Swasthya, Yoga and Yog Attain Sukha Sthanam a Potential

Compiled and Edited By
Yogacharya Jnandev Giri
Dr. Diana Skibniewski-Woods
Yogachariya Dr Ananda Balayogi Bhavanani

The Institute of Salutogenesis and Complementary Medicine (ISCM), Puducherry,

Ananda Ashram (ICYER) Puducherry, India

Gurukula UK & Portugal

First Published October 2023

ISBN 978-1-914485-14-5

Printed in Great Britain
by Design Marque

Dedicated to Our Guru Yogacharini Ammaji Meenakshi Devi Bhavanani Ji

Content List

Lesson-1.   Swasthya - Holistic health   13

Lesson 2   Holistic Health management through Yoga   23

Lesson 3.   Ashtanga Yoga or Yoga of Eight Limbs   27

Lesson 4.   What Yoga Offers for Holistic Health, Well-Being
and Yoga Chikitsa   29

Lesson 5.   What is Yoga Therapy?   31

Lesson 6.   Yoga as The Science and Philosophy of Wholistic Being   37

Lesson 7.   A Holistic Life Philosophy   38

Lesson 8.   What do we study in Gitananda Yoga Chikitsa?   42

Lesson 9.   12 Point Yogic Diagnosis- Dr Swami Gitananda Giri Ji
(Modified from Original Article by Dr Ananda Balayogi Bhavanani)   45

Lesson 10.   Key Yoga Therapy Models   49

Lesson 11.   Key Yoga Scripture For Yoga Therapy   56

Lesson 12.   Yoga as Life Style   63

Lesson 13.   Living Mindfully for Health and Happiness   65

Lesson 14.   Finding Balance in Life- Moderate Living   67

Lesson 15.   Discipline Key to Success in Life   68

Lesson 16.   Yoga is Stilling our Mind   69

Lesson 17.   Yoga is Path and An Ultimate Goal to Self-Realisation   71

Lesson 18.   Yoga Skill in Action (Karma Yoga)   72

Lesson 19.   Yoga is To Live in Equanimity (Yoga Samatva)   73

Lesson 20.   Be Aware to avoid the Miseries Yet to Come   75

Lesson 21.   Learn to Act and Never to React   76

Lesson 22.   Shat Karmas or Cleansing Practices   77

Lesson 23.   Yoga, Health and Diet   78

Lesson 24.   Yogic Diet   80

Lesson 25.   A Balanced approach always helps   82

Lesson 26.   The Science of Yogic Vyayama   84

Lesson 27. Simple Ayurveda to Assist Yoga Therapy 92

Lesson 28. Tri-dosha: Three Doshas (Vata, Pitta, Kapha) 97

Lesson 29. Dosha, Dhatu and Malas 104

Lesson 30. Asthi Dhatu: Ayurveda and Yogic Perspectives 109

Lesson 31. Ayurveda and Skeletal System 116

Lesson 32. Yoga, Ayurveda and Digestive Health 118

Lesson 33. A Yogi, Bhogi, Rogi and Drohi 124

Lesson 34. Adhi Vyadhi Concept of Diseases and Yoga Chikitsa 128

Lesson 35. Shavasana (Yogic Relaxation) and stress management 132

Lesson 36. Pancha Kosha – Yogic Principles of Existence and Yoga Therapy 141

Lesson 37. Pancha Prana Vayu Model of Diagnosis and Yoga Therapy 153

Lesson 38. Yoga for Emotional Release 160

Lesson 39. Muscle Tension Caused By Trapped Emotions and Yogic Remedial Healing 164

Lesson 40. Healing Powers of Yoga Nidra 182

Lesson 41. Neuroscience of Breathing and Pranayama 188

Lesson 42. Pranayama- is Not the Breathing Exercise 196

Lesson 43. Classical Eight Pranayama 200

Lesson 44. Dr Swami Gitananda Giri Ji on Pranayama 203

Lesson 45. Classical Pranayama Abhyasa or Sadhana and Applications 206

Lesson 46. Vasanas – Past Impressions and Deep-Rooted Desires 211

Lesson 47. Understanding Health and Evolutionary Concept of Karma, Samaskaras and Epigenetics 220

Lesson 48. Chakras and Yoga Therapy 229

Lesson 49. The Neurophysiology of Chakras 238

Lesson 50. Mantra or Naada Yoga and Health 249

Lesson 51. Yoga Sutras and Mental Health 261

Lesson 52. Obstacles in Yogic Evolution 272

Yogachariya Jnandev Giri (Surender Kumar Saini)

This book on Swasthya and Yoga Chikitsa is a research work compilation for all the sincere Yoga, Health, Spiritual Seekers and Yoga Chikitsa or Yoga Therapy professionals who wish to use fundamental yogic principles to support the yoga Chikitsa /therapy Program. Yoga is path, a lifestyle that includes practices, principles, Kriyas and Prakriyas and their applications to help the yoga seekers to be free from all forms of suffering or Dukha. In a wholistic sense Yoga Chiktisha is part of yoga itself as Yogachariya Dr. Ananda Balayogi Bhavanani mentions that "If we see Yoga as a big circle then yoga Chiktisha is small circle within it", which makes them inseparable. For me Yoga is one of the sincerest efforts of ancient yogis and life scientists to find the way to attain our wholesome potential.

The journey of this work began in 2019 when we started the first online yoga therapy course under the guidance and mentorship of Dr. Yogachariya Ananda Ji. As I started to study, research and teach a lesson week by week I realise how much the in-depth teachings and practices yoga provide us with as human beings, to deal with our day-to-day sufferings and improve our health and wellness. In recent times yoga therapy has become very popular, as yoga is one of the best tools for the management of most of psycho-somatic problems as well pains and injuries, which has also led to the progression of yoga therapy into Yogopathy (symptomatic relief).

In this book we are following the fundamental principles of Gitananda Yoga as per our Guru Dr. Swamiji Gitananda Giri Ji Gurumaharaj Ji as well Yogic Life teachings of Yogacharini Ammaji Meenakshi Devi Bhavanani. Working under guidance of Dr. Ananda Ji who is a pioneer of yoga therapy with his in-depth knowledge of yoga, medical science, yoga therapy and yoga research has been an honour for me and I feel privileged to have been able to compile this work around the Gitananda Yoga Chiktisha principles.

I would also like to mention here, that this work is still a work in progress and all feedback and suggestions are wholeheartedly welcome.

Yoga is to live in harmony with our truest nature and yoga Chiktisha is the application of yoga itself to help care-seekers to find peace and harmony within themselves. May we all attain our full potential. May our diet support our body, mind and life. May we live virtuously and be able to use these truly amazing tools for a healthier body, mind and spirit.

I would like to offer my gratitude and special thanks to my dearest Guru Ammaji Meenakshi Devi Bhavanani, Swamiji. I would like to offer my sincere gratitude to Yogachariya Dr. Ananda Balayogi Bhavanani for guiding me and for giving us all his unconditional love, support and blessings to move forward. I would like to express my gratitude to Dr. Diana for helping to compile this book and I also express my deep gratitude to all the authors, and resources we have used as part of this compilation.

I would like to offer my special thanks and gratitude to Yogacharini Deepika Saini and my three divine boys, Siddha, Mahadev, Krishna, for all their love and support as well as motivation in my life.

I am very grateful to Sarah Ray (Design Marque, Pembrokeshire) for the truly amazing design work as always. Finally, I also offer my thanks to all my Yoga Family and the local Welsh community, all of whom have supported both Gurukula UK and me on the yoga path of teaching, writing, and living a yogic life.

With Love and Gratitude
Yogachariya Jnandev Giri (Surender Kumar Saini)
Founder & Director Gurukula UK & Portugal
Yoga Chiktisha Achariya, Ananda Ashram (ICYER), India.

Param Pujya Ammaji, Yogacharini Meenakshi Devi Bhavanani, Ashram Acharya and Director ICYER at Ananda Ashram, Pondicherry, India.

One of the unique features of the timeless wellness system of Yoga is that it provides a complete discipline of body, emotions, mind and spirit. Every aspect of the human being is refined by practices which have been proven through generations of the Rishiculture Yoga Parampara.

To take responsibility for one's life in an intelligent manner is indeed Yogic. All other societies, including political and religious societies, put the blame onto contrary systems or even onto God, for what is happening to us individually and for humankind as a whole. What also happens is that we become wise enough to accept responsibility for what we are doing now, but want to deny any responsibility for what we have been previously doing. Accepting the Law of Karma doesn't wipe out the past mistakes. It has to be worked out in conscious living. The idea that simply "feeling sorry" or feeling remorse for mistakes, thoughts, words or deeds, sins, lapses, etc which we have done will free using the effects of our deeds is a nonsensical concept devised by immature minds which cannot face the reality of irrevocable Universal Laws. Nothing can "wash away our sins" but we can with conscious effort "work out" the unhappy effects of past foolish action.

Unfortunately, the body, emotions and mind have all been conditioned by previous life styles, attitudes and actions. It may take some time for things to come into balance. Also as we grow older it is more difficult to change body problems that are deeply entrenched. It is easier, however, to change one's emotions and mind as we grow older. That is why maturity gives some semblance of balance of compensation for the past. At least we can look forward to a limited future that is in our control. The past has to be worked out by present action.

Yogamaharishi Dr Swami Gitananda Giri Guru Maharaj, Founder Ananda Ashram at ICYER, Pondicherry, India.

Yoga as a life style has an answer to depression, stress, strain and anxiety. Engaging in the Asanas, Kriyas and Mudras along with the proper Pranayama goes a long way to aid in relieving the condition. Yoga practice is basically isometric, rather than isotonic. Therefore, it has an advantage for all types of depression. Isometric Yoga plays body movement against the breath, while isotonic activity is to be observed in heavy work sports and recreational play. Although the latter does give a false sense of relief from tension, only a personality change can relieve the condition totally. It is to be sadly noted that Western culture has advanced a long way in using relaxation techniques in every form of recreation, sport and medicine, while here in India, little or nothing is known about Hatha Yoga relaxation or Jnana Yoga counselling which are both fields producing dynamic recovery from depression and repression. It is to be hoped that leading Research Centres devote time to this valuable research field. More people are dying daily from conditions caused by anxiety, stress, and tension than by all other diseases put together. Yet, this is hardly recognized in the statistics of death from so-called "natural causes."

Dr Diana Skibniewski-Woods

My background is in nursing, I have a PhD. in Health Science with a special interest in mental health. I have completed Therapeutic Yoga Teacher training with Yogacharya Jnandev Giri and Dr. Ananda Baloyogi Bhavanani and have a basic understanding of Yoga Philosophy and health. My role as co-author was in seeking to understand, searching for definitions and clarifications in order to ensure that this wisdom is as accessible as possible to the reader. This is an incredible piece of comprehensive Yoga wisdom written by Yogachariya Jnandev under the inspiration and guidance of Dr. Ananda. I have been honoured to be a part of it. Its contents come highly recommended to anyone seeking in-depth knowledge about yoga philosophy for Therapeutic Yoga Chikitsa.

Introduction: Salutogenesis and Yoga Therapy

Salutogenesis, may be defined as all the factors involved in manifesting and sustaining a sense of wellbeing and wholesome wellness. It is derived from the Latin "salus" meaning "health" and the Greek genesis meaning "source". Hence in combination it implies, "Sources of health".

The equivalent concept in Indian tradition is "Swastha" that implies a sense of being at ease with oneself. Acharya Sushrut (~600 BC) defined this positive sense of wholesome wellness as a "dynamic balance of the elements and humors, normal metabolic activity and efficient elimination coupled with a tranquil mind, senses and contented soul". Yoga is truly the best means to achieve such a dynamic state of wholesome health and wellness at all levels of existence.

Salutogenesis has become a key word in modern healthcare and this is very welcome. Healing in a holistic sense has faded from medical attention and is rarely discussed in modern medicine especially in therapeutics. To heal is to achieve or acquire wholeness as a person. The wholeness of personhood involves physical, emotional, intellectual, social, and spiritual aspects of human experience.[1]

The Indian tradition of healing on the other hand understands health and well-being as a dynamic continuum of human nature and not a mere 'state' to be attained and maintained. The lowest point on the continuum may be understood as having the lowest speed of vibration and manifests as death whereas the highest point with the highest vibration is that of health, well-being and even a conceptual awareness of immortality. In between the extremes of this continuum lie the states of normal health and disease. For many, their state of health is defined as that 'state' in which they are able to function without hindrance whereas in reality, health is part of our evolutionary process towards Divinity.

This is in tune with the concept of eudemonia described by Aristotle as a "well-lived" life that fulfills a person's ultimate purpose and gives them meaning. Eudemonic happiness is a steadfast, abiding contentment marked by flourishing vs. a short-term pleasure or comfort. This may related also to the concepts of self-actualization of Abraham Maslow [2] and to the meaning/purpose of life known in the Japanese culture as Ikigai [3] and as self-responsibility (Swadharma [4]) in Indian tradition that enables the individual to attain a sense of coherence that is essential for wellbeing [5].

Aaron Antonovsky proposed that the experience of well-being is based on a "Sense of Coherence". This SOC can be considered the heart of salutogenesis and may be understood as a pervasive, long-lasting and dynamic feeling of confidence that one's internal and external environments are predictable and that there is a high probability that things will work out as well as can be expected" ([6]). SOC has strong positive correlations to perceived health, mental health, and quality of life as it helps the 'diseased' to manage their condition and 'be well'. ([7])

The three components of SOC are based on a sense that -

1. One's life is comprehensible,

2. It is manageable and

3. It is meaningful.

The sense of life being comprehensible is a cognitive process where the individual has the sense "My world is understandable". The coping skill in the second component enables the individual feel, "My world is manageable" while the motivational aspect of life having a sense of meaningfulness manifests in the individual feeling, "My world has meaning".

The comprehension, meaningfulness and manageability (SOC approach) in chronic diseases keeps them 'well' despite any limitations and is similar to 'physically disabled' becoming 'differently abled'. When an individual has these three aspects manifesting in their life, they have a sense of health, wellness, wellbeing and wholesomeness.

As Yoga therapist, though our words and actions we need to communicate with our clients in such a way that these three aspects come alive. It is only then, that the health promoting aspects of healing start to manifest in them.

We as a friend and guide need to help them comprehend their life better. This is only possible if we truly 'know' them. This takes time and patience. Can we help them tap into their own potential to manage their life? Often people are not aware of their inherent capacities and potential and it is we as an external observer who can help them understand it.

We need to help them move from a state where "being healthy" seems "impossible" to one of a confident "I Am Possible". This is where the very stressor in their life becomes a catalyst for transformative positive health, rather than induce degenerative disease.

To live a healthy life it is important to do healthy things and follow a healthy lifestyle. Yoga places great importance on a proper and healthy lifestyle whose main components are: [8]

- **Achar** - Yoga stresses the importance of healthy activities such as exercise and recommends Asana, Pranayama and Kriyas on a regular basis. Cardio-respiratory health is one of the main by-products of such healthy activities.

- **Vichar** - Right thoughts and right attitude towards life is vital for wellbeing. A balanced state of mind is obtained by following the moral restraints and ethical observances (Yama-Niyama). As Mahatma Gandhi said, "there is enough in this world for everyone's need but not enough for any one person's greed".

- **Ahar** - Yoga emphasizes need for a healthy, nourishing diet that has an adequate intake of fresh water along with a well-balanced intake of fresh food, green salads, sprouts, unrefined cereals and fresh fruits. It is important to be aware of the need for a Satwic diet, prepared and served with love and affection.

- **Vihar** - Proper recreational activities to relax body and mind are essential for good health. This includes proper relaxation, maintaining quietude of action-speech-thoughts and group activities wherein one loses the sense of individuality. Karma Yoga is an excellent method for losing the sense of individuality and gaining a sense of universality.

- **Vyavahar** - Healthy interpersonal relationships that enable us to be the best "we' that we can be. Learning to adapt to the other people in our life and create a sense of teamwork, enable the sublimation of the ego into a positive energy that sustains relationships rather than harm them. When we learn to live with gratitude, respect, love and acceptance; life becomes much better and we grow as an individual.

According to Param Pujya Ammaji Yogacharini Meenakshi Devi Bhavanani, Director ICYER at Ananda Ashram in Pondicherry [9], Yoga has a step-by-step method for producing and maintaining perfect health at all levels of existence. She explains that social behaviour is first optimized through an understanding and control of the lower animal nature (Pancha Yama) and development and enhancement of the higher, human nature (Pancha Niyama).

The body is then strengthened, disciplined, purified, sensitized, lightened, energized and made obedient to the higher will through asana. Universal Pranic energy that flows through body-mind-emotions-spirit continuum is intensified and controlled through pranayama using breath control as a method to attain controlled expansion of the vital cosmic energy. The externally oriented senses are explored, refined, sharpened and made acute, until finally the individual can detach themselves from sensory impressions at will through Pratyahara.

The restless mind is then purified, cleansed, focused and strengthened through concentration (Dharana). If these six steps are thoroughly understood and practiced then the seventh, Dhyana or meditation (a state of union of the mind with the object of contemplation) is possible. Intense meditation produces Samadhi, or the ecstatic feeling of Union, Oneness with the Universe. This is the perfect state of integration or harmonious health.

I would like to reiterate at this point the need of the modern age which is to have an integrated approach towards all forms of therapy. We must try to integrate concepts of Yoga in coordination and collaboration with other systems of medicine such as Allopathy, Ayurveda, Siddha and Naturopathy. Physiotherapy, osteopathy and chiropractic practices may be also used with the Yoga Chikitsa as required. Don't forget that advice on diet and adoption of a healthy lifestyle is very important irrespective of the mode of therapy employed for the patient.

Yoga can help us to regain the ease we had lost through dis-ease (as implied by sthira sukham asanam- Yoga Darshan II: 46). [9] It can also enable us to attain a dynamic state of mental equanimity (samatvam yoga uchyate- Bhagavad Gita II: 48) where the opposites cease to affect us any more (tato dwandwa anabhigatha- Yoga Darshan II: 48). This enables us to move from a state of illness and disease to one of health and wellbeing that ultimately allows us to move from a lower animal nature to a higher human nature and finally reach the highest Divine Nature that is our birthright.

References:
1. Egnew TR. The meaning of healing: transcending suffering. Ann Fam Med 2005;3(3):255–262.
2. www.psychologytoday.com/intl/blog/theory-and-psychopathology/201308/the-theory-self-actualization
3. https://en.wikipedia.org/wiki/Ikigai
4. https://moayush.wordpress.com/2017/05/09/the-yoga-of-responsibility
5. www.ncbi.nlm.nih.gov/books/NBK435839
6. Antonovsky A. Health, Stress, and Coping. San Francisco and London: Jossey-Bass Publishers; 1979.
7. Antonovsky A. The salutogenic model as a theory to guide health promotion. Health Promot Int. 1996; 11: 11–1
8. Bhavanani AB. Yoga Chikitsa: Application of Yoga as a therapy. 1st ed. Pondicherry, India: Dhivyananda Creations; 2013.
9. Bhavanani Ammaji Meenakshi Devi. Demystifying the Basics of Yoga. The Vedanta Kesari. Dec 2012: pg 88-93.
10. Bhavanani AB. Understanding the Yoga Darshan. An exploration of the Yoga Sutra of Maharishi Patanjali. 1st ed. Pondicherry, India: Dhivyananda Creations; 2011.

Lesson-1.
Swasthya - Holistic health

Swamiji Dr. Gitananda Giriji mentions that "health and happiness is everyone's birthright", but points out that we can't take it for granted. We must claim our birthright and do everything we need to do be healthy and happy. This chapter intends to introduce the concepts surrounding Sukha Sthanam, the dynamic sense of physical, mental and spiritual well-being. We will look at our understanding of Swasthya to define what we mean when we talk about health in a holistic sense, so that we can reflect on what it means to be healthy.

According to The Practical Sanskrit - English Dictionary, Swasthya means "self-reliance, self-dependence, fortitude, resoluteness, firmness, sound state of being, health, prosperity, well-being, comfortableness, ease and satisfaction of spirit". The Cologne Digital Sanskrit Dictionary: Shabda-Sagar Sanskrit- English Dictionary similarly translates Swasthya as "health, contentment, happiness, complacency, satisfaction, fortitude, firmness, self-dependence, prosperity, comfortableness, and competence".

The Sushruti Samhita explains that a person who is in union with the true self, whose doshas (primary life forces) are balanced, who has balanced and active Agni (digestive fire and life force), well-formed and aligned Dhatus (tissues and body formation), healthy elimination of Malas (waste products), optimum functioning of body process with sensory discipline, a calm mind and a blissful soul, is known as Healthy or Swastha.

> **Samadoṣa samāgni cha sama dhātu mala-kriyah**
> **Prasanna ātma indriya manah Swastha iti abhidhīyate**
> (Sushruti Samhita 15/48).

In the above sloka we have following concepts or basics of health-

❖ *Samadosa*- Ayurveda explains the concepts of three doshas - vatta, pitta and kapha. Imbalance of the doshas is one of the root causes of health problems and a causal factor in the aggravation of many diseases.

❖ *Sama-Agni*- Ayurveda explains that having a healthy and balanced digestive fire (Koshtagni) and cellular or metabolic fire (dhatugani) is essential for healthy life functions and vitality.

❖ *Sama-Dhatu-Mala-Kriya*- Next we need a balance and healthy system of essential elements known as dhatus for good health and excretion of waste products known as malas. There are seven known Dhatus in Ayurveda - Rasa, Rakta, Mamsa, Medas, Asthi, Majja and Shukra. These excrements or Malas include - Purisa (faeces), Mutra (urine) and Sweda (sweat).

❖ *Prasanna ātma indriya manah* - Ayurveda also explains that discipline of our sensual energy, functions of our sensory organs, perception, experience and mind are also very important for Swasthya or health and Swasth Jeevan or a blissful and healthy life.

In Sanskrit and Yoga, we use the word Swasthya for health. Health means absence of diseases for many of us. The word Swasthya comes from two Sanskrit words, 'Swa' meaning self and 'asthya' meaning established at ease, hence Swasthya means 'a complete state of being at ease with our own self'. It is said that pain may or may not exist in our life, as many times we don't have the choice, but suffering is our own choice. When we are at ease with our individual self, every life situation becomes opportunity, and we take every problem as a challenge that we can deal with.

Our health can be seen as a state of holistic being where all our faculties are functioning at their full potential in perfect harmony with each other. Our duty is not only to cure any illness but also to look after and maintain our health and well-being and prevent the health issues that we can. i.e. as it is said in Yoga Sutras of Patanjali, "we should live consciously and make each and every choice wisely so we can avoid miseries yet to come".

According to the Charak Samhita (The Scripture on Ayurveda), Swasthya or health is to be maintained by keeping the balance of three Doshas and constitutions, and with maintaining a healthy and sound mind. These bring a healthy posture, good muscular and organ health and a peaceful mind.

Yoga and Vedantic scriptures explain that our life is a divine blessing, to fulfil our dharma and workout past life karmas, it is not a punishment. This idea advocates self-care, self-respect, gratitude, and equality. There is famous Indian saying-

If you lose your business, you can rebuild it; If you lose money or wealth, you can regain it; If you lose your health, you lose everything else as without health everything else is lost!

We must look after our health and well-being, having sound health and a peaceful mind enables us to live and enjoy our life and fulfil our true potential.

The word 'health' refers to a state of complete emotional and physical well-being. We now have healthcare system to help us to cure and manage and rehabilitate our bodies to maintain the optimal state of health. In 1948, the WHO definition of health stated that "Health is a state of complete physical, mental, and social well-being and not merely the absence of disease or infirmity". In 1986 this was updated and rectified to define health as "A resource for everyday life, not the objective of living. Health is a positive concept emphasising social and personal resources, as well as physical capacities".

In this way our health becomes our resource and right and not the end goal. Our health supports us to function as individuals in our wider society and fulfil our true potentials. A healthy lifestyle becomes the means to lead us to live our fulfilled holistic life with true meaning and purpose. In 2009, researchers published in The Lancet further defined health as "the ability of a body to adapt to new threats and infirmities". This was the conclusion of the past few decades of medical research and discoveries that we may not be able to completely free ourselves from some of the health issues, but we can still thrive to live to our full potential.

Dr. Ananda Balayogi Bhavanani states that, "Yoga is an excellent tool of promotive health that can enrich modern medicine. The practice of Yoga leads to the efficient functioning of the body with homeostasis through improved functioning of the psycho-immuno-neuro-endocrine system. A balanced equilibrium between the sympathetic and parasympathetic wings of the autonomic nervous system leads to a dynamic state of health".

Types of Health
Mental and physical health are the two most discussed aspects of health. Spiritual, emotional, ethical and financial health also contribute to our overall holistic health. Medical science links these aspects of health to stress levels, how we deal with things and cope affects our physical and mental health.

People who have some kind belief system or faith may deal with many stressful events with more positive attitude. People with financial stability, may worry less about finances and have the means to buy fresh food more regularly. Those with good spiritual health may feel a sense of calm and purpose that nourishes good mental health.

Physical health

Having good physical health means all our physiological functions and processes are at their best. This is a state of health that doesn't merely mean an absence of disease. Good physical health demands regular exercise, healthy nutritional diet, and adequate rest or sleep. Hatha Yoga and Pranayama provides us with all the tools, kriyas and prakriyas, techniques and applications to maintain good physical health.

Physical health involves cultivating and maintaining a moderate and healthy lifestyle as described in the Yogic scriptures. Hatha Yoga also helps us in developing endurance, enhanced flexibility, strength through our breathing and in our heart, digestion, and muscles.

To look after our physical health and well-being, we also need to avoid or reduce the risks involving injury or health issues, for example -

❖ Having a safe workplace
❖ Avoiding active or passive smoking
❖ Maintaining good hygiene
❖ Avoiding drug and alcohol consumption
❖ Avoiding unprotected sex
❖ Avoiding junk or unhygienic food and drinks

According to a study published in 2008, "mental illness, such as depression, may increase the risk of drug use disorders. This can go on to adversely affect physical health".

Mental health

The U.S. Department of Health and Human Services mentions that "Mental health is a person's emotional, social, and psychological well-being. Mental health is as important as physical health as part of a full, active lifestyle".

Understanding mental health is far more complex compare to physical health as psychological diagnosis depends on everyone's perception, experience, and perspective. It is easily to label people with learning disabilities if someone is not good in maths or science, unless we can change our perspective to see what everyone can do. Many of mental health issues are caused due to our expectations, and family, social, academic, and economical pressure.

Good mental health is not only the absence of mental problems. Mental health is a person's ability to-

- ❖ Live and enjoy life
- ❖ The ability to cope and adapt in difficult situations
- ❖ To achieve balance in all aspects of life, such as family, finances, social responsibilities, and spiritual aspects
- ❖ To have feelings of safety and security
- ❖ To attain their full potential
- ❖ To achieve the ability to bounce back after every fall.

Physical and mental health are interconnected. Yoga mentions the relation of body-mind health thousands year ago as Adhi-Vyadhi, which in modern terms is known as psycho-somatic. For example, a long-term physical health issue may lead someone to depression and stress due to financial or social pressure.
A mental illness like depression or anorexia, can affect the body's weight and overall physical health.

Our mental and physical health have strong connections. For example, if a chronic illness affects a person's ability to complete their regular tasks, it may lead to depression and stress. These feelings could be due to financial problems or mobility issues.

What is Emotional Health?
Our emotional health is our ability to accept, cope and manage our feelings during an adverse change, and challenge. An emotionally healthy person can manage and digest the emotions. Our daily life hassles offer us an opportunity to grow and learn new ways of dealing with situations. We learn how to respond, rather than reacting, this helps our emotional health to blossom.

Our holistic health includes physical, mental, emotional, intellectual, social, and spiritual well-being. When all these aspects are in balance and alignment, we can thrive to our full potential. Each of these areas will influence the rest in our life.

Emotional health includes emotional regulation and emotional intelligence. Experience of various emotions is subjective and may be appropriate over a sustained period. Our emotional health enables us to distinguish between our true feelings and emotional reactions. Emotional health will fall under the broader aspects of mental health. Lack of emotions does not mean emotional well-being. If we keep suppressing our emotions long term, especially in childhood, this may lead us to have difficulties and be vulnerable around expressing our emotions.

Each day of life brings its own lows and highs like the waves in the ocean. An emotionally healthy and balanced person can ride the waves of feelings and various situations without getting stalled or experiencing bursts of disruptive and eruptive emotional reactions.

Emotional distress has significant role in physical health problems. A study by Stewart-Brown (1998) showed that "ailments like cardiovascular disease and immune system repression can be linked to emotional distress". A study on emotional distress and the underlying neurological circuitry by Sinha et al. (2004) indicated a connection with substance abuse and other dysfunctional behaviours.

What is Social Health?

Our social health encompasses our ability to interact and form meaningful relationships with others and how comfortably we can adapt in social situations. Our social health has a significant impact on our mental health, physical health, and mortality risks .

Many social research studies are showing that there is direct link between of social relationships and general health and well-being. Our social relationships in quality and quantity are having a short- and long-term effect on our health.

Social health includes: -

- ❖ Assertive skills rather than passive or aggressive skills
- ❖ Balance in personal and social time
- ❖ Engagement in the community
- ❖ Adapting in social situations.
- ❖ Ability to be our individual self in all situations
- ❖ Respecting others and ourselves
- ❖ Ability to develop and maintaining friendships and connections
- ❖ Supporting others and being able to receive or ask for support
- ❖ Fun and joy in life

Further studies are showing that "people with poor social interactions are more likely to suffer with mental and emotional health problems and die younger than those with high social involvements". These studying have linked following health issues to poor social health: -

- ❖ Heart disease
- ❖ Chronic illness
- ❖ Mobility issues
- ❖ Blood pressure issues
- ❖ High stress hormones
- ❖ Poor mental health
- ❖ Emotional instability
- ❖ Anxiety and Depression
- ❖ Week immunity

What is Spiritual health?

Our discussion on spiritual health in medical terms is very difficult, spirituality is commonly associated with religion or faith of worship which has its own history of pain, and suppression in name of God or heaven in many cultures. In simple terms our spiritual health is associated with our 'spirit', 'life force', 'individual self' or in yogic terms 'atman'.

The World Health Organisation (WHO) refers to spiritual health as "that part of the individual which reaches out and strives for meaning and purpose in life. It is the intangible 'something' that transcends physiology and psychology". In 1998 WHO proposed that, "Health is a dynamic state of complete physical, mental, spiritual and social wellbeing and not merely the absence of disease or infirmity".

In a study conducted at the National Institute of Health and Family Welfare (NIHFW), New Delhi, for developing a spiritual health scale, the research group described the following definition of spiritual health-

"Spiritual health is a state of being where an individual is able to deal with day-to-day life in a manner which leads to the realisation of one's full potential, meaning and purpose of life and happiness from within".

Our spiritual health is an issue of our core values and happiness, which we will deal with in detail when come to the yogic idea of Swasthya or health and well-being. Many of our physical, mental and emotional problems can be elevated or managed better by nurturing our spiritual well-being. Bringing devotion, purity, dedication, charity, forgiveness, connectedness, faith in oneself and dealing smoothly with issues of death and death anxiety through prayer, yoga, meditation and other mind healing practices has a significant role in our overall health and well-being.

Within Yogic concepts, true health is the complete state of oneness of our body, mind and soul. Our highest state of ease of Swasthya is a state of self-realisation or Samadhi where a Sadhana becomes free from duality, pain and suffering. I pray to the divine for us all to attain that highest potential and live-in harmony within our individual self and our universal self.

Common Factors for good health

Good health depends on a wide range of factors including genetics, environmental factors and lifestyle.

Genetic factors

Each one of us is born with variety of genes and epigenetic memories. For many people, an unusual genetic pattern can lead to various health issues. We may inherit genetic health conditions from our parents which increases the risk of certain health conditions.

Environmental factors

Our environmental factors play a significant role in our general health. In many cases environment alone is enough to cause an impact on health, environmental factors can also become triggers, which flare up illnesses.

WHO suggests that the following environmental factors play a more significant impact on our health-

- ❖ The area or state we live in and around
- ❖ The state and quality of our surroundings
- ❖ Our genetic make up
- ❖ Income
- ❖ Level of education
- ❖ Employment
- ❖ Our family and social relations

These factors can have significant relevance to our health through our social and economic environment, the financial status of a family or community, as well as the social culture and quality of relationships, physical environment including which germs, viruses and pollutants exist in an area. A person's characteristics and behaviours, genetic makeup and lifestyle choices can affect their overall health.

According to some of the social studies, people with lower socioeconomic status and security are more likely to suffer with physical and mental health problems compared to people with higher socioeconomic status. The second group enjoy better health care, education, food and hygiene. People with low socioeconomic status are more likely to face the day-to-day stress due to daily living costs, financial difficulties and unemployment. The culture and social issues, traditions and customs of a society or family can also have a good or bad impact on health.

According to the Seven Countries Study people eating a healthy and nutritional diet live and longer and have a better-quality life. This study further mentions that people eating a healthier diet tend to consume more fruits and vegetables than those who regularly consume fast food.

The International Journal of Environmental Research and Public Health finds that a healthy diet can help protect a person's heart and reduce the risk of several diseases, including type 2 diabetes, cancer and diseases that cause the brain and nerves disorders. Correspondingly the National Institute of Mental Health, people who smoke tobacco, drink alcohol, or take illicit drugs to manage stressful situations are more likely to develop health problems than those who manage stress through a healthful diet, relaxation techniques, and exercise.

How to Preserve Health?

We need to follow a healthy lifestyle throughout our life to preserve and maintain a good and sound health, rather than waiting for health issues and sickness to manifest and then address them. It is said that 'prevention is better than cure'. We must take care of our health and well-being and do everything we can to maintain this wellness.

The World Health Organisation defines wellness as follows-
Wellness is the optimal state of health of individuals and groups. There are two focal concerns: the realisation of the fullest potential of an individual physically, psychologically, socially, spiritually, and economically, and the fulfilment of one's

roles and expectations in the family, community, place of worship, and other settings.

Wellness promotes and demands active awareness of and participating in activities that preserve health, both as an individual and in the community. Maintaining wellness and optimal health is a lifelong and a day-to-day commitment.

Following simple steps can help us in supporting and maintaining wellness, including having-

- ❖ A balanced, nutritional diet from natural and organic sources
- ❖ Daily exercise from moderate to high intensity
- ❖ Frequent screening for disease to prevent the risk or address them at primary level
- ❖ Stress management
- ❖ Engaging in activities providing meaning and purpose to life
- ❖ Connecting with positive and caring people
- ❖ Maintaining positive outlook on life
- ❖ Moral and ethical values or virtues in practice

It is said that 'it may not be possible to avoid disease altogether', however, each individual should try to do as much as they can do develop the resilience and prepare the body and mind to deal with the health problems as they may arise. This chapter has considered health from many different perspectives. Holistic health includes physical, mental, social, emotional and spiritual health. It is the ability to consider and attend to all of these aspects that can promote health in our day-to-day lives.

References and resources
https://www.who.int/healthpr
The Lancet Publication: - https://www.thelancet.com/journals/lancet/article/PIIS0140-6736(09)60456-6/fulltext
https://www.medicalnewstoday.com/articles/150999#what_is_health
https://www.ncbi.nlm.nih.gov/pubmed/18281835
https://www.mentalhealth.gov/basics/what-is-mental-health
https://positivepsychology.com/emotional-health-activities/
https://www.ncbi.nlm.nih.gov/pmc/articles/PMC3150158/#
Spiritual health – definition and applications in clinical care Dipak Shukla*, Kaustubhi Shukla*
https://www.sevencountriesstudy.com/dietary-patterns-and-all-cause-mortality/
https://www.ncbi.nlm.nih.gov/pmc/articles/PMC6466433/
https://www.nimh.nih.gov/health/publications/stress/index.shtml

Lesson 2:
Holistic Health management through Yoga

Yoga is known today for a set of postures or asanas, kriyas and vinyasa (flow or movement of body from pose to pose), however in its true meanings yoga offers us so much more than exercise. It is said by many Rishis or followers of Yoga that asanas are actually only a very small part of Yoga. In this Lesson 2 we are going to study the history, meanings, concepts, philosophy and benefits of yoga.

What is Yoga?

"Yoga is the science of the sciences. Yoga is an art, a philosophy, a religion, a fad and a fanaticism" (Swami Gitananda).

Yoga is a philosophy, a path, a set of practices, a discipline: it contains concepts and ideas to understand our mind, our consciousness and soul to achieve harmony and balance between the body, mind and soul in order to achieve inner peace, health, and wellbeing.

The Meaning or definition of yoga depends on the individual person, according to their level of consciousness and evolution. Yoga can be simply described as the process to control the perception and the conceptions, which develop the conscious, rational thinking and Viveka (discernment).

Yoga has many overlapping ideas, concepts, practices and principles which include forms of static postures, kriyas or vinyasa, sun salutations, mudras and pranayama, deep relaxation and visualisation techniques, adaptation of a healthy lifestyle and a positive, optimistic, and virtuous attitude and living.

Yoga is one of most precious jewels of the Ancient Hindu ways of attaining liberation. Even then yoga is not concerned with religion. Yoga can help us to live with greater harmony. Today you can find people practicing yoga everywhere. Especially Hatha-Yoga (asanas and Pranayama) which has become the synonym of yoga. So, to enhance the meaning of your life, religion, faith and practices, yoga is the tool, which is free from religion, caste, or creed, and available for one and all. The term 'Yoga', which is multivalent and derived from the root 'yuj', generally means 'union', 'to join', 'to yoke together', or 'to unite as one'. The word yoga comes from the most ancient language known to man Sanskrit. In India, Sanskrit is considered to be the language of God and is formed in a mathematical way.

Yoga in India is also considered as one of the six Ancient Indian Philosophies. Primarily we should keep in mind that yoga is the 'way of union'.

The Bhagavad Gita uses it in many ways:
- ❖ i.i.48 to mean sole desire for supreme divinity (paramesvarikaparata-sridharasvamin)
- ❖ i.i. 50 yoga denotes skill in work (karmasu kausalam)
- ❖ IV. 1,2,3, yoga means Karma yoga (desire less action) and Jnanayoga (acquisition of time knowledge)
- ❖ VI. 16, 17, the term yoga means Samadhi in which the mind is united with the Atman
- ❖ VI. 23, yoga means a state of mind, which having realized the Supreme Being, is not disturbed even by great suffering
- ❖ i.i. 48 and vi. 33, 36, yoga means samatva or equanimity, i.e., indifference to pleasure and pain.

Yoga can be accepted as a way of life, a way of integrating your whole awareness with the true nature of the self. Physical, mental, emotional, and spiritual aspects of your life should work in integrated harmony with each other.

In arithmetic, yoga means addition; in astronomy it means conjunction, lucky conjunction and also conjunctions which may warn us of a danger, etc.

In the Upanishads, yoga generally means union; union of Jivatman with Parmatman. Similarly Patanjali in his Yoga Sutra (i.2) defines yoga as "yogah-chittavrattinirodha", this means control of the whirlpools of the mind: by yoga, Patanjali means the effort to attain union, or oneness of Self with the Supreme Self.

What is union? In the normal sense of yoga this union means harmony of body, mind, emotions, and spirit. This means living in the present, moving, and accepting all situations as they are with a positive attitude.

Yoga has many paths or divisions that deal with various aspects of our health and well-being and our evolutionary journey. These include:

1. ***Karma Yoga*** – which is also known as Karma marga is one of the three spiritual paths in Hinduism, based on the 'yoga of action'. To a karma yogi, right action without the desire for fruit is a form of prayer or Sadhana our daily spiritual practice. Of the various paths to spiritual liberation in Hinduism, karma yoga is the path of selfless action (niskam karma).

2. ***Hatha Yoga*** - is the most commonly practised path of yoga in West. The Sanskrit term HATHA is derived from the Sanskrit HA, meaning 'sun' and THA, meaning 'moon'. The Hatha yoga Sadhana aims to balance and unite the two opposite energies to attain a perfect polarity. Hatha Yoga includes cleansing practices, asana, kriyas, mudras, pranayama, relaxation techniques and some dharna or concentration practices for our body, prana, mind, and soul.

3. ***Raja Yoga / Ashtanga Yoga*** - Raja yoga is more commonly known as Ashtanga yoga, or the 'eightfold path of yoga' leading to self-realisation. In ancient yoga texts like the Hatha Yoga Pradipika, the Gheranda Samahita and the Shiva Samhita, Raja Yoga is described as the ultimate goal of yoga or the highest path of yoga, the other paths preparing our body and mind for Raja Yoga. Raja means 'king', or 'royal' or 'highest' and hence Raja Yoga is known as royal or the highest path of yoga. Raja Yoga is the science of our mind, consciousness, and soul and details all the hindrances to our self-realisation and how to remove them. The Yoga Sutras of Patanjali are the main source for the teachings of Raja Yoga.

4. ***Bhakti Yoga*** - is the path of devotion, worship and service to the divine, a way of life or sadhaka leading to divine-realisation or union. This is the commonly followed path by Hindus in India. The word Bhakti comes from the Sanskrit root 'bhaj' meaning 'to adore, worship, sing praise, or service to divine'. The concept of Bhakti as the path of love and devotion to the divine is described in the Bhagavad Gita and the Upanishads and it involves surrendering to the Divine or Supreme Consciousness.

5. ***Jnana Yoga*** - Jnana is Sanskrit word for 'knowledge or wisdom'. It is the path of knowledge of the true nature (Prakriti) of the Atman (soul) and Parmatman (Supreme Consciousness) through the practices of meditation, self-inquiry, and contemplation. Jnana Yoga aims to attain the 'awareness of absolute or supreme consciousness' and Swadhyaya or self-study is the key practice.

6. **Kundalini Yoga** - is an ancient Yoga and Tantra science dealing with the transformation and expansion of consciousness and the awakening and raising of Kundalini. Kundalini Yoga describes seven principal energy Chakras or wheels. The activation, balance and tuning of the chakras begins with the activation and union of the Prana and Apana Vayus through the Pingala and Ida Nadis by means of Asana, Pranayama, Bandhas, Kriyas, Mantras, and Visualisation to attain our full potential.

7. **Tantra Yoga**- is a path of yoga that teaches us to experience the universe (macrocosm or supreme consciousness) through various practices through the human body and consciousness (microcosm, individual consciousness). The Sanskrit word Tantra means 'leading principle', 'woven together' or 'the body as a tool'. Tantra yoga advocates for the balance and union of two opposites and not renunciation in the attempt to reach liberation. Tantra Yoga Sadhana is practiced to awaken the Chakras and raise the energy towards higher energy Chakras or Brahmarandra. It encourages its participants to build up kundalini energy in the top chakras so it 'spills from the top'. Tantra uses Asana, Pranayama, Mudra, Dharna, Dhyana, Mantras, Visualisations. Jnana Yoga Kriyas and Yantras or Mandalas are the key practices in Tantra.

8. **Mantra Yoga** - The Sanskrit word Mantra means 'sacred word, phrase, verse, charm, spell, or counsel'. Mantra Yoga uses mantras to free the mind from mundane activities and transcend to experience our True Self, leading to absolute union or divine realisation. Mantra yoga engages the mind through focusing on chanting, sound, duration, number of repetitions and the essence of the mantra. Repetition of the mantras creates a healing positive vibration and benefit to the one who chants and the one who listens. Mantra Yoga is also referred to as Japa Yoga. A Japa or Mantra chant can be chanted mentally or verbally out loud.

9. **Laya Yoga** - dissolves or transcends the individual self to the higher or supreme self through visualisations and mantra chanting. Laya is a Sanskrit term meaning 'dissolve' or 'transcend'. Laya yoga leads to the state of samadhi, which is the highest unification with the Divine; it includes asanas, pranayama, mudras, mantras and bandhas.

10. **Dhyana Yoga** - Dhyana is a Sanskrit word meaning 'meditation'. It is derived from the root, Dhi, meaning 'receptacle' or 'the mind' and Yana, meaning 'moving' or 'going'. Some scholars use the root word, dhyai, meaning 'to think

of'; Dhyana is a state of union or oneness with the focus point. Lord Krishna explains the Dhyana Yoga as a Path, in which the sadhaka or spiritual practice focuses the mind on one single object to transcend the mundane mind and experience cosmic consciousness or Samadhi.

11. Swara yoga - is a path to the study, control and manipulation of the breath through nostril breathing or Nadis, as a means to achieve Samadhi or self-realization. Swara yoga explains that we have two energy currents or Swaras, the Ida-Pingala, Chandra-Suriya or left-right nostril. We are predominately in governance of one or other of these subtle energy currencies, which has its own effects and influence.

This lesson has looked at what Yoga encompasses; it has considered the main paths of yoga and has examined how the Yogic Scriptures can support our understanding.

Lesson 3:
Ashtanga Yoga or Yoga of Eight Limbs

This lesson describes the eight limbs to the Yoga Sutras. The Yoga Sutras of Patanjali offer guidance on our spiritual path, so that all of our authentic decisions and actions come from a considered higher self-place.

1. Yama or five ethical restraints - These are the five ethical and moral virtues to live our life by, which fulfil all our needs to live in harmony with and within our individual, family, social and universal perspectives.
   ❖ Ahimsa: non-violence
   ❖ Satya: truthfulness
   ❖ Asteya: non-stealing and not taking anything for granted
   ❖ Brahmacharya: sensual energy discipline and living in harmony
      with bio-rhythms
   ❖ Aparigraha: Non-greed and non-possessiveness

2. Niyama, observances or codes of conducts- These are the five spiritual and self-discipline observances.
   ❖ Saucha: external and internal purity

❖ Santosha: contentment in fruits of our actions, acceptance of ourselves, others and situations own circumstances
❖ Tapas: Sincere and disciplined actions or practice with perseverance, determination, and persistence
❖ Swadhyaya: Introspection, Study of self, self-reflection
❖ Ishwara Pranidhana: Seeing life and each event as divine blessings, faith or trust in divine

3. Asana (posture, pose, pause): These are the physical yoga postures that help the body to be strong, flexible and healthy, to attain the sense of ease so we can progress further towards advance higher practices. Asana is also a state of being or self-mastery.

4. Pranayama (Subtle Vital Life Force Expansion): Pranayama help us to refine, extend and enhance the pranic energy flow to heal our body, mind and soul through using our breath as a tool.

5. Pratyahara (Sensory withdrawal): This limb is to withdraw our mind or conscious from sensory stimulus to transcend from mundane awareness to subtle consciousness.

6. Dharana (concentration practice): Dharna is effort towards single pointed focus on an inner or external object of awareness.

7. Dhyana (meditation): Dhyana is not a practice; it is result or success in Dharna or effort to focus our mind at one point. Here our mind is completely absorbed in single point of focus.

8. Samadhi (union): Samadhi is ultimate goal of Yoga Sadhana where sadhaka becomes one with the divine or supreme consciousness. This is a state of absolute bliss known as SAT-CHIT-ANANDA.

The guidance offered by these teachings helps us to live our lives in accordance with spiritual principles, which support our holistic health and well-being. The next lesson develops the practical understanding of yoga Chikitsa, which we can use to support our health.

Lesson 4:
What Yoga Offers for Holistic Health, Well-Being and Yoga Chikitsa

The yoga practices described in this lesson are the tools that we can use to support our health and well-being.

Jattis- These are also known as Sukshma Vyayama or subtle therapeutic exercises. They are unstructured, conscious movements like shaking, bouncing, circling, rotating, movements of limbs, joints and body parts. These Jattis can help many to bring sense of ease, remove toxins and develop body sensitivity.

Kriyas- These are more structured movements of body carried out with conscious breath as you flow from one to other position. Kriyas help through improving flexibility, strength, endurance, breathing, blood and energy circulation. These simple and complex kriyas can help us in a preventative way and also heal and rehabilitate our body and mind back to our best.

Yoga Vyayama- While Kriyas are very subtle, gentle and relaxing movements Vyayamas are more vigorous or stronger forms of Kriyas where it also becomes a physical, mental, emotional or energy workout.

Suriya Namaskars- In traditional Yoga there are many variations to offer our greetings and gratitude to the Sun or Suriya for our physical, mental, pranic and spiritual healing.

Hatha Yoga Kriyas- These are a set of movements moving from an asana to asana (posture to posture) with conscious breathing and focus on energy flows, physical points or chakras (subtle energy points). These generally include classical Hatha Yoga Postures, according to scriptures there are 84 classical postures.

Asanas- Asana are described by Patanjali as a "comfortable and stable seat or posture" to be held for long time while focussing the mind on various body points, chakras, energy flows. They are generally known as the more advanced or higher practices of Yoga. Each of the asana has significant preventive and therapeutic role for healing our body and mind.

Mudras- Mudras are body-mind-energy gestures to tune into the universal cosmic prana and channel it inward towards various chakras, naris, consciousness and body parts.

Pranayamas- Pranayamas use breath as a tool to enhance our Prana, the cosmic universal energy to refine, and vitalise our body, mind and energy. Pranayamas can be a great tool for refining, balancing and recharging our body, mind and soul for better health and well-being.

Jnana Yoga Kriyas- These are Pratyahara or relaxation techniques used to either enhance the energy subtle flows or to reverse the flows, so that energies can flow back to the point of their origin leading us to better health and well-being. The relaxation techniques are one of the best tools as part of yoga therapy as so many of our health problems now have their roots in stress.

Dharna or Meditation Techniques- These are classical concentration techniques for focussing our minds, leading to Dhyana or meditation. These practices help us to reconnect with our true self and see the higher perspectives of life and its meanings.

Ashtanga Yoga- This is based on Yoga Sutras of Patanjali, Ashtanga Yoga has eight steps leading the individual self to attain union with the higher self.

Yoga Philosophy- Yoga philosophy provides us with all the tools to enhance our mental, emotional and spiritual well-being, leading us to higher states of consciousness and joyfulness. We use the Yoga Sutras, Samkhya Yoga, Vedanta, Bhagavat Gita, Yoga Vashishtha and the Upanishads as reference scriptures. Yoga Philosophy provides us all the tools, concepts, principles, ideas and practices to deal with our mental, emotional and spiritual problems.

Yoga Anatomy and Physiology- We study general anatomy and physiology, along with yoga-anatomy including the pancha-kosha, naris and chakra system, adhi-vyadhi (psycho-somatic) and spanda-nispanda (homeostasis, stretch-relax). This brings a holistic perspective, with kriyas and prakriyas to work on ourselves at the core of our existence from gross to subtle and subtlest to gross for true healing.

Jnana Yoga- This is Yoga of wisdom to improve our lifestyle, attitude, thought process to live our life with health and happiness.

Many Paths of Yoga- Various paths of yoga like raja yoga, Bhakti Yoga, karma yoga, mantra yoga etc. provide us with tools to work on our health and well-being at various levels.

Lesson 5:
What is Yoga Therapy?

Yoga Therapy is an adapted, modified or applied form of yoga using asana, kriya, pranayama, visualisation and relaxation techniques to help prevent, heal, or rehabilitate people with different health issues. Yoga has proved to be significantly supportive with all stress related disorders, including mental and emotional problems.

Dr. Swami Gitananda Giri, my Guru, says that Yoga Chikitsa is virtually as old as Yoga itself, indeed the return of the mind that feels separated from the Universe in which it exists represents the first Yoga therapy, it is-

"Man's first attempt at unitive understanding of mind-emotion-physical distress and is the oldest holistic concept and therapy in the world".

Dr. Swami Gitananda Giri.

Ancient and traditional forms of Yoga have a wide range of applications including preventive, therapeutic and rehabilitative approaches as well as being concerned with spiritual and evolutionary growth. Hatha Yoga provides us with all the tools for our body and mind, while Raja Yoga provides us with holistic tools, concepts and ideas to deal with mental and emotional problems.

Modern medical science and Psychology describe more than 4,000 diseases and disorders of the body and mind. Yoga explains that many of these disease or health problems are the outcome of stress and strain caused by our Vasanas (desires), Kaam (our desire to seek sensual pleasures), Krodha (anger), Ahamkara (ego) and Asmita (i-ness). Now we also need to add abuse caused to our body-mind-spirit by 'junk' food, religion and modern stressful lifestyles. Holistic health, or Swasthya, in the Yogic sense means to be at ease within and without of ourselves.

Swamiji Dr. Gitananda Giriji further states that all diseases, maladies, tensions, are manifestations of divisions in what should be man's complete nature, the Atman or Self. This Self is 'Ease', a loss of 'Ease' creates 'Dis-ease'. Duality is the first insanity, the first disease, the unreasonable thought that 'I am different from the whole.... I am unique.... I am me'. The ego is a manifestation of disease, only a distorted ego could feel alone, suffer from 'the lonely disease', in a Universe, a Cosmos totally filled with the Self. It is of some interest to note that one of the oldest words for man in an Indian language is 'Insana'. Man is 'insane'. A return to sanity is the purpose of real Yoga Sadhana and Yoga Abyasa. Yoga Chikitsa is one of the methods to help the insane man back to the path of sanity. A healthy man or woman is known by the term 'Yogi'.

Dr. Ananda Balayogi Bhavanani, ICYER, India in his Yoga Chikitsa book writes that-

Yoga as a mode of therapy (Yoga Chikitsa) has become extremely popular and a great number of studies and systematic reviews offer scientific evidence of its potential in treating a wide range of psychosomatic conditions. Yoga understands health and well-being as a dynamic continuum of human nature and not merely a 'state' to be reached and maintained. Yoga helps the individual to establish sukha sthanam, which may be defined as a dynamic sense of physical mental and spiritual well-being.

Understanding the applications of Hatha yoga and Yoga philosophy and bringing them in to our practice (abhyasa) to the best of our ability, will help us gain the optimum level of health and state of ease within our individual selves, which is known as Swasthya.

Yoga is a path, which gives us sets of practices, guidelines and tools to support our health and well-being needs. Each path of yoga like Raja Yoga, Jnana Yoga, Karma Yoga, Bhakti Yoga etc. leads us from duality to oneness: disturbed mind to still mind; imbalance to balance; disequilibrium to equanimity; and gradually to absolute self-realisation. The highest form of yogic therapy aims to free us from all our physical, mental, Karmic, Samsarik, Bhautik and Adhibhautik sufferings to a state of absolute bliss.

The IAYT Educational Standards for the Training of Yoga Therapists defines it as follows-
Yoga therapy is the process of empowering individuals to progress toward improved health and well-being through the application of the teachings and practices of Yoga.
TKV Desikachar and Kausthub Desikachar explains that-

Yoga therapy is a self-empowering process, where the care-seeker, with the help of the Yoga therapist, implements a personalised and evolving Yoga practice, that not only addresses the illness in a multi-dimensional manner, but also aims to alleviate his/her suffering in a progressive, non-invasive and complementary manner. Depending upon the nature of the illness, Yoga therapy can not only be preventative or curative, but also serve a means to manage the illness, or facilitate healing in the person at all levels.

Yoga in its various forms provides us with tools, kriayas and prakriyas, the concepts and practices, which can be easily adapted to each and every individual according to their needs. Patanjali guides us in the Yoga Sutras to free ourselves from mundane suffering, we need to follow Abhayas, do our practice to heal and Vairajna, let go of our attachment with pain and suffering and our associations with them.

Gary Kraftsow of the American Viniyoga Institute defines it as follows-
Yoga therapy, derived from the Yoga tradition of Patanjali and the Ayurvedic system of health care refers to the adaptation and application of Yoga techniques and practices to help individuals facing health challenges at any level manage their condition, reduce symptoms, restore balance, increase vitality, and improve attitude. In addition Yoga Therapy requires a skill in teaching, adapting and modifying practices, so they are accessible and achievable for the sadhakas to regain optimum physical, mental, emotional and spiritual well-being. One may see yoga as part of prevention, cure, or rehabilitation. Yoga paths and practices are diverse, and each individual can choose which one of them is suitable for their health and well-being and as a yoga therapist or teacher, we can help someone in finding that suitable path or practice.

Joseph LePage, M.A., Integrative Yoga Therapy (U.S.A.) explains this as follows-

Yoga therapy is that facet of the ancient science of Yoga that focuses on health and wellness at all levels of the person: physical, psychological, and spiritual. Yoga therapy focuses on the path of Yoga as a healing journey that brings balance to the body and mind through an experiential understanding of the primary intention of Yoga: awakening of Spirit, our essential nature.

Ultimately yoga leads us to absolute realisation where the self becomes one with the higher self. If we study the Yoga Sutras, Bhagavad Gita, or Yoga Vashistha, there is a step-by-step scientific approach of dealing with our mental, emotional, spiritual, and karmic issues and how we can transcend them. Each of the scriptures can be seen as a focussed, organised spiritual counselling for our wellness and evolution. Dr. Ananda Balayogi Bhavanani in one of his recent talks mentioned the understanding that some of these spiritual teachings are actually thought to be from the future and these Rishis travelled back in past to put them in place to help the humanity.

Larry Payne Ph.D. from the Samata Yoga Centre (U.S.A.) defines yoga therapy as adapting the practices of Yoga to the needs of people with specific or persistent health problems that are not usually able to be addressed in a group class.

In Yoga as therapy, we will need to address each person individually at least in the beginning, as part of the assessment, diagnosis and understanding the needs of each individual. Later on gradually introducing a group class can enhance the benefits of therapeutic yoga in many ways through meeting with like-minded people, making new friends, social interactions, etc.

Robin Monro, Ph.D. Yoga Biomedical Trust (England) explains that Yoga therapy is the adaptation of yoga practices for people with health challenges. Yoga therapists are able to prescribe specific regimens of postures, breathing exercises, and relaxation techniques to suit individual's needs. Dr. Monro explains that research has shown Yoga therapy to be among the most effective complementary therapies for several common ailments; challenges may be an illness, a temporary condition like pregnancy or childbirth, or a chronic condition associated with old age or infirmity.

The Hatha Yoga Pradipika, Gheranda Samhita, and Shiva Samhita mention many physical, mental and spiritual benefits of asanas, mudra, bandhas, shat karmas, pranayama's and relaxation techniques. Marie Quail, from the Yoga Therapy and Training Centre (Ireland) writes that-

Yoga comprises a wide range of mind/body practices, from postural and breathing exercises to deep relaxation and meditation. Yoga therapy tailors these to the health needs of the individual. It helps to promote all-round positive health, as well as assisting particular medical conditions. The therapy is particularly appropriate for many chronic conditions that persist despite conventional medical treatment.

Yoga scriptures and texts thousands of years ago mention the idea of Adhi-Vyadhi or psychosomatic illnesses and offer us the tools to deal with problems at the root level of our mind. Avidya which can be translated as 'lack of knowledge', 'lack of awareness', or 'denying the truth' is described as a root cause of all our problems. Judith Hanson Lasater, Ph.D., says that the techniques of Yoga can create, stimulate, and maintain our optimum state of physical, emotional, mental, and spiritual health. Our Hatha Yoga practices stimulate our body, muscles, organs, nervous system and endocrine system through means of stretching, twisting, compressing, and messaging with deep conscious breath. This enhances our body's ability to relax, rejuvenate and heal. Relaxation techniques, Jnana Yoga Kriyas and Yoga Nidras will help de-stressing our mind and emotions and bring a sense of balance and equanimity. Meditation and Jnana yoga practices will help us release old memories, traumas and samskaras and find inner peace to connect with our true self.

Art Brownstein, M.D. explains that Yoga therapy is preventive in nature, as is Yoga itself, but it is also restorative in many instances, palliative in others, and curative in many others." Our Jattis -subtle or sukshma Vyayama or exercises can be done by anyone at a certain level to stimulate our joints, muscles and peripheral nerves to improve our body awareness, and motor skills. Similarly short, guided meditation and relaxation practices can help improving our mental and emotional wellbeing. Dr. Richard Miller Ph.D. summarises that Yoga therapy may be defined as the application of yogic principles to a particular person with the objective of achieving a particular spiritual, psychological, or physiological goal. The means employed are comprised of intelligently conceived steps that include Ashtanga Yoga practices of Yama, niyama, asana, pranayama, pratyahara, dharana, dhyana, and Samadhi; also included are the application of meditation, textual study, spiritual or psychological counselling, chanting, imagery, prayer, and ritual to meet the needs of the individual. Importantly Yoga therapy respects individual differences in age, culture, religion, philosophy, occupation, and mental and physical health. The knowledgeable and competent yogi or yogini applies Yoga Therapy according to the individual's needs, age, strength and ability.

There is a modern application of yoga through therapeutic approaches, which as Georg Feuerstein Ph.D. writes integrate traditional yogic concepts and techniques with Western medical and psychological knowledge. Whereas traditional Yoga is primarily concerned with a personal transcendence on the part of a healthy individual, Yoga therapy aims at the holistic treatment of various kinds of psychological or somatic dysfunctions ranging from back problems to emotional distress. However both approaches share an understanding of the human being as an integrated mind-body system that functions optimally only when there is a state of dynamic balance.

Michael Lee, of Phoenix Rising Yoga Therapy writes that-

Yoga therapy is a holistic healing art. Rather than prescribe treatments, it invites presence and awareness. Using age-old yogic approaches to deeper presence and awareness, we are able to know ourselves more fully. Out of that knowing, we are more easily moved to embrace the opportunity for change, growth, and enhanced well-being in body, feelings, thought, and spirit.

Ganesh Mohan, Swastha Yoga and Ayurveda inform us that Yoga therapy encompasses the application of Yoga to individuals to empower them to progress toward greater health and freedom from disease.

This chapter has discussed what is Yoga Therapy? There has been recent research work looking at the effects of yoga on health, which have shown how various, yoga practices can assist in the prevention and management of physical, mental, and emotional health needs and help healing. Applying Yoga Philosophy practices can help us change our perspective and attitude and reframe our mental and emotional health to support our quality of life. Understanding our body, our psychology, our life governing principles and spirit of consciousness will bring the subtlest and deepest of healing we all are seeking for. Hatha Yoga, Asana, Pranayama, Mudra and Jnana Yoga Practices will help preparing our body, mind and energy for that healing to manifest and be received.

References and Resources

Step By Step Course in Rishiculture Gitananda Yoga by Swamiji Dr Gitananda Giriji. www.icyer.com
Yoga Chikitsa By Dr Ananda Balayogi Bhavanani, www.icyer.com
 An article by Dr Ananda Balayogi Bhavanani, Yoga Therapy for Conscious adulthood
https://www.svastha.net/
https://www.iayt.org/page/ContemporaryDefiniti
http://khyf.net/
https://www.viniyoga.com/
https://samata.com/
https://www.yogatherapy.org/
https://www.yogaireland.com/
https://www.judithhansonlasater.com/
https://www.irest.org/
http://www.traditionalyogastudies.com/

Lesson 6:
Yoga as The Science and Philosophy of Wholistic Being

In this lesson we consider the meaning of wholistic or holistic. For our concept of Wholistic Being we have to look at several components of life including the physical, social, personal, global and spiritual. It includes the quality of our mind which allows us to connect with ourselves and the rest of the world and enjoy life and participate creatively in the life events. When we become caught in a negative mind, we let our life to fall into spiralling whirlpools of the mind known as chitta-vrittis and kleshas, where we can easily suffer with frustration , depression, carelessness , self-centredness and selfishness . Hence our mental component becomes very important for our wholistic and blissful being.

As we come to understand the scientific and methodological approach of Patanjali in the Yoga Sutras; the understanding of our mind, its qualities, characters and states and basic principles or philosophy of a healthy mind-set becomes far more important than all other practices. Understanding our mind enables our ability to diagnose the problems we are facing. As a practitioner, you cannot write a prescription unless you know the problem itself. As part of our growth, we need to have understanding, awareness and a philosophy in life.

The development of our holistic being and wellness begins with the foundation of a virtuous mind and a holistic life philosophy; this helps us in making day-to-day life choices. In a way yoga is science and philosophy of life, mind and soul. Here we are not talking about religion, or a belief system, but more practical values, virtues, attitude and a mind-set that enables us to experience joy, peace and tranquillity within our hearts.

The components of wholistic wellness include:
- ❖ A holistic life philosophy
- ❖ A healthy and moderate lifestyle
- ❖ A healthy routine in our daily lives
- ❖ A nutritional diet
- ❖ Healthy associations and relationships
- ❖ Healthy desires, ambitions and goals
- ❖ A healthy attitude or Drishti

Lesson 7:
A Holistic Life Philosophy

Lesson seven considers how we develop a health life philosophy and the tools that Yoga gives us to do this. A healthy life philosophy is not just about the theory, principles or ideas about Gods and the Universe, or Life and Soul, but it is the practical and applied understandings of our evolutionary life processes and how we can maintain a healthy and happy life. It is of great importance in our healing processes.

Each and every one of us is going through a continuous evolutionary process from birth, till death and beyond. Our body, mind and intellect are all evolving. Since our birth our body has evolved from a little baby; our bones, muscles and organs have evolved. We are continuously going through physical change in our bodies. Our mental, emotional and intellectual processes are changing too. We must learn to have the right attitude and mind set to enable us to look after, nurture, and care for our bodies, minds and our emotional well-being. Through the practices of Yoga, we are provided with Hatha Yoga: Kriyas, Asanas, Pranayama, Mudras, Shata-Karmas, Relaxation techniques, meditation techniques, mantra and bhajans and so much more for our physical, mental, emotional well-being.

We also need to look into the spiritual aspects of our life philosophy and evolutionary journey. Remember not to confuse our spiritual life with religious philosophy; our spiritual and religious life philosophies can be seen as our two eyes, which can never see each other, but they can see everything else together. Our spiritual eye, drishti or life philosophy connects us with our own inner self, the auspiciousness and goodness that is within us and enables us to live a healthy and virtuous life. Spiritual life philosophy also helps us to be fearless and live in harmony with all our living and non-living beings in this universe.

Yoga Provides us with the following tools for a healthier holistic life philosophy -

1. ***Yamas*-** Patanjali details five Yamas for our moral and social discipline, on how to live and fulfil our day-to-day needs. These are five universal laws to live in peace and harmony within our individual self and with everything and everyone else:
   ❖ **Ahimsa-** (non-violence or non-injury) is the first of five yamas which means abstaining from causing pain or harm to all living creatures, either by thought, word, intention or action. The Ahimsa in our life supports us to practice love

and compassion towards all living creatures. Ahimsa is the highest virtue according to Hindu and Jain philosophies as it helps us finding the peace within our heart, behaviour and choices.

❖ **Satya-** (or truthfulness) is honesty and authenticity in our thoughts, speech and actions. Satya is being true to ourselves and living our life to our full potential and doing everything we can do to be healthy and happy. Satya also includes keeping ourselves free from manipulated ideas, expectations, desires and thoughts.

❖ **Asteya-** (non-stealing) means to not take anything that doesn't belong to us, or that we haven't earned. The concept of non-stealing at a material level is very easy to understand; however at a personal and social level it also involves not stealing someone's time, energy, thoughts, ideas or credits. Swamis Gitananda Giri ji explains that stealing our own or someone else's time that could have been used for their health, or evolution is the subtlest form of stealing.

❖ **Brahmacharya-** is generally translated as sexual abstinence, but in its true sense, the concept of brahmacharya means to live in harmony with the natural rhythms or laws of nature. Brahamachaya encompasses our capacity to channel our energy for the good of everyone's health, peace and evolution. It is the life philosophy or lifestyle that guides us to live in harmony with our natural biorhythms. This can be as simple as eating, sleeping, waking, exercising, working or socialising at appropriate times, in appropriate situations, around appropriate people and with appropriate attitudes.

❖ **Aparigraha-** means non-greed or non-possessiveness of all the material and non-materials, which are not necessary for our health and wellness. At subtlest level it means letting go of our old negative experiences and memories that are causing distress to the balance of our mind and emotions.

2. **Niyama-** Niyama are the second limb of Ashtanga Yoga and are understood as self-discipline, or moral and ethical observances. These are the virtues or values that we need to follow or practice to enable us to live a healthy, peaceful life and attain our highest potential:

❖ **Saucha-** or purity is the first of five Niyama which is the means to maintain purity of our body, mind, sense, thoughts, desires, and environment. Saucha can help us to have the right mindset and attitude towards our own self and others and maintain a sense of clarity in perception and experiences. Hatha Yoga describes very extensive cleansing practices known as Shata-Karmas to support our Saucha.

❖ **Santosha-** or contentment is being satisfied with the fruits and outcomes of our actions. It is also the ability to free our minds from expectations and desires. Santosha enables us to live and enjoy our lives without judging our comparing ourselves with others in any form.

❖ **Tapas-** can translate as austerity and discipline in our practice to achieve success in life. So many of us know what to do in day-to-day life for being healthy, but how many of us actually do it. Doing what needs to be done is Tapas.

❖ **Swadhyaya-** is the ability to know ourselves in our true meaning. It involves a process of self-study, or introspection by means of self-enquiry, conscious awareness, and acquiring the life wisdom or knowledge through scriptures and other sources. Through this tool we can understand our true nature in its mundane form and then experience the divine self by removing all the obstacles and layers of whirlpools of the mind.

❖ **Iswara Pranidhana-** means to dedicate, devote or surrender. It is our ability to see the divine purpose and opportunity in each and every life event and experience we are going through. It is also our ability to offer all our actions for divine purpose and surrender our ego to this higher purpose; in this way becoming one with divine consciousness.

3. *Maitri-* Maitri is a Sanskrit word which can be translated as 'friendship', 'friendliness' or 'benevolence'. It can also be used to describe the mental union that takes place when two people are on the same wavelength. The Pali version of this word that is often used is 'metta' which encompasses unconditional love for all beings. Another way of describing Maitri is a form of love which excludes the suffering that can arise from attachment (known as upadana).

4. *Karuna-* means compassion. Karuna is one of the nine virtuous emotions described in Hindu life style as important for peace and harmony. In this life principle one needs to be free of self-centredness and feelings of pity, resentment, anger, frustration and guilt. We all must cultivate compassion in our thoughts, feelings, emotions and actions. It is a further reflective practice of friendliness towards each and every one. The virtue of compassion or Karuna needs ability to let go and forgive; we can be extremely harsh to ourselves and others for little mistakes and these are the things that can be one of the causing factors of many health issues.

5. *Mudita-* is detailed as one of the tools that deals with obstacles in our lives. Mudita is a state of inner joy, happiness and cheerfulness towards our own as well as other peoples accomplishments; it is without any form of self-interest. It is also a living concept, an attitude of looking forward to every event and opportunity in life and trying to see the goodness in all things. When we are happy or cheerful, our body and muscles relax and release endorphins, the feel good chemicals in body which help with the healing and rejuvenation processes

of our body and mind. This attitude of mudita can greatly enhance our life quality and purpose.

6. *Upeksha*- Upeksha means detachment, a balanced mindset, tolerance and equanimity. Yoga explains four elements in our behaviour with others and ourselves for living a healthy and happy life and attain our full potential. These are loving-kindness or friendliness (maitri), compassion (karuna), joyfulness (mudita) and equanimity (upeksha). These are four basic qualities of a Yogi who is free from all mundane, mental and emotional afflictions. Upeksha is to be cultivated in all adverse situations to keep ourselves calm and help us to not react to various situations or stimulus.

7. *Samatva*- Samatva is a further subtler aspect of Upeksha and Karuna. It is a state of equality and equanimity where we remain balanced in all adverse situations. This helps us to practice absolute equality in speech, thought and action towards each and every one. Krishna mentions in the Bhagavat Gita that Samatva is the virtue that treats failure and success alike and helps us remain in balance. It involves not getting over excited or developing ego for our success and also not getting stressed and depressed for our failures or mistakes. This state of balance and equality can free us from many mental and emotional problems. Krishna further explains that enlightened beings see everyone with equal respect and in the same way, regardless of their colour, cast, religion, race, and social and economic status; because everyone is eternally equal in their true form as Self, or Atman.

8. *Kshama*- Kshama is a Sanskrit word, which means forbearance and forgiveness. This is one of the greatest virtues, forgiving others and letting go of the past, as well as not judging them on past events. Self-forgiveness and letting go of our own mistakes and learning from them is also another aspect of Kshama. It is a virtue of patience and of having a non-judgemental attitude.

9. *Vairajna*- Abhyasa and vairagya are central principles in Ashtanga yoga that deal with our mental whirlpools and help us attain inner quietness and peace. The Sanskrit word Vairajna means detachment from mundane worldly desires. It is an attitude of letting go and freeing our mind from all the sensory information. In a therapeutic sense Vairajna is actually non-attachment to problems themselves, keeping our mind and energy focussed on all the positive and creative aspects of life, health and wellness.

This lesson has described the tools that yoga provides us with to develop a healthy life philosophy.

Lesson 8:
What do we study in Gitananda Yoga Chikitsa?

This lesson lays out a brief summary of what we need to study within Yoga Chikitsa for the prevention and treatment of medical conditions. We will go on to look at these in more depth as we continue to develop our understanding and practice.

Human Anatomy and Yoga - While modern science deals with only one body, yoga science enumerates the Pancha-Koshas or five body system. Within our yogic perspective anatomy also includes the pancha-pranas and Chakras, Bindus and energy points.

Human Physiology and Yoga - Likewise Anatomy in Yoga also goes further into the subtle aspects of our physiology with concepts of Doshas, Tri-Gunas, Loma-Viloma, Swaras and Vasaanas. These are the are underlying forces which govern our body and all its functions.

Yoga Philosophy - Yoga Darshan provides us with insight into life, our minds and the conflicts causing distress, pain and disease. It guides us on the way that we view the world. Yoga Philosophy also provides all the tools, kriyas and prakriyas to free ourselves from all these conflicts and become one with our higher-selves.

Yoga Psychology – This is where we begin to bring all of yoga's philosophical ideas and principles into practice. Yoga Darshan is one of the most advanced holistic and applied psychologies and psycho-therapeutic approaches, which identifies that the goal in life is union with the ultimate reality, a state of enlightenment or samadhi.

Hatha Yoga - Hatha Yoga provides us with details of many Asanas with their therapeutic and spiritual benefits. The static postures help us with: healing injuries; healing past traumas; improving our flexibility, endurance and strength; and removing accumulated toxins causing distress in our bodies.

Pranayama - Gitananda Yoga teaches around 130 Pranayamas. These breath control practices are to enhance Prana and are some of the best Yoga Therapy tools. Even the classical pranayama's can be modified for their therapeutic applications for respiratory problems. Pranayama or modified breathing techniques are proven to be significantly beneficial for mental, emotional and nervous disorders. It has particular benefit for long-Covid sufferers and other chronic lung conditions such as asthma.

Mudras – The word Mudra means seal or energy gesture. Various Yoga Mudras can help to channel our vital forces to the desired parts of the body, Bindus or Chakras for healing and rejuvenation. Mudras work directly at glandular and endocrine level to bring health and well-being.

Vyayama Yoga - There is also a wide range of yoga-based exercises in the form of Vinyasa or movements from one position to another. Gitananda Yoga offers a wide range of Jattis (loosening up movements to release and remove stress and toxins from joints) and Kriyas (sets of simple movements from one to another posture for bringing mobility and enhancing prana and blood circulation). Hatha-Yoga provides us with Kriyas (sets of asanas to work on the subtle energy flows within body parts and between our chakras) and Suriya-Namaskar (sun-salutations for strength, flexibility, endurance, weight loss, enhanced body immunity and vitality).

Ahara-Vihara – The next step is ensuring a healthy diet and life style to enjoy health and well-being. Ahara is what we eat and drink for our body. It is also what we watch, see, hear, read and engage with; this is the food for our mind. Remember we become what we feed into our body-mind system. Vihara means lifestyle or the habits that we follow. It includes our sleeping, waking, working, exercise, eating and leisure activities. Yoga therapy includes a healthy nutritional diet rich in fresh fruits, vegetables, sprouted grains, dry nuts, lentils, etc. Vihara includes having a moderate life style with a good balance of exercise, sleep, work, leisure time, etc.

Fasting and Mauna - We can give physiological rest to our constantly working digestive system and vocal cords by fasting from food and speech. Fasting from food can be whole day without food, or one day a week eating only fruits. Mauna or silence is the practice of not speaking which heightens our other senses. When we are silent we are able to observe the world around us and turn our reflection inwards. It can be for 30 minutes to hour every day or if possible few hours a week if not a whole day. This gives us time to reflect and listen to our inner body and mind.

Shavasana and Yoga Nidra - Many stress related problems can be healed by using various relaxation and yoga nidra techniques. These practices help our body systems to experience rest and regain the state of ease, which they tend to forget as we live in states of chronic stress, distress and dis-ease.

Jnana Yoga Therapy - Jnana Yoga provides us with a strong foundation of moral and ethical principles in the form of yamas and niyamas, which can help us with healing our mental, emotional, karmic and spiritual problems. Some of the typical Jnana Yoga therapy practices and remedies offered by Patanjali are in the form of: mudita (cheerfulness); karuna (kindness, compassion); maitri (friendliness, harmony); and upeksha (equanimity and letting go).

Postural Manipulation or Assistance - Many Postures or Kriyas can be assisted by a yoga therapist or teacher to help people with limited mobility or strength to improve their physical and mental well-being.

Naris and Muscle Manipulations - By the use of our hands, feet and fingers a yoga therapist can manipulate naris, muscles and even chakras to heal or rejuvenate parts of points within the body.

Yoga Cleansing or Purification - Hatha Yoga details six cleansing practices to remove all the toxins from our body. The three types of doshas (the bodies constitutional imbalances) - vata, pita, and kapha can be re-balanced by these cleansing practices. The six kinds of purifying practices are: Dhauti, Basti, Neti, Trataka, Nauti and Kapala Bhati.

Mantras and Bhajans - Various Mantras and Bhajans can help us enhance our manomaya kosha or mind body and heal many karmic and spiritual causes of health problems.

Dhyana or Meditation - Meditation enables us to rest our body and mind consciously. Regular meditation can help us release stress, anxieties and worries, which cause many health problems by focusing on the present moment and removing our thoughts from past concerns or future anxieties. Meditation can help improve our sleep and our general brain function.

This lesson has laid out important areas of study within Yoga Chikitsa for the prevention and treatment of medical conditions. The focus is on the ways in which we can heal and support our health and well-being.

Lesson 9:
The 12 Point Yogic Diagnosis

This lesson on the 12 Point Yogic Diagnosis - Dr Swami Gitananda Giri Ji is Modified from Original Article by Dr. Ananda Balayogi Bhavanani.

Yoga offers us a path of holistic body, mind and conscious management to attain our full potential, and similarly yoga therapy is the application and modification of yogic Kriyas and Prakriyas, concepts and principles to enhance our health and wellness and regain our sense of balance, coherence and optimum health. The science of Yoga as a therapy (Yoga Chikitsa) has its own system of diagnosis and health evaluation like other therapeutic approaches. Dr Ananda mentions that "the mere use of Yoga techniques to suppress symptoms is Yogopathy".

Yogamaharishi Dr. Swami Gitananda Giri describes a twelve step diagnostic method or dwadasha rogalakshna anukrama. It is one of the most comprehensive yogic diagnosis tools, which incorporates a method for self-introspection and self-analysis (Swadhyaya). This wholistic diagnostic tool will enable a yoga therapist to understand the needs, health issues and underlying factors of care seekers and it will help the care-seeker to understand himself or herself better. Remember that your aim is to regain the lost health, happiness and wholesomeness through unitive path of yoga.

The twelve important tools of yogic diagnosis used in yoga therapy described by Swamiji are as follows:

1. Triguna: Lord Krishna describes three primary qualities or Gunas express the nature of each individual: they are Sattva (Pure, calm and coherence), Rajas (active, and energetic) and Tamas (dull, inactive and lazy).

Each individual due to his or her own inert nature must be treated differently. Dr. Ananda explains that within western medicine everyone is treated democratically in the same way and this turns simple toxicity into permanent sickness. The trigunic nature must first be evaluated to bring about self-healing in a patient. The more sensitive and evolved the person, the more sensitive must be the treatment.

2.Tridosha: Ayurveda evaluates individuals on the basis of the three different natures of individuals based on their constitution or Doshas. Dr. Ananda explains that-

Without evaluating patients according to their dosha, modern medicine dries up the kapha, increases chemical poisoning and produces pressure conditions that are all chronic disorders, while the original dosha imbalances may be easily rectified and balanced.

The three doshas are **Kapha**, **Pitta** and **Vata**.

3. Trivasana: Vasanas are the deep-rooted behaviour patterns, desires, and belief systems which can be understood as the psychological background to one's personal nature. These Vasanas represents personal propensities of each individual and bind them to the wheel of birth-cycles (Jivan-Mrityu-Bandha-Chakra). Yoga describes three types of vasanas: Deha Vasana (desires and behaviour patterns attached with body and physical pleasures); Loka vasana (desires, behaviour patterns and attachment to one's position in life and society); and Jnana vasana (desires and behaviour patterns attached with education, and knowledge).

4. Prana: Prana is the subtlest cosmic energy that governs all the living and non-living mechanisms which exists eternally and is described as an 'all-pervading cosmic force'. The Yoga tradition describes five movements or functions of prana known as the vayus or winds of Pancha Prana Vayus including Prana, Apana, Samana, Vyana and Udana. These five vayus govern different areas of the body and different physical and subtle activities. A Yoga Therapist or health seeker will need to determine which of the prana vayu and upa-prana vayu is active or recessive, and which one is out of harmony. Improper and out of harmony of prana-vayus may lead to various health issues associated with the areas and functions it is involved in. Optimum and balanced flow of Pancha-Prana Vayus is health: malfunction of prana-vayus is diseases; and loss of Prana is death.

5. Abhyasa Krama: Abhyasa means continued practice to the extent that it becomes part of your personality or nature. An individual with a certain order of discipline can be trusted to follow the practices and direction to regain health and wellness; while undisciplined ones are very difficult to be helped and healed. Dr. Ananda Balayogi Bhavanani explains that if we are disciplined we may be seldom ill, but as we suffer from ignorance or avidya this can cause us to be ill; however when truth is revealed we can immediately follow the truth. Having said that whereas most real Gurus will refuse to accept students unless they are disciplined, Yoga therapists don't always really have that choice!

6. *Jiva Karma:* Jiva is our living sentient substance, many of our modern illness are rooted in our unhealthy lifestyles. Yoga teaches us the tools of Yamas and Niyamas as part of a healthy lifestyle. The only way to attain freedom from suffering is by adhering to these moral and ethical virtues. Lack of virtues in life leads us to sickness, pain, suffering and violence. Moral and ethical life is a fundamental necessity of health and happiness in life.

7. *Chetana:* Chetana is the field of thoughts and consciousness. The quality of thought of the individual plays a very important role in their health, life choices, view-points and perspectives as well as life-philosophy. Individuals can be idealistic, positive, outgoing, negative, reserved, etc. Our thoughts are the cause of all physical actions. Our state of mind manifests the state of body and state of body manifests the state of mind (adhij-Vyadhij and Vyadhij-Adhij).

8. *Vacha:* Our speech is a very important aspect of our health and wellness. Dr. Ananda mentions that so much can be diagnosed from the way a person speaks, how they pronounce and enunciate language and how they deliver the "power of sound in speech". Refined speech should be met with refined results, whereas crude and rough speech can elicit crude and rough responses. Sounds can be easily relate with the regions of their production, tone, energy and pitch to each individual state of body, mind and awareness. A great saint Tyagaraja explained that sounds can be classified in association with the area of their production: the nabhi (navel), hridaya (heart), kantha (throat), Jivya (tongue), nasagra (nasal area) etc. Saint Thiyagaraja who was a great south Indian music composer delineated these regions and their importance in producing the seven sacred notes of Indian music in his krithi (song) shobillu saptaswara (the seven beautiful heavenly notes of music).

9. *Ahara:* Our physical body or Annamayya Kosha is primarily assembled from our food and it is well known in Yoga, Ayurveda, Naturopathy and other alternative medicines that our food plays an important part in health or sickness, dietary habits must be examined in great detail. Also food carries its own memory and energy and the source of food, way we prepare or cook our food and energy we put in to the process from buying to eating also plays significant role in our health or sickness. Yoga and Ayurveda promotes a nutritional vegetarian diet to attain a healthy body and peaceful mind as well as emotional balance. Junk food and unhealthy dietary habits must be changed to regain health and wellness. The philosopher Thiruvalluvar described that the one who eats on an empty stomach attains health, while the one who eats for greed and pleasure develops ill-health. He further explained that "he who eats after the previous meal has been digested, needs not any medicine" and advised us on the yogic concept of Mitahara that "eating moderate quantity of easily digestible foods leads to health and wellbeing".

10. *Viparita Buddhi:* Good health demands that we have healthy life habits. When we deliberately misuse tobacco, alcohol and other drugs or substances it can only lead to diseases or illness. There are many other habits like over or under eating, sexual risk-taking, over or under sleeping, over use of modern screens and social media that also induce many health problems. Dr. Ananda describes that "Viparita Buddhi is considered one of the final steps on the road to self induced disaster as made clear by the common statement "vinashkale viparita buddhi" (when the end is near the intelligence is lost)." This relates to the concept that when faced with our own destruction we can act against reason.

11. *Jiva Vritti:* The observation and evaluation of more subtle psycho-biological life patterns and biorhythms of each individual, for example the periodicity of the nasal cycle, number of breaths per minute, quality and pattern of breathing (like deep or shallow, diaphragmatic or thoracic, easy or laboured), the periodicity and rate of the heart, blood pressure, regularity of passing urine and emptying of bowels etc. are classified under Jiva Vritti.

12. *Sankalpa:* Sankalpa means intention and guides us to know an individual's inspirations and aspirations which may involve a desire to regain health and wellness. A health seekers or care-seekers beliefs, attitudes and perspectives including their religion and faith, positive or negative attitudes, high or low temperament etc. are included here. Are they open to take a yogic advice and willing to follow the practices?

It is inspirational to contemplate the wisdom of the great minds (Rishis) who devised and codified such a complete system of diagnosis and health evaluation. When we make the effort to incorporate these concepts into our Yoga therapy practice, then we start to be real Yoga Chikitsaks (those practicing yoga as a therapy).

Lesson 10:
Key Yoga Therapy Models

In this lesson we aim to give an introduction and brief outline of the ten key Yoga Therapy models. Important concepts of therapeutic care and practices are briefly outlined here to give us a foundation to our understanding of Yoga Chikitsa.

1. Symptomatic or Instant Relief and Healing or Short-term plan

According to medical dictionary Symptomatic treatment is "a therapy that eases the symptoms without addressing the basic cause of the diseases". Symptomatic treatment is also known as palliative treatment. As a yoga therapist you may use some asanas, Kriyas, Pranayamas and relaxation techniques to help ease the symptoms, relieve pain and gain some flexibility, mobility and strength. These are generally known as one-to-one Hatha Yoga lessons, where a care-seekers seeks for general advice for a particular health issue or injury. Postural adjustment, muscles manipulation, guided relaxation or jnana yoga kriyas and mantra are few of the many tools a yoga therapist may use in these one or two sessions with the care seeker. As a yoga therapist you can aim to motivate these health seekers during these initial one-to-one sessions to join appropriate yoga classes, where they can benefit from the support of the group and be motivated to continue their practice.

2. Adhij-Vyadhij (Psycho-somatic) and Vyadhij-Adhij (Somato-Psychic)
                                                    (Dr. Ananda Balayogi Bhavanani)

Psychosomatic Disorders
Within the Nirvana Prakarana of the Laghu Yoga Vashishta, one of the ancient Yoga Texts, is a detailed description of the origin and destruction of mental and bodily diseases. The great Sage Vashishta teaches Lord Rama that there are two major classifications of disease. Those that are caused by the mind are primary Adhija Vyadhi, the psychosomatic, stress disorders; while those that afflict the body directly are the secondary Anadhija Vyadhi , infectious disease, accidents etc.

The Adhija Vyadhi primary diseases have two sub divisions: these are the Samanya or ordinary physical diseases and the Sara, the essential disorders of rebirth that may only be destroyed by Atma, Jnana or knowledge of the Divine Self. The Samanya diseases are the ones that affect us physically and may be destroyed by the correction of the mind-body disharmony. It is with these psycho-somatic disorders that the actual practical application of Yoga practices as a mode of therapy can be very useful.

From the Yogic viewpoint of disease, it can be seen that psychosomatic, stress related disorders appear to progress through four distinct phases. These can be understood as follows:

❖ **Psychic Phase**- This phase is marked by mild but persistent psychological and behavioural symptoms of stress like irritability, disturbed sleep and other minor symptoms. This phase can be correlated with vijnanamaya (intellect or wisdom sheath) and manomaya (mind or mental sheath) layers of the koshas. Yoga as a mind body therapy is very effective in this phase.

❖ **Psycho-somatic Phase**- If the stress continues there is an increase in symptoms, along with the appearance of generalized physiological symptoms such as occasional hypertension and tremors. This phase can be correlated with manomaya (mind or mental sheath) and pranamaya (life force sheath) koshas. Yoga as a mind body therapy is very effective in this phase.

❖ **Somatic Phase**- This phase is marked by the disturbed function of organs, particularly target, or involved organs. At this stage it becomes possible to begin to identify the diseased state. This phase can be correlated with pranamaya (life force sheath) and annamaya (physical sheath) koshas. Yoga as a therapy is less effective in this phase, however, may be effective in a palliative way, in conjunction with other methods of treatment.

❖ **Somato-psychic phase**- Yoga understands the influence of the body on the mind as well as that of the mind on the body. This is the principle of Adhi-Vyadhi elucidated in the Yoga Vasishta more than 5000 years ago! As we continue to study and understand the Psycho-somatic and the Somato-psycho Mechanisms of Yoga, it is interesting to contemplate that modern medicine has only realised this connection in the last hundred years, whereas the Yogis of India have been teaching and practicing it for thousands of years. It is no wonder that Yoga may be considered as the original mind-body medicine.

We are what we think, yet we also start to think that which we do. Yogic concepts and techniques enable the development of right attitudes towards life and enable us to correct the numerous internal and external imbalances we suffer due to our wrong lifestyle/ genetic potential. Yoga enables us to take responsibility for our own health and happiness and as Swami Gitananda Giri would say, "If you want to be healthy do healthy things, if you want to be happy do happy things".

In this yoga therapy model, we aim to address the stress and stressors and use the yogic tools, kriyas and Prakriyas to relieve the stress and develop better coping mechanisms. This model requires the use of yogic counseling and lifestyle assessment followed by the use of bespoke Hatha Yoga practices, jattis, kriyas, yoga vyayama, pranayama, relaxation practices and lifestyle changes to promote health and wellness.

3. Spanda-Nispanda (Stress-relaxation) Yoga Nidra and Yogic Visualisations
This model follows the primary concepts of Adhi-Vyadhi and understands the importance of relaxation in enabling symptomatic relief as well as in long term healing plans. This is a much simpler model, easily accessible by care seekers at all levels as these Jnana Yoga Kriyas and Prakriyas can be followed on the floor, in a chair, or in a bed easily. Yogic kriyas can be physical movement with breath or simple visualisations; their variations or adaptations are Prakriyas. We have a wide range of Jnana Yoga Kriyas and Yoga Nidra Practices within Gitananda Practices for psycho (soul; mind) cleansing, stress relief, polarity and energy balances. This model's approach addresses the re-activation of our para-sympathetic or relaxation response, which allows our body, mind and vital energies to do the necessary repair or healing.

4. Pancha Kosha (five body system)
The Pancha Koshas are a concept in yoga darshan or philosophy, in which there are five layers of our existence and awareness through which all experiences are filtered. This concept of Pancha Kosha is described in the Taittiriya Upanishad, a Vedic Sanskrit text embedded within the Yajurveda (one of the four Vedas of Hinduism). The Yoga Science describes our being or existence in five sheaths, layers or bodies (pancha-koshas), where each person has-
   ❖ A physical body, made of matter, the Annamaya Kosha
   ❖ An astral body or psychic energy body, containing prana and vital energy currents, the Pranamaya Kosha
   ❖ A mind body, the Manomaya Kosha
   ❖ A cosmic intellect or wisdom body the Vijnanamaya Kosha
   ❖ A bliss or consciousness body the Anandamaya Kosha

This model follows the use of yogic kriyas and Prakriyas through Hatha Yoga, Jnana Yoga, Kriya Yoga, Karma Yoga and Mantra Yoga practices, alongside lifestyle changes through Yogic Diet and Yogic Lifestyle. It is a wholistic approach whose purpose is to regain vitality and balance or harmony of all the five bodies to their optimum potential.

5. Prana Vayus (subtle energy currents)

The word Vayu is a Sanskrit term meaning wind or current and Prana means the vital life force or subtle energy current. Within Yogic and Ayurveda philosophy, the concept of the Pancha-Mahabhutas and their association of Pancha-Prana Vayus are described. The Pancha Mahabhutas understand man as a microcosm of the world that he lives in, made up of the same basic elements of Akasa (ether), Vayu (air), Tejas (fire), Ap (water) and Prithvi (earth); which are held in balance.
There are five major Prana Vayus-
- ❖ Prana
- ❖ Apana
- ❖ Samana
- ❖ Udana
- ❖ Vyana

There are also seven Up-prana Vayus, including naga, kurma, devdatta, krikala and dhananjaya. The Chakra system also associates the Prana Vayus with respective chakras and their psycho-neuro-biology.   It is the management of prana, the vital life force that animates all levels of being. This model follows the use of asana, bandhas, pranayama, mudras, nada, yogic diet and yogic jnana yoga kriyas to balance or harmonise these vital life currents to regain health and wellness.

6. Tri-Dosha

Ayurveda defines disease as the progressive end result of living out of harmony with our own constitution. Our constitution within the Tri-Gunas of Vata, Pitta and Kapha, constitute the inherent balance of energies within our body, mind and lifestyle choices. They describe our constitutional principles and energies and the most fundamental level. The unique balance of energy determines everything from our bone structure to our predisposition toward certain health challenges.

Our tri-dosha constitution defines what we are naturally attracted to (raga), as well as what repels us (dvesha). It enables us to understand what is in harmony with our nature and what will lead us towards being out of balance, which naturally leads towards sickness and disease. Because we all have a different balance of energy, Ayurveda shows that the path to optimal health is different for each person depending upon their constitution.

In this module we choose appropriate asana, mudra, pranayama, kriyas, yogic diet, lifestyle, cleansing practices etc. to enhance the health and wellness of individuals.

7. Tri-Guna

The Tri-Gunas are the primordial qualities of all living and non-living matter in for energetic principles weave together to form the universe and all that exists within it. Our body, mind, thoughts, food, lifestyle choices and so on can be classified and understood with the tri-guna principle. These are: **Tamas** (inertia or stability), **Rajas** (activity, transformation) and **Sattva** (essence, purity, consciousness). The Gunas can help us understand our habitual patterns, tendencies and life patterns.

All three Gunas are present in each experience too and are constantly changing. Lord Krishna in Bhagavad Gita details the teachings on Gunas and their role in our health, happiness and spiritual evolution. Through modifications in diet, yogic practices, pranayama, jnana yoga kriyas and lifestyle adaptations we can help our care-seekers to find a good balance in tri-Gunas and their energy principles known as balance between "energy, action, relaxation and consciousness".

8. Yogic Mind and Life Management (Yoga Darshana)

The Yoga Sutras of Maharishi Patanjali, the Yoga teachings of Yoga Vashistha and the teachings of the Bhagavad Gita are our scientific guide, giving us practical and applied science for the management of our mind, psychology, habits and spiritual growth. They provide detailed teachings on the mind and its various stages of evolution, they identify adverse factors, obstacles and how to deal with them for better health, happiness, perspective and perception. These life teachings are teachings of the science of the mind, life and soul, and how we can make our life better through mind management. This model is significantly important for yoga therapists who aim to work on mental, emotional, social, relationships and spiritual health.

9. Swaras Yoga and Yoga Chikitsa

Swara Yoga is the science of breath and vital energy currents associated with nasal breathing cycles on our body and mind, through right nostril the **Pingala Nadi**, the left nostril the **Ida Nadi** and both nostrils or **Shushumna Nadi**. The different patterns and nature of the breath indicate the active elements of the Pancha

Mahabhutas ie. Prathvi, Jala, Vayu, Agni and Akasha, in our physical (Sthula Sharira) and psychic body (Sukshma Sharira).

Within Swara Yoga, practices are connected with the flow of our nadi in a systematic pattern, primarily with the sun and moon phases, along with other planets. The elements are connected with different planets in different nasal flows. When a planet effects the earth's gravitational field and electromagnetic fields, they will alter human energy patterns in the psychic body on a feedback basis. Swara Yoga explains that when our Swaras or nasal breathing cycles are out of harmony we lose health and inner balance leading to disease. In order to balance and harmonize these subtle forces, Swara yoga details easily accessible and applicable effective tools to regain our health and inner balance.

10. Kundalini and Chakras.

In our pranic body we have seven chakras. These are junction points where our major nadis – Ida, Pingala and Sushumna meet or criss-cross each other. If you imagine shapes of eight on top of each other, that is how it will look with a straight line through the middle of them.

When you walk around in your garden and see so many plants, flowers and vegetables, these all are growing in same soil and environment. They all get the same air, water and sun; but they are all so are different. It is so fascinating that each seed takes what it needs be able to grow. It's also so interesting to notice that each of them has their own shaped leaves, flowers or seeds. This is all written in their genetic code and so it is also the way they receive or absorb various ingredients, light, air and water.

The same applies to us human beings, even though we all have similar physical structures with bones, flesh, muscles and organs, our physical, mental, emotional and spiritual behaviours are completely different. Even the response or reaction to the same stimulus is very different between all of us. Furthermore, if you look into it further, our own behaviours, reactions, responses or actions can be different when exposed to the same stimulus in different situations, events of phases of our life. Our Chakras have a main role to play in all our psycho-physio-spiritual activities.

The first chakra is located at the base of the spine and is known as the **Mooladhara** (the root or foundation) Chakra. This is the chakra where the kundalini rests coiled up in the form of a serpent. Our seventh chakra is known as the **Sahashrara** (thousand petals) chakra and it is located at the top of our head or crown. All the Yogis aim to open these two chakras to attain self-realisation or Samadhi.

The other five chakras define our personality and who we truly are. They also govern various psycho-physiological functions in our body and hence blockages or imbalances of any of these chakras will result in physical or mental health problems associated to those chakras; the balance of these chakras is key to a balanced health and well-being.

Our second chakra is known as the **Swadhisthana** (self-dwelling place) chakra. This is based around our pelvic area and it is associated with the reproductive organs and kidneys. This chakra is naturally active or awakened in most human beings as part of the natural process to reproduce life and to sustain the life processes. The energy from this chakra flows and expresses itself through sensual or sexual pleasures in a gross form. While in subtle form it expresses or fulfils life through arts and creativity.

Our third chakra is known as the **Manipura** (jewel city) Chakra. This chakra is associated with the solar plexus, stomach, liver, pancreas and upper digestive system. This is the centre of the fire element and provides us with the necessary life forces to fulfil our karma and dharma. When this chakra is fully open, we feel strong, brave and fearless while, if it is blocked, we are fearful, anxious and worried.

Our fourth chakra is the **Anahata** (unstruck) chakra. It is associated with heart and lungs. This chakra gives us force to give and receive unconditional joy, love and happiness. When this chakra, is blocked, we feel a lack of faith or trust in ourselves or others and tend to be more self-centred. While, when it is open fully, we feel positive, confident, caring and nurturing towards ourselves as well as others.

The fifth chakra is known as the **Vishuddha** (purity) Chakra. This chakra is associated with our throat and thyroid. This governs our general well-being and outward personality. If it is open freely, we always feel positive and confident in expressing ourselves to others.

The sixth Chakra is known as the **Ajna** (command) chakra. This chakra is associated with our pineal gland and brain. We have to train ourselves to full activate this chakra. This chakra governs our will power and self-worth. It helps us to follow our thoughts, ideas and practices wilfully.

In this model we follow the Tantric practices of Hatha Yoga, pranayama, cleansing practices, mudras, bija mantras, mandala visualisations to help our care-seekers to enhance their health, wellness and vitality.

In this lesson we have given an introduction and brief outline of ten key Yoga Therapy models. This is an introductory foundation which will support our further learning. All these practices and models are available to us as Yoga Therapists. We can use one or a combination of models to meets the individual needs of each care-seeker. As we learn more about each of these models, we can skill ourselves to become able Yoga Therapists.

Lesson 11.
Key Yoga Scriptures For Yoga Therapy

Yoga is mentioned in many Hindu and Vedic scriptures including the Vedas, Upanishadas and the Bhagavat Gita. In this lesson we will discuss the key scriptures that we need to be familiar with in order to practice Yoga Therapy.

The Yoga Sutras of Patanjali

The Yoga Sutra of Patanjali is a completely dedicated work on yoga philosophy and each of its limbs, practices, obstacles and solutions. The Yoga Sutras are really a guide map for every human being to reach higher states of mind.

Patanjali complied and connected many concepts, ideas, practices and principals of yoga that we are able to use as guide map for our Self or Purusha (individual soul), to free ourselves from worldly mental bondage and attain Self-realisation or Union with Parmatman (our higher self or divine self).

The word Sutra means a thread, or verse; Yoga Sutras are verses or threads of wisdom. These Yoga Sutras were written in a complex coded Sanskrita language and to explore and understand them we need to experience each one of them through Sadhana. There are four chapters in the Yoga Sutras, containing 195 or 196 Sutras (as in some schools one of the sutra is divided in two verses). The four chapters or Padas are Samadhi, Sadhana, Vibhuti and Kaivalya-

❖ **Samadhi Pada**- This first chapter contains 51 verses about Samadhi or enlightenment, focusing on our states of mind. Samadhi Pada expresses the goal of concentration as a means of achieving vairagya or detachment. Patanjali explains that this is only possible when we have a balance between effort and letting go. Obstacles to mental stillness and tools like abhyasa or practice are discussed here.

❖ **Sadhana Pada**- The second chapter details the Sadhana or practice in forms of The Eight Limbs of Yoga, Karma yoga, Kriya yoga and Ashtanga yoga. It details first six limbs from Yama to Dharana in detail.

❖ **Vibhuti Pada**- This third chapter is about the Siddhis; the fruits, power, and manifestations that occur once mastery in practice is achieved. In the 56 verses in this chapter Patanjali explains last two limbs- Dhyana and Samadhi and all the Siddhis one attains as milestones on this yogic path. Patanjali advices that Siddhis are just the fruits on path and not the goal itself.

❖ **Kaivalya Pada**- The last chapter is about enlightenment, liberation, or moksha. These 34 sutras details about liberation and all the higher states of mind, describing how someone on the yogic path can free their consciousness.

Who was Patanjali?

Patanjali is considered to have lived between 200BC to 2000BC. Patanjali was a great Yogi, who attained liberation through following disciplined path of Yoga. Gonika a great Yogini and worshipper of Lord Shiva was praying for child to pass on her yogic wisdom. Once she was praying while bathing in river with holding water in her palms (anjali). A little snake fell her hands as she was praying to Shiva, he blessed that snake to transformed into a child or yogi, who represents half snake, half man. Pata means fallen, and Anjali means palms joined together. That's why he was named Patanjali.

Patanjali was represented by a snake because it is the symbol for un-manifested potential energy stored in all of us in form of Kundalini.

The Bhagavata Gita

The Bhagavad Gita, often known as Gita is one of the key Hindu and Yoga scriptures; it is written in poetic form and is known as the 'Song of the Lord'. It forms part of the Mahabharata which is an ancient Indian epic.

In the 18 chapters of the Gita there are 700 verses written in poetic form. The Gita describes the beginning of an epic war between Pandavas and Kauravas, where Arjuna is the greatest warrior and head of Padava army. Within these dialogues between Arjuna and Krishna, Krishna represents the Divine or Supreme Soul (parmatman), Arjuna represents the individual soul (purusha) and the battle represents the ethical and moral struggles of our human mind and life. Arjuna is filled with doubt and despondency on the battlefield and refuses to fight at the beginning after realising that he is fighting against his own family, friends and relatives. He puts his weapons down and askes Krishna, for his advice. Responding to Arjuna's confusion and moral dilemma, Krishna explains to Arjuna his dharma or duties as a warrior and prince. Through the counselling verses of the Gita, the paths of yoga, Jnana, Bhakti, Dhyana and Karma yoga awaken the wisdom of Arjuna.

The Gita details all the psychological tools for the body and mind, including all four paths of yoga, with karma yoga as most important of all in form of selfless service or performing all the actions devoted to divine cause. The Gita is often thought of as a summary of the Upanishads (the Vedanta or essence of the Vedas) and is called 'the Upanishad of the Upanishads'.

Yoga Vashistha

The Yoga Vasishtha is philosophical contemplation on human suffering, it was written by Valmiki between the 6th and 14th century (CE) and contains 19,000 verses. This work is named after Vasishtha who is described as the first sage of the Vedanta School by Adi Sankara. It is written in the form of inspiring stories and fables of the great Sages, Rishis and Yogis who attained Liberation through various paths of Yoga and focuses on the counselling dialogue between Lord Rama is his youth and his Guru Vasishtha. It contains six parts; the first part details Prince Rama's mental and emotional dilemma of confusion and frustration with the nature of human life, its desires and sufferings. In the second part the nature and desire of those who seek liberation is described through the character of Rama. The third and forth chapters explains that liberation can be attained through spiritual life, self effort and understanding of the universal principals of existence, truth and reality. The fifth part describes meditation and its powers of bringing liberation for the individual self and in the last chapter, Vasishtha describes Rama's progression to consciousness and enlightenment.

Shiva Samhita

The Shiva Samhita is the oldest Hatha Yoga Scripture. This scripture details the teaching of Lord Shiva to his wife Paravati or Shakti. This is a complete text on Hatha Yoga mentioning 84 classical postures; it details four asanas and five types of Prana, Tantra, Mudras and Meditation techniques and also covers yoga philosophy. There is no actual evidence of dates when this scripture was actually written. Shiva Samhita covers following subjects in detail-

❖ Naris, sushumna, ida, pingala
❖ Prana, 10 types of prana
❖ How to attain success in yoga
❖ Who is Adhikari or worthy of doing yoga

❖ The qualities and characters of someone who is worthy of doing yoga
❖ The signs of someone whose naris (energy channels in the astral body) have been purified by nari shodhana (alternate nostril pranayam)
❖ The obstacles in yoga
❖ How to attain mastery in yoga
❖ Mentions 84 asanas (postures) of which only 4 are described as most important
❖ Only describes nari shodhana as pranayama and the method of doing it
❖ Mantra yoga, and trataka like shadow gazing, anahat sounds

Yoga Chudamani

The Yoga Chudamani Upanishad commentary on the Sama Veda literally means 'Crown Jewel of Yoga'. It has 121 verses and as it says in its name, it is for Yoga Sadhakas seeking for liberation and Samadhi through yoga practice and purification of the mind. The Yoga Chudamani explains that a Yogi should use every breath as Pranayama with the mind focussed on the 'Hamsa' Mantra. Unconsciously we are chanting this mantra with every breath, meaning 'I am Super-Consciousness'. This chanting is known as Ajapa Jap. If we focus on this breathing and the mantra, it will awake our Kundalini.

This Upanishad explains the Naris, especially the Sushumna, the central channel and its connection with all the Chakras. Through this Nari, Kundalini energy can flow upward into the Sahashrara or crown centre bringing peace, bliss and enlightenment. It opens the doors to for us to realise our Higher Self or Param-Brahma. Brahma is the universal self and Para Shakti manifests in the form of our Individual self. All the five elements also manifest from Para-Shakti or the creative-mother-energy. This Upanishad also details the five elements or tattvas, the four states of consciousness and our body organs and their ruling divine forces. The specific element's of Pranayama are detailed as Pooraka (inhalation), Rechaka (exhalation) and Kumbhaka (retention). This Upanishad also explains the benefits of pranayama, pratyahara and asana too.

Vijnana Bhairava Tantra

The Vijana Bhairava Tantra is a classical Tantra Yoga text, it is very beautiful and is a typical example of the Guru-Shishya system. According to many scholars its writing dates from around around 7th century (CE). Vijnana means 'knowledge', which comes direct from experience and Bhairava means 'Supreme Reality or Divine'. The Guru here is our teacher Lord Shiva and Shakti or Parvati is his Shishya (pupil or student). It is in the form of a dialogue between Shiva and Parvati; she explains her own doubts and desires to know how to attain union of her individual self with her higher self. The term Shiva is used for 'Higher' and Shakti for 'Individual Self'.

Lord Shiva explains how we are under influence of Maya (illusion) and duality due to ego and mental bondage. He explains that Supreme-Consciousness or Reality cannot be described by the human mind but it can only be experienced. This yoga can be practised by using body, mind, breath and subtle life force-prana in a process of self- enquiry to realise the Self and Higher Self.

This scripture details 112 techniques of enquiry and meditation to attain Self-realisation. These are aimed at stilling and focusing the mind, awakening kundalini and bringing union of our Shiva and Shakti. The techniques include breath awareness, mantra, contemplations and subtle energy visualisations. This path has two branches known as North and South. It has more liberal approach compared to other paths of yoga in regard to food, life style, sex and material possessions.

Shiva Swarodaya

This scripture is for advanced yoga seekers, it contains a dialogue between Lord Shiva and his wife Parvati. This knowledge has been passed down within the Guru-Shishya tradition where teachings are transmitted from a guru to a seeker; imparted through the relationship of respect, commitment, devotion and obedience: which is considered to be the best way to pass on subtle or advanced teachings. This scripture gives details on the Swaras (nostril) breathing and their associations with the five elements (prithvi-earth, jal-water, agni-fire, vayu-air, akasha-ether), states of mind and how to transform our body, mind and life through manipulating and changing our Swaras and breath. It associates the right nostril with the pingala and the left nostril with the ida nari, while the shushumna (main energy channel of the subtle body) is associated with both nostrils when flowing freely together.

Hatha Yoga Pradipika

The Hatha Yoga Pradipika is one of the most detailed works on Hatha Yoga, it is written by Svatmarama Suri as a compilation of texts from earlier Hatha Yoga Masters teaching lineages. Hatha means forceful, vigorous, zeal, endeavour, steadfast approach to attain the goal of Yoga as Meditation and Samadhi (stilling of the mind and unification with the cosmic). This literature provides a scientific and experienced approach to asana, pranayama, mudra, bandhas and dharana (concentration) practices by many Yogis and Masters in the Hatha Yoga lineage.

The Goddess Parvati wife of Lord Shiva asks Lord Shiva how to attain Jnana or Knowledge and in order to set herself free from the experience of suffering and mental whirlpools, she asks how human beings can be free of their physical, mental and emotional suffering. In response Lord Shiva teaches her Hatha Yoga science for the holistic development of the self. Parvati passed this knowledge to Brahma, who passed this knowledge to many sages like Narada, Sanka, and Sanatkumara. Although this Vidya (knowledge) was written down later in 12th to 15th century (CE) as the Hatha Yoga Pradipika, the actual authority of teachings goes much further back; Svatmarama mentions in a list of 35 Gurus and Yoga Masters, his lineage from which the knowledge was passed down to him.

The Pradipika is divided into four parts-
- ❖ The first chapter details Yamas (restraints on behaviour), Niyamas (observances), Asanas (posture) and discusses diet
- ❖ The second chapter explains pranayama (enhancement of subtle energy) and the shatkarmas (internal purification practices)
- ❖ The third chapter details the mudras (seals or energy gestures), bandhas (locks), naris (channels of energy through which prana flows) and the kundalini power
- ❖ The fourth gives details about pratyahara (sensory withdrawal), Dharana (concentration), dhyana (meditation) and Samadhi (union)

The Hatha Yoga Pradipika incorporates teachings and practices of the Yoga Sutras, the Bhagavat Gita and other key scriptures. It has practices to attain purify, strengthen, empower and balance our body-mind-energy system to prepare for Raja or Ashtanga Yoga. The literature begins with showing gratitude to Lord Shiva who taught this science of Hatha Yoga and closes with the understanding of the practices which serve to prepare us for Raja Yoga.

Gheranda Samhita

The Gheranda Samhita or Gheranda's Collection is one of three primary texts on classic Hatha yoga, along with the Hatha Yoga Pradipika and the Shiva Samhita. It was written in Sanskrit in the late 17th century and is sometimes considered to be the most comprehensive of the three texts as it provides a detailed manual for yoga. The Gheranda Samhita describes Ghatastha yoga which means 'vessel yoga' where the mind and body are the vessels that serve the atman (soul), understanding form as truth, consciousness and bliss.

The yoga text has seven chapters dealing with various limbs of yoga. These seven chapters of the Gheranda Samhita follow the sevenfold path of yoga, which was taught by the sage Rishi Gheranda to his student Chanda Kapali.

These seven are-

- ❖ **Shatkarmas**- for purification of body and mind through six cleansing practices
- ❖ **Asana**- for strength, stability and ease of body and channeling the subtle energy- includes 32 postures
- ❖ **Mudra**- channeling the energy in various Naris and Chakras to focus the mind and awake consciousness- describes 25 mudras
- ❖ **Pratyahra**- sensory withdrawal to concentrate the mind
- ❖ **Pranayama**- to attain lightness, cleanse naris and enhance Prana- describes 10 classical Pranayama techniques
- ❖ **Dhyana** to attain realisation of single pointed awareness
- ❖ **Samadhi** or Union – Describes techniques of levels of Samadhi

There is mention of 84 classical Asanas and out of them only 32 are described in detail in Gheranda Samhita, most are seated postures and there is only one standing posture, which is the Vrikshasana or Tree Pose.

Yajnavalkya Samhita

Another classical text on hatha Yoga, the Yogayajnavalikya Samhita is a dialogue between the great sage Yajnavalkya and his learned wife Gargi. Considered as one of the most learned women of all times, Gargi asks him about how to reach the highest state of consciousness or Samadhi and Yajnavalkya teaches a systematic path of Hatha Yoga to her in twelve chapters in this text. There are several versions of this Hatha Yoga text including the Yajnavalkya Gita, Yajnavalkya and Yajnavalkys Yoga. Yajnavalkya is the name of a legendary sage from Verdic times, who was estimated to have lived in around the 8th century (BCE). The Verdic period covers 1500 to 500 BCE in India.

The Yajnavalkya Samhita discusses how to start and develop meditative practices with the use of Om and other resonating sounds, going on to advanced meditation that is reflective of the mind, feelings and nature and the development of Samadhi (concentration) to become aware of equality with universal ultimate reality.

This chapter has introduced the key scriptures that we need to be familiar with in order to practice Yoga Therapy. The depth of wisdom that we have inherited through these texts are our yogic heritage which equips us with all the tools that we need to become Yoga Chikitsaks.

Lesson 12:
Yoga as Life Style

Yoga is one of the most comprehensive systems, it provides us with step by step tools, practices, asana and pranayama, kriyas and prakriyas, concepts and ideas, principles and code of conducts, philosophical and spiritual practices to grow physically, mentally, emotionally and spiritually. In this lesson we will consider how we understand our own lives and how we are living. To bring a positive change, we need to understand our life style and the life practices that we follow. These few simple questions can help us understand ourselves and what we do, what is our focus, what are our habits and pre-occupations.

I would like you to ask and put the answers together on a paper if possible-
- ❖ What are the things I do every day?
- ❖ What sort of food do I eat?
- ❖ What kind of drinking habits do I follow?
- ❖ Do I sleep or rest enough?
- ❖ Do I do enough physical exercise or not?
- ❖ How do I entertain myself?
- ❖ What type of social circle do I have?
- ❖ What kind of work do I do?
- ❖ What occupies my thoughts and my energies?
- ❖ Do I have time to meet my own needs
- ❖ What do I do to support my own physical, emotional and spiritual needs

These answers will give you a little idea on what kind of lifestyle you are living. Our lifestyle includes physical, mental, emotional, social, economical and spiritual activities we take part in regularly. If you follow sedentary life style with unhealthy food and drinking habits, you can be prone to suffer with mental and physical disorders.

The foundation of a yogic life style is based on Jattis, Kriyas, Asana, Pranayama and Mudra which provide us with balanced tools for our body, mind and soul to keep us active, healthy and balanced. Regular Hatha Yoga practice will keep you away from many physical and mental illness.

Then yoga advocates that we have healthy dietary habits including eating healthy fresh foods, vegetables, fruits, raw food, following a vegetarian diet and avoiding consumption of any toxic food, alcoholic drinks, smoking and mind altering substances. A Yogis life style describes Shaucha or purity, including our food and drink, our body, mind and spiritual activities and pre-conditions for health, well-being and spiritual evolution. In Ayurveda it is explained that we become what we think and we are what we feed into our bodies.

The third important aspect of yoga is its strong foundation of ethical and moral character. Yoga teaches five Yamas (restrains) and five Niyamas (observances). As part of human life progression and evolution, we all have our basic biological needs; these are hunger, thirst and sex. These primary forces naturally enforce all living beings to sustain life and also reproduce to keep our species alive. The Yamas and Niyamas moral and ethical values provide us with healthier and more holistic ways to fulfil our day-to-day needs.

The fourth Part is our Karma (actions or deeds) and Dharma (duties). We all have certain duties to fulfil. We all are born with certain qualities and potentials, yoga really emphasises attaining our true potential. Within Yoga and Hinduism all the physical, mental and verbal activities that we do are classified as Karma. Even our breathing, eating, sleeping, thinking, talking, etc. are classified as Karma or Actions. Doing everything mindfully without worrying for the fruits of our actions is one of the key Yogic ideas to free ourselves from our Karma.

Regular practice (Tapas), self-discipline (Anushasanam), self-awareness (Swadhyaya), contemplation and meditation (Chintan and Dhyana), companionships with truth seekers (Satsanga), Faith and devotion (Shradha and Viriya), and seeing life and life events as divine blessing (Iswara Prashadhana) are some of the key philosophical ideas that Yoga teaches us to practice in our day to day lives.

Key Factors to contemplate as part of healthy or Yogic life style include-
- ❖ Balance between exercise, rest and energy
- ❖ Moral and ethical character
- ❖ Healthy vegetarian diet
- ❖ Cleanliness or purity of body, mind and soul
- ❖ Balance, Harmony and peace within ourselves and others
- ❖ Doing our duties and taking every action mindfully.
- ❖ Making every choice consciously and responsibly.

Lesson 13.
Living Mindfully for Health and Happiness

In this lesson we will consider what it is to live mindfully. Swamiji Dr Gitananda Giriji tells us that it is every human being's birth-right to be healthy and happy; he further states that everyone must claim it. Simply if you like to be healthy, you need to do everything that makes you healthy. If you like to be happy, you need to do everything that brings happiness.

We learn through Yoga and scriptures such as the Upanishads that all our unhealthy and immoral acts have their roots in Avidya or ignorance. Ignorance is not only not knowing the truth or what it is right to do, but it is also not following the truth or practices that we know are good for our health and happiness.

We have natural drives and forces within us, which evince the pleasure seeking principle. This may lead us to do many things that our Viveka (reasoning) and Buddhi (intellect) tells us not to do, or not to do in a certain way, or situations not to get into. Our Viveka (reasoning) guides us in a more healthy ways to fulfil our desires. We all have intuition or what is sometimes known as gut-instinct. In order to empower this, we must live mindfully.

In our day-to-day lives, we wake up, do daily tasks, eat, drink, go to work, talk to family and friends, look through social media and do many other activities without even knowing them as part of our daily habits. Yogic or mindful living advocates giving our awareness to each and every activity that we take part in every day. Every choice we make from waking up, to eating, drinking, working, sleeping, entertainment, etc. should be a conscious choice.

If we can be mindful to every activity that we follow, it will naturally bring balance and appreciation into our lives. We tend to always act or respond better when we are aware within a situation. Our prana or energy flows where our mind goes; hence if we start doing things consciously, our energy will flow into the right parts of our body and mind. Lets say, if you are eating and also watching television, your body has to decide where to supply the more energy. Naturally if you are eating, energy should be supplied to your mouth, slavery glands, and stomach, but if you are also watching something on television, then the priority becomes our brain. This will lead to many digestive problems.

This mindful living also allows us to appreciate day-to-day activities, which normally many people don't value much like eating, resting, social times, entertainment etc. Many people have such big ambitions that they don't have moment to care for their body, mind and soul.

Simple Mindful Activities-

- ❖ Sit down enjoy every sip of your cup of tea or coffee
- ❖ Go for a walk and enjoy every step, notice the movement of your body and notice detail of your walk, things you see and hear, touch or smell
- ❖ Make a time to relax or meditate and let go of everything else for few minutes
- ❖ While you are eating your meals, focus on your food and enjoy the flavours, textures, smells
- ❖ Light a candle or incense that you like and enjoy the fragrance
- ❖ Play your favourite music and try to become fully absorbed in it

The four foundations of mindfulness are-

- ❖ Mindfulness of the body: this foundation involves paying attention to the physical sensations of the body, such as breathing, posture and movement
- ❖ Mindfulness of feelings or sensations: this foundation involves observing and becoming aware of our feelings or emotions as they arise and pass away, without judgement or attachment
- ❖ Mindfulness of the mind: this involves being aware of our thoughts, mental states and mental qualities such as greed, anger and delusion
- ❖ Mindfulness of mental objects: this last foundation involves paying attention to the nature of mental phenomena, such as perceptions, intentions and our consciousness

In this lesson we have considered the need for living mindfully, to be aware of our thoughts, emotions and our actions. Through mindfulness we aim to develop insight into the nature of our reality and support ourselves to be well and happy.

Lesson 14.
Finding Balance in Life- Moderate Living

Balance is very important in life. As Lord Krishna teaches in the Bhagavat Gita Yoga is Equanimity (yoga samatva ujyate). But how do we attain this balance or harmony. Lord Krishna further states that to be successful in Yoga or any other aspect of life, we need to follow things moderately. He explains that anyone who eats too much, or does not eat enough, exercise too much or does not do enough exercise, who works too much or does not work enough, who sleeps too much or does not sleep enough, will never succeed in life.

This clearly gives us healthy guidelines on working on our own health, well-being and spiritual evolution. If you not eating enough, you will have no energy to fulfil all your Dharma or duties and take part in day-to-day tasks. On other hand if we eat too much that causes toxicity and burden on our digestive system and liver. This may result in obesity, lethargy and heaviness of body and mind. If we are not doing enough physical activity, work and exercise, we are prone to suffer with stiffness, physical weakness, joint immobility, arthritis, blood and heart problems. Not fulfilling our duties may also result in family, social and economic problems. Overdoing things, exercise or work will cause exhaustion and tiredness, which will also result in many physical, mental and emotional health issues. Sleep is another important aspect of our life; healthy sleep allows our body to heal, rejuvenate and prepare of another day of activities and tasks. Where as a sedentary life style, sleeping too much may result in physical problems like obesity, muscle and joints pain, heart problems, depression, anxiety, stress and lack of self-confidence.

The Key idea is very simple and profound here, live your life in harmony and balance between your energy, action and rest. So if your work demands physical activity, then you need to eat more than someone who has a less physically demanding job. If your job demands mental activities, then you must find time to do physical exercise, relaxation and meditation.

When we consider how to achieve balance in our lives, we need to be honest with ourselves and reflect honestly about our life style choices, the demands that are placed on us and what resources we have to achieve balance. This is on on-going challenge for us as we go through our lives.

Lesson 15.
Discipline Key to Success in Life

In the last lesson we looked at finding balance in modern life and moderate living. Patanjali begins explaining the yogic journey of self-realisation in the first yoga sutra by describing "Yoga as a Path of Discipline" (atha yoga anushasanam). This sutra also explains that we all have the potential to attain success in field of yoga or any other goal in life, if we are willing to go inward and find the answers as well as do what needs to be done. There is always a deeper meaning and reason to everything that is around us, or is happening in our life. We just need to look deep within and follow the path with right attitude.

For many of us these days, discipline seems to be a negative term. The moment we say that I have to follow something, our mind starts to debate against it. We all are looking for freedom. We like to be living under our own free will, we like to do what we want to do or feel like doing. But we keep forgetting that we can only be free by following discipline in our life. If we do everything as it should be done, with right intention, attitude and intellect, we are free. We all are individuals and need to look after our individual health, well-being and happiness. But we are also collective beings, and hence we have to be mindful of everyone around us.

Patanjali begins with the word 'ATHA' which literally means 'here and now'; living here and now and paying attention to the right now and not to the past or the future. So if we follow this discipline, here and now, we will benefit.

It can also be seen as it is for 'I' or 'You' or the one who follows.

The word Anu from anushasanam means 'atom', the smallest or minute, that which cannot be broken down any further and that which makes the 'whole'. This whole universe is composed from various forms of atoms. The word Shasanam means ruling or governing. Atoms can be seen as the subtlest form of our existence and energy while Shasanam is to govern or master this true essence or nature. Anushasnam is Sanskrita and means the discipline of our body, mind and actions. Anushashnam or discipline is to live in harmony with our true nature and essence. It is our Dharma or duty to look after our health and well-being and grow in our lives, hence anushasanam means also to do everything that we need to do attain health, well-being, happiness and spiritual evolution.

When we live in the here and now and follow all the discipline with great humane virtues of honesty, love, compassion, forgiveness, self-awareness and live in deeply harmony with our true nature, it opens the doors of limitless possibilities.

There are natural laws of geometry bringing harmony, dynamic life transformations and beauty, which we can see through flowers, butterflies, birds, plants, fruits, animals, trees, planets, stars, moon, sun etc. We can see how alive the whole universe is and how harmony within the dynamic dance of energy of existence is there. Living in the here and now, with discipline will bring this whole dynamic harmony and peace to us. Our life will become full of joy, abundance and love. The discipline of the here and now is to also appreciate everything that we have in our life. It is to respect, value and be grateful. Whenever we are living in the past or future, we suffer mentally and emotionally for what we don't have or couldn't get, or are fearful of getting or not getting in the future. We are so obsessed about exploiting our resources, nature, mother earth, to make our life comfortable or gain power and wealth. Yogic attitude and virtues will enable us to look deep within the laws of nature and live in harmony within our own true nature and with external universal living and non-living beings.

Remember, if you are planning to go for an adventure, or journey, where will you start? You have to start your journey from where you are. Once you begin your journey, to get to your destination, you need to follow the right path and you need to also follow it till you get there. If you want to reach the top of a mountain, you must keep climbing up as well as choose the right path and prepare yourself for the journey.

Lesson 16.
Yoga is Stilling our Mind

In the second Sutra, Patanjali says, "Yoga is stilling or quietening whirlpools of our mind" (yogah-chitta-vritti-nirodha). There are a few things to remember here, the path of yogic conscious or mindful living is not to control or supress our mental and emotional whirlpools, but gradually be free of all the ups and downs and remain in peace or balance. This is where disciplined, mindful, virtuous yogic living will lead us to.

Our mind is subject to our senses, desires and ego. It is driven around by deep rooted behaviour patterns, attitudes, belief systems and personality types. If we see, hear, or feel something, there is always an outcome experience of 'liking or disliking', which leads us to 'attraction or repulsion'. We are happy if we get what we want and we are unhappy if we don't get what we want. Our Chitta or mind in general has to respond to every stimulus that we receive. Stimulus can be internal or external. When we see something we may like it or not like it according to our memories, experiences or pre-conceptions.

Patanjali explains five categories of stimulus or Chitta vrittis the whirlpools of our minds-

- ❖ **Pramana**- This is correct knowledge, our direct cognition or experiences like seeing, listening, watching, feeling, touching, smelling
- ❖ **Viprayaya**- This is misconception, experiencing what is not real, like seeing a snake in rope in dark, feeling upset because someone doesn't pay attention to us thinking they don't like us, etc.
- ❖ **Vikalpa**- We understand this as conceptualisation, imagination or fantasy, like stressing about things or events haven't happened yet for example, imagining what happens if you get a job or lose it
- ❖ **Nidra**- Lack of awareness in the moment here and now, or sleep
- ❖ **Smriti**- This is our memory of past events and experiences

Patanjali explains that each of them can bring pain or pleasure. All these mental and emotional process leads us into duality or the experience of two opposites knows as Kleshas or colouring, causing modifications of our states of mind and experiences. These are like-dislike, pain-pleasure, good-bad, hot-cold, happy-unhappy. Patanjali's fifth yoga sutra describes five different mental states, the first three categories are classified as negative or disturbed states of our mind. The next two categories of the whirlpools of our mind are more positive and classified as yogic *or mindful states of our mind.*

- ❖ **Kshipta**- The monkey mind, disturbed or distracted
- ❖ **Muddha**- The donkey mind, dull, lacking in concentration and energy
- ❖ **Vikshipta**-The butterfly mind, distorted, alternating between clarity and distraction
- ❖ **Ekagra**- One pointed attention, concentrated or focused
- ❖ **Niruddha**- Fully focused mind, still, quite or ceased. Here your mind is fully focussed in tasks you are doing or things you are involved with.

We all experience these negative states in day-to-day life situations due to stress, tiredness, over-exertion, over stimulated life styles, interpersonal relations, work, finances etc. These states will further influence our experience and judgement.

Many times our outer world is simply a manifestation of our mind or what is going on within our minds. If we are sad and upset, we see everything that upsets us; If we are stressed, we will find so many things out there that will annoy and stress us; but when we are happy, everything seems to be good and positive around us.

Yoga provides us all the tools to free ourselves from whirlpools, thought process, and emotions causing disturbed, distracted and dull states of our mind. Yoga means union, it helps us navigate and move through mental fluctuations to find peace . Yoga means union of our body, mind and emotions. Yoga means living here and now in this moment. Yoga means everything that we do, act or engage, we do that fully consciously and responsibly. When we are in relaxed and focussed states of mind, we will be unaffected by external factors and in union with our highest consciousness. This state we can attain through regular practice (abhyasa) and detachment (vairajna). Abhyasa includes our life style, diet, attitude, belief system, physical and mental exercises or practices like Hatha, Jnana, Bhakti Yoga.

In this lesson we have examined how to reflect on the quality of our minds and our thoughts and emotions. We have guidance from Patanjali on the vrittis and the states of mind that support us in gaining accurate and true knowledge.

Lesson 17.
Yoga is Path and An Ultimate Goal to Self-Realisation

In this lesson we will consider yoga as a path and as a goal for self-realisation. Yoga is disciplined, mindful and responsible living. In his first Sutra Patanjali explains that yoga is living in the moment, here and now in union or awareness with the subtlest form of our existence. This means yoga is a path, or life style that can lead us to health, well-being and self-realisation.

In the second Sutra Patanjali mentions Yoga as a goal or success point where we attain purity, clarity, stillness or oneness of mind. Here our mind becomes free from all the whirlpools and fluctuations. Yoga is living our life with full intent, heart and energy. So this stillness or oneness of mind is also state of equanimity or serenity in day-to-day life, as we are not running away from life's challenges. Here we become free from the ups and down of our mundane or judgemental mind.

In the third Sutra Patanjali explains that "Yoga is to become one with our True or Higher Self" (tada drasta swarupe avasthanam). Here the seer, seeker, or Sadhaka becomes one with itself and attains Self-realisation. This is the highest state great Yogis, Sadhus and Spiritual seekers are searching for, here our conscious mind becomes free from our mundane mind.

You might think, what keeps us away from our own true self? It is our Ego, and Asmita or I-ness, vasanas or desires and all the mental and emotional conditioning. If you see your Atman as a light, with your conscious mind as a glass shade around it, your ego, i-ness, desires, mental and emotional conditioning are like coloured layers on a clear glass shade. It gradually hides the shine and light of our true self.

This disciplined path of Yoga provides us with all the tools, kriyas and prakriyas, asana and pranayama, jnana yoga practices, yogic life style, and moral and ethical way of living and aspiring for us to spiritually evolve. This helps us in removing all these colours shading away that radiant glow, purity, joy and unconditional bliss of Chetana or consciousness. In this way we can understand yoga as a path, as well as a goal.

Lesson 18.
Yoga Skill in Action (Karma Yoga)

Having the right energy and focus in our lives means being able to hold things in balance. In the Bhagavat Gita Lord Krishna explains that "yoga is skill in action" (Yogah Karmeshu Kaushalam). This can also be seen within yoga as living in the moment here and now. Putting your intention, energy and effort in what needs to be done or doing all your duties (dharma) as and when it should be done. If you are a teacher, it is your duty to teach. If you are a musician it is your duty to make music. Developing this attitude of Karma Yogi that I must do what needs to be done by me with my best intention.

Lord Krishna explains that we all have Karma and no one can be free of doing Karma. Karma includes all our mental, emotional, physical, and spiritual activities. You might think, that if your sitting back or resting, you are not doing anything. But still you are breathing, you are resting, sitting, thinking, feeling and much more. We have choices on what to do and how to do it; however we do not have control on the fruits of our actions or the outcomes of what we do. You have control on planting a seed and looking after it, but you don't have control on, if it is going to fruit or not.

People who can manage all their daily tasks at home and in their work place will naturally tend to have less stress or burden, which will bring positive energy and attitude. We can let our life become chaotic and struggle with everything or we can get everything done, which allows us to relax and be happy. This part of yoga is also our attitude towards life. We all know that to live healthily, we need to eat and drink healthily, do exercise, take time to relax and sleep well. Also for our peace of mind and comfort, we need to be able to pay our bills; actually respecting and appreciating the daily tasks we need to do. We need to clean the place we live, wash dishes, do our laundry, do our duties at work, and it is all part of healthy living and growth. We can be grateful and appreciative, instead of worrying and stressing and letting things pile and becoming a burden by not doing them as and when we need to do them.

Swamiji Gitananda Giriji explains this as "do your best and leave the rest". We also need to remember that once we have done our best, we can't do anything more than that. So letting go and not being too hard or too critical is a further step of Karma Yoga. Some time we can expect too much from ourselves and we want to achieve beyond our abilities; this causes a burden and we can feel burnt out.

This concept is also concept of acceptance of who we are, being realistic about our abilities, skills, energy and time. Taking time to reflect and think about our karmic activity is important in our yogic life. This lesson has helped us be aware of the need to reflect and be aware of where we put our intention, effort and energy.

Lesson 19.
Yoga is To Live in Equanimity (Yoga Samatva)

Samatva is one of the commonly known as very important practice in Yogic, Vedic and Vedantic traditions. It means living and maintaining the state of equanimity, equality, indifference or uniformity in all the ups and downs of our life. The term Samatva comes from the Sanskrit root, sama, which means 'equal'.
Lord Krishna in the Bhagavat Gita explains to Arjuna that to master life and live in a balanced, calm, and even-mindedness-

You have the right to work, but never to the fruit of work. You should never engage in action for the sake of reward, nor should you long for inaction. Perform work in this world, Arjuna as a man established within himself- without selfish attachments and alike in success and defeat. For yoga is perfect evenness of mind. Ch.2 v.47-48.

We are taught that a Yogi should remain calm and mindful in adverse and favourable situations. This can also be practiced by maintaining body and mind equanimity. Our body and mind respond, react or act to our and other's states of being. If we are not feeling happy, our body feels stress too, similarly if our body is in pain, our mind feels sad too. This is also a state of awareness where our body and mind are doing same thing. If you are going for a walk, walk fully conscious, not letting your mind to wander around in other activities.

In mastering this state of equality, we become free from transitory states of duality like – like-dislike, pain-pleasure, good-bad and life-death. In this way we can overcome the transitory conditions of birth and death. Do everything, as it needs to be done by you or it is your duty to do, not because you like or do not like it. Lord Krishna in the Bhagavat Gita explains that success and failure should be treated alike. In understanding and following this you will attain indifference to such ups and downs, success or failure and thus attain liberation from them. He further teaches us that one who practices equanimity, sees all beings in the same way, regardless of their outward appearance, cast, colour, or status because everyone has the same potential and divine Self or Atman.

Samatva can be mastered through Karma Yoga, Hatha Yoga and Jnana Yoga practices as they bring tranquility and stability.

Lesson 20.
Be Aware to avoid the Miseries Yet to Come

Yoga advocates that we should try to live in harmony with our true nature, be in the moment, here and now, and take responsibility for everything that we do or every choice we make. This allows us to be in tune with our true nature.

We all have gut instincts or gut feelings that tell us what to be done and what is to be avoided. Many adverse situations can be avoided by following our heart and inner self. Arjuna asks Krishna why do we do immoral, unhealthy or wrong things; Krishna explains that it is because of our desires, asmita or I-ness and ahamkara (ego-consciousness) that leads us to do many things that even we wouldn't approve of ourselves. According to Patanjali, Asmita is one of our five kleshas or afflictions of the mind, in which physical, emotional and mental aspects of the mind and body are mistaken for the true self. When desire takes over our viveka or discriminative mind, we want to fulfil them at any cost. When we can't fulfil them, it leads to anger, irritation, and discontentment, which causes further physical, mental and emotional imbalance and turmoil.

Swamiji Dr. Gitananda Giri ji reminds us that health and happiness are our birthright, but we all need to claim it and maintain it in our day-to-day lives. We can't take our health and well-being for granted. We need to avoid all that is causing discomfort, pain or stress to our body-mind health. We need to avoid all the junk food or any food that we are intolerant or allergic to. We need to make sure that we follow our day-to-day physical exercise, yoga, pranayama, relaxation etc. to keep our bodies healthy, fit and strong. This is what Patanjali says here- "take responsibility, be aware and listen your heart, to avoid many problems yet to come".

We can also avoid many adverse situations in our day-to-day lives and interactions to prevent conflicts. Many people can be quite fragile and volatile, if we can hold ourselves back and give a bit of space in our relations and when we find ourselves in adverse situations, we can find much better clarity in our thoughts and emotions. When we are in the middle of crisis or conflict, we tend to lose our reasoning and intellect and tend to make choices or actions under the volcano of anger, frustration or guilt. If you can allow some space and try to evaluate the events and situations without being victim to them, you will find much better and calmer ways to deal with the same situation or issue.

Lesson 21.
Learn to Act and Never to React

This brings us to take our journey of self-transformation deeper into the concepts of Karma and Samatva Yoga. We have habitual patterns of doing things, responding and reacting to things. Our society, life and social structure is very competitive and we can have a huge amount of pressure with targets and deadlines. Many people live within such a huge amount of pressure that they don't remember there is any pressure at all.

In our body, we have the autonomic nervous system, which includes our lower brain and spinal or reptilian memory. Our spine and brain stem or the reptilian part of brain, deals with the fight-flight response. This functions to keep us safe even when we are not fully aware of it. If you are resting on your couch and your finger goes close to a candle or fire, your lower brain response will send the message to your arm to pull your hands away without you consciously thinking of it. Your higher or intellectual brain will then assess and analyse the situation and make a secondary choice for example to put the candle in safe place, or move away further away, or blow the candle out.

If you have someone running down towards you, your first response may be to feel threatened and prepare for fight or flight. The secondary response comes a little later where your brain analyses the situation and decides if there is actual danger or someone is just going to run past you. When we have conflicts at work or home, there is always the first response or reaction. If we let ourselves burst into a volcano of emotion in that moment, it becomes very hard to turn around and see if there is a better way to deal the situation. Dr Ananda says that "while your problems, feelings, emotions and issues are within your own mind, you have to deal with only one mind to make things right. Once you have spoken out or burst out on others, then you have to deal with all those minds and people to make the situation right". It is best to wait and watch even at least for few breaths before we respond.

This is what English word 'responsibility' means, 'ability to respond'. To master this ability to respond, we need to learn 'to act and never to react'. This is our work within yoga.

Lesson 22.
Shat Karmas or Cleansing Practices

Shat-karma is the Sanskrit term composed of two words, Shat (six) and karma (kriya or practices). Hatha Yoga details six cleansing or purification practices to get rid of all the malas or toxins accumulated within the body. Ayurveda and Hatha Yoga teach us that "A healthy body is home to healthy mind and healthy mind is foundation of healthy body". According to ancient yogic teachings, a toxic body is cause to toxic mind. Hence to attain peace of mind, we need to free ourselves from these toxics substances from the digestive system, nasal cavity, blood circulation, and tissues. Removing toxins will also remove blockages in pranic energy flows.

The Shat-Karmas internally and externally purify our body, which helps preparing our body, mind and energy for the pranayama and dharma practices without distraction, discomfort or fatigue.

The shat-karmas should always be learned and practiced under the supervision of an experienced Yoga teacher.

The six Shat Karmas are:
1. **Neti:** a nasal cleansing practice to purify the nasal passages and enhance the health and well-being of the sinuses. There are two types of Neti practice- Jala Neti (saline water nasal cleanse) and Sutra Neti (use of thread or catheter for nasal cleanse).

2. **Dhauti:** This is a cleansing practice for the alimentary canal, including the mouth, oesophagus, stomach, intestines and rectum. There are 11 types of dhauti practices to cleanse different parts with the help of swallowing a muslin soft cloth and taking it out.

3. **Nauli**: This is an abdominal cleansing practice which provides deep massage and stimulates the digestive organs by using the abdominal muscles on contraction, extension and rotation to create a wave like effect. This enhances digestive fire.

4. **Basti:** This is a cleansing practice for the rectum and large intestinal areas by means of an anima or enema. According to ancient practice, you can sit in warm saline water and gently draw the water into the rectum by practising the

uddiyana band and nauli Kriyas. We expel all the water to remove the toxins at the end. Our anima and colonic irrigation can be seen as a modernised Basti Kriya.

5. **Kapalabhati**: is a pranayama technique which means 'skull cleanser', it is a sharp short outbreath, followed by a relaxation of the core which allows the body to inhale on its own.

6. **Trataka**: is for the eyes, ophthalmic nerves and is a cortex brain cleanser to refine our senses, mind and enhance our focus or concentration. This practice involves focussing our eyes on one object without blinking for a few minutes or until they are tired.

These practices aim to remove gross impurities and prepare the body for vital energy work.

Lesson 23.
Yoga, Health and Diet

As we have come to understand various holistic aspects of our health, we recognise that we cannot attain this state of holistic health purely by doing regular exercise or hatha yoga and relaxation. We also have to consider how to keep our minds calm and think about what sort of life style and life philosophy will support our holistic health.

A complete yoga health program includes harmony of the following things-

- ❖ Availability of nutritious foods for growth and dynamic energy
- ❖ Regular practice of physical activity including asana, mudras, relaxation and pranayama
- ❖ Choosing to live a healthy and natural life
- ❖ Consumption of fresh air, water, food and sun light
- ❖ Proper rest, relaxation and sleep for repair of the whole body
- ❖ The use of techniques for cleansing the toxins from the body
- ❖ Motivation to develop a positive attitude and healthy mental state

Another important aspect we need to consider for our physical and mental health is our diet and nutrition. When the connective tissues of the body, for example bone cells and skin cells wear out, they use materials present within the bodies system to replace themselves. This is one of the automatic and perfectly organised processes in our bodies. This process requires healthy organic material for repair and rebuilding of tissue. If your blood stream is full of toxins, nicotine, alcohol, opiates, caffeine, protein or carbohydrate poisoning, or waste products; then the cells cannot carry out this perfect replacement, repair and reconstruction. A person who has toxic material in their system is poisoning their body and mind, and developing a faulty unhealthy structure, instead of a healthy and optimum functioning body. We are reminded that our health begets a healthy life; disease is the cause of death.

If we are seeking good health, we must ensure that our body is getting all the nutrients and food elements necessary for health, energy, cellular replacement, defence mechanism and body immunity against diseases. Our regular diet should have all the nutrients in the correct balance for the healthy functioning of all our body systems. This must be supported with access to sunlight, fresh air, exercise, rest and relaxation. Too little or too much of anything is harmful and degenerating. We must find the correct balance for our own good.

Our mental attitude around and about food is also a very important aspect of our healthy diet. The environment surrounding us during food preparation, when we eat and afterward should be pleasant, peaceful, cheerful and relaxed. Any stress, tension and emotional negativity during all these processes can cause negative effects on our health. Your positive attitude and cheerfulness helps in digesting the food properly. So take care of your health by eating healthy with the right attitude, love and care. Taking care of our mental and emotional needs can support us to eat a healthy diet, not over or under eating, but meeting the nutritional needs of our body. Stress and negative emotions can affect appetite differently, inducing some people to eat more and others to eat less. Food can put a damper on stressful feelings temporarily, foods high in fat, sugar and salt can become more appealing when you are under stress, or feeling bad about yourself.

Over and under eating are common ways to cope with feelings like stress and anxiety and being overwhelmed. When the body is stressed it activates the fight or flight response which directs the bodies resources away from things that we don't need in the moment, like digestion. Additionally stress and anxiety are often accompanied by physical symptoms such as nausea, cramping and diarrhoea, which can cause lack of appetite. Overeating may be more common with chronic stress and trauma. During chronic stress, cortisol the body's stress hormone is released promoting cravings and an increased drive to eat and seek comfort. Eating for comfort can release dopamine the feel good hormone. Being mindful of our eating habits and mindful as we eat can support us to eat healthily. Taking care of our emotional needs and mental health is important in living a balanced healthy life.

Only healthy people can enjoy all of the aspects of life. All our material possessions are of no value if we are unhealthy. There is no pleasure greater than the pleasure of health known as Swasthya Ananda (joy of health).

Lesson 24.
Yogic Diet

Simply put a yoga diet references to the pure vegetarian diet. Our Indian yogis are the best examples of health through a vegetarian diet. They could stay in the high mountains, both hot and cool places, without having any modern mundane resources, where the normal person like us cannot imagine surviving. Their diet is very simple, free of meat, fowl, fish and other animal products and even some times they cease the by-products of the animals and follow a strict vegan diet.

According to Swamis Dr Gitananda Giri Ji, non-vegetarian people say that they could not survive without these animal products, because these are the richest sources of proteins. This is a totally false concept and it is proved by the large numbers of healthy vegetarians. Many Hindus are vegetarian to fulfil the Yama of 'non-killing', or 'Ahimsa' non harm. All of the natural food that we eat possess a large number of proteins. A simple question you need to answer is Where does a cow get its protein from? and Why do you want to get the second hand nutrients then?

Yoga Diet means total balanced nutritious healthy vegetarian food. Your daily intake of the food should possess the desired amounts of the proteins, fats, carbohydrates, minerals, vitamins, and resins. Then clean and cool water, fresh air, natural living, exposure to sunlight and physical exercises are very essential parts of the complete yoga diet. One of dearest students and yoga follower Annapurna (Helen Wilson) who follows a very strict vegan life style says "the simple rule for a healthy, nutritional and balanced diet is to have all seven colours on your plate, on at least one of the meals every day".

There should be balance in between our action, energy, and rest. Only we can find out these balancing measures for ourselves with awareness of our own particular body, mind and energy needs. Do the self-study with the awareness and then make a balance chart for yourself. The balance of action, energy and rest is very important to be understood. How much and which type of physical and mental work you have to do? Is it balancing for all aspects of body, mind and emotions? If not, then try to balance it through selecting and practicing a group of the hatha-yoga practices and changing your diet and lifestyle.

Then try to find out the energy requirements of your body according to your work, body makeup and environmental conditions. We should eat the food grown in the area we are living, this will help our bodies maintain homeostasis within ourselves and with our surroundings; we will enjoy our health better if we are in-tune with nature all around us. Finally rest, a sound sleep makes you fresh and energetic. So enjoy your sleep, enjoy your work, enjoy your food, enjoy your social and family times, enjoy your individual nourishing times in a balanced and moderate manner. Lord Krishna in Bhagavat Gita mentions that the middle or moderate lifestyle or path is the way to life, grow and evolve.

Important Diet Rules for Natural Health

1. Include at least 40% raw, fresh foods in your diet, concentrating on seasonal fruits and vegetables. You can grow your natural health by following nature through eating seasonal foods, vegetables and fruits, belonging to that particular area. Nature has its own cycle and produces food, fruits and vegetables for the requirement of the area. So don't avoid this if you are seeking good health.

2. In the 60% cooked food, consider whole grains to keep in balance the acid-alkaline ratio of the body. Never over cook the food; to save the essential ingredients of the food try to also consume the water used for boiling the vegetables, this uses the most essential ingredients of the vegetables.

3. The skin of fruit and vegetables is a rich source of alkaline content, so don't throw them out. Wash the fruits and vegetables properly under tap water and use them fully with their skins on. Don't throw away your health producing food with the peelings.

4. The use of animal fats in cooking even the ghee, increases the acid amount of the food. Poly-unsaturated, cold pressed vegetable oils are the most satisfactory for the maintenance of smooth working body processes and nerve tone.

5. Adding white and refined sugar to fresh fruits and juices makes them highly acidic; if you need sweetener then add the natural sweeteners like honey or jiggery (coarse dark brown sugar).

6. Avoid any unnatural, junk, processed or long stored foods. They are rich in calories, but having no nutrients. The producers may claim that they have proteins and vitamins in them, and that this can be proved in laboratory testing; but they are of a chemical or inorganic nature and cannot be assimilated by the body and should be chucked out. You should avoid the preservatives and chemical fresheners used in all these types of foods.

7. Be aware of the psychological causes creating the feelings of unnatural appetite. Many of the negative emotions, thoughts, feelings and situations may create this appetite. Remember that appetite is mental while hunger is the body's process.

8. Eat to satisfy the hunger and fulfil the bodily needs of all the nutrients and not to satisfy the appetite or not to satisfy the sensory pleasure.

Lesson 25.
A Balanced approach always helps

Having a balanced approach to life is important for us to combat stress. As we have considered, a wholesome change is required which includes health, life style, emotional and attitude changes.

Where the physical aspect is concerned, the basic stress buster is yoga Vyayama, conscious relaxation and sleep. Adequate sleep fuels the mind and body. Feeling tired only increases the stress because it may cause us to think irrationally. A few light isometric asanas, conscious breathing and hatha yoga kriyas and deep relaxation or yoga nidra can be helpful to aid sound restorative sleep.

On the emotional level, beginning each day with a mudita (smile), cheerfulness and joy really helps us. A right start to the day will help develop the right perspective and happy mood, which is very important.

Seeing problems as opportunities is a quality that will enable us to handle stress better and be at our own optimum level. We can try to release and replace the negative thoughts with positive thoughts for transformation. Once we have started the day well, we can try and follow the uplifted mindful attitude throughout the day.

Ignorance can surely prove to be bliss at times, especially when it comes to ignoring the people who always add to our stress levels at work or otherwise. Keeping ourselves on a positive path, in our thoughts and attitudes and not letting ourselves get drowned in negativity can support us with the various life situations that we may face.

At the level of our intellectual aspect, it is a good practice to challenge ourselves in order to achieve a goal. A positive approach will help us achieve, without affecting our stress levels. If we are realistic about how much we can do in both our professional and personal lives, our stress levels will be controlled.

References and Further Resources
1. Yoga Step By Step by Swamiji Dr Gitananda Giriji
2. Talks and Teachings on Yoga by Dr Ananda Balayogi Bhavanani; Youtube link :- https://www.youtube.com/user/yognat2001
3. Authentic Teachings of Yoga during six months intensive 2006-07, course at ICYER, Ananda Ashram, Puducherry, India with Ammaji Meenakshi Devi, Dr Ananda, Smt Devesana and Dr Nalini Devi.
4. Ashtanga Yoga of Patanjali by Swamiji Dr Gitananda Giriji
5. Yoga and Modern Man by Dr Ananda Balayogi Bhavanani
6. Yoga for Health and Healing by Dr Ananda Balayogi Bhavanani
7. Understanding of the Yoga Darshan by Dr Ananda Balayogi Bhavanani
8. Exploring Yoga Philosophy, 121 Authentic Yoga Lessons, By Yogachariya Jnandev
9. Swamij.com by Swami Rama.
10. Yoga Questions and Answers by Yogachariya Jnandev
11. Yoga way of Life by Yogachariya Jnandev

Lesson 26.
The Science of Yogic Vyayama

Vyayama means exercise or movement of the body, Hatha yoga provides us with the tools to balance our Ha (solar) and Tha (lunar) energies that can be associated with the functions of our nervous system, breathing and subtle life energy. Ha is associated with the sun, warmth, masculine, action, activeness, and sympathetic nervous system. Tha is associated with the lunar, cool, feminine, restorative, calming energy and parasympathetic nervous system. Hatha Yoga holds the balance between these two opposing forces and establishes healthy polarity. This is the balance between our solar-lunar, prana-apana, loma-viloma, yin-yang, action-reaction, sympathetic and parasympathetic nervous system.

Our muscles are controlled by a continuous communication within the nervous system. Our skeletal muscles have some contraction even while we are resting known as muscles tone and this is under the control of our central nervous system. This muscle tone helps in maintaining the firmness of muscles and maintains posture against the force of gravity. Muscle tone is equally important in the smooth muscle tissues found in the arteries and veins, which maintains blood pressure. When we stretch or cause any form of pressure on our muscles, along with stimulating and massaging the muscles, we are also stimulating the nervous system. When we are moving through postures such as with a kriya, or holding the postures in a static position as with an asana; we are significantly changing the nervous systems communication and response in relation to our muscles.

Spanda - Nispanda or The Stretch Reflex- Relaxation Response

When we want to stretch or move our body, our nervous system creates a stretch reflex, which causes a reflex contraction of a skeletal muscle in response to the movement and stretching of that muscle. A group of muscles achieve this action by generating a series of nerve impulses that move along sensory or afferent neurons in the spinal cord. In the spinal cord we also have nerve plexuses where the sensory neurons produce excitation within the synapse, which activate motor or efferent neurons.

If this excitation is strong enough, the nerve impulse is transmitted across into the motor nerves and passed down though neurons to stimulate the muscle. The neuromuscular junctions are formed at the ends of the motor neuron fibre along with the skeletal fibres of the muscle in action or stretch. A neurotransmitter known as acetylcholine is released by nerve impulses at the neuromuscular junctions triggering the muscle action or stretch. A muscle stretch is followed by muscle contraction, which relieves the stretching and prevents a possible injury.

For example if you are trying to stretch forward in Hasta-Pada-Asana, the postural muscles connected with the vertebral column in the back will stretch; for all that to be coordinated, we need a well-organised stretch reflex. Our actions are governed by nerves and reflexes, our conscious actions are stimulating the nerves and producing reflexes, which stimulate the relevant areas of the brain, spinal nerves and nerve plexuses. Yogis realised this thousands of years ago through their Sadhana and found a way to utilise this process to stimulate the nervous system, nadis, muscles and organs through the practice of asanas, kriyas and mudras. In Yogic terms our action or doing, is known as Spanda where our body, mind and breath follow the one action. When we do our practice, we understand the transformative benefits for example as with conscious breathing; this is a typical example of traditional hatha yoga sadhana.

MONOSYNAPTIC REFLEX ARC

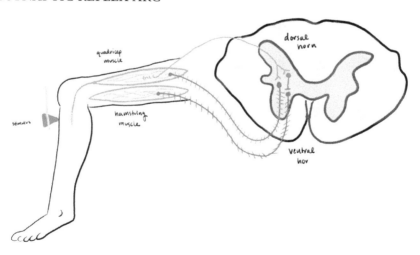

At the end of the muscle stretch reflex, our nervous system in health follows the counter balancing process to bring our muscles and nerves back to a relaxed state. In medical terms we know this as homeostasis. Hatha Yoga explains the concept of Nispanda, a conscious relaxation and letting go at the end of our action or stretch to allow healing.

Dr. Herbert Benson describes, the term 'relaxation response' as our personal ability to encourage our body to release chemicals and brain signals that make our muscles and organs slow down and increase blood flow to the brain. Yogic Nispanda explains that after a stretch, kriyas, asana or practice, when we relax, our vital energy flows as it should in those areas and helps rejuvenating the muscles, organs and nerves involved. Traditionally in Yoga it is accepted that our relaxation, our shavasana and yoga nidra is an equally important part of our sadhana as the hatha yoga practice itself.

Daily stress, pressure and life hassles are dealt with in our lives with our fight-flight, freeze responses. Our body, mind and nervous system uses this mechanism to cope with various situations and find the best possible way to maintain our life. Due to excess exposure to stress and pressure of life in various forms, we gradually lose the ability of our muscles, nerves and energy to return us back to relaxed states where healing and rejuvenation takes place. Ancient Yogis taught us how to stretch and move our body's joints and muscles using our pranic energy, breath and awareness to enhance the neuro-muscular connections and develop the relaxation responses where we are able to relax our body at will and restore our vital energy.

Types of Hatha Yoga Stretching

Hatha Yoga explains three types of stretching that are used in Santana Hatha Yoga classes.

1. *Isometric Hatha Yoga* - This is a gentle and passive approach of hatha yoga, where we hold a static asana or pose and use conscious breath and stretching of muscles to stimulate our organs and energy fields. This is a very relaxed way to improve strength, flexibility, endurance and energy balance to gain health and wellness. It is amazing for stimulating our muscles, peripheral nervous system and pranic energy system or Nadis. Static stretching is used to stretch muscles while the body is at rest.

2. *Hatha Yoga Kriyas or Vinyasa* - This is a mix or flow of movements of the body between poses and through some static poses in active Hatha Yoga Sadhana. In Ancient times, it was known as Hatha Yoga Vyayama, and commonly practised in Hatha Yoga Shalas (meeting places) for health and wellbeing. These practices work by activating the agonist muscle to contract, inhibiting, releasing or

stretching the antagonist muscle. Traditionally Sanatan Hatha Yoga kiryas also involve the flow of pranic energies nadis and chakras.

3. ***Classical Hatha Style*** - This was followed by Natha, Giri and Tantric Yoga traditions, it involves a forceful and deep static holding of the posture to awaken our subtlest potential energy or kundalini for spiritual awakening. This requires a static stretch followed by a strong isometric contraction of the muscle against an immovable force to create resistance.

Why do we need to stretch?

In our busy life many of us are overstressed, overworked and exhausted, the nervous systems is often under the fight-flight response and is hyper-alert due to stress, trauma, anxiety, fear and life pressure. Our healthy and properly functioning nervous system and homeostasis enables us to transit between the sympathetic and parasympathetic nervous system. Problems begin when we lose the ability of harmonious transition to perform the desired action and return back to relaxation.

If you are riding a bike and going up a hill, you will need to peddle harder, while if you're riding a bike down hill, you will not need to peddle, instead you may need to use the brakes to slow down. We need to master our body and mind for both situations to live our life to its full potential. Our body has this amazing inbuilt system, regulated by our nervous system and hormones to quickly adjust and find a way to deal with various situations and opportunities.

If we are living under constant pain, pressure, stress or strain gradually our nervous systems and muscles forget how to relax, which further impairs the healing and rejuvenation process at a cellular level. Yoga can help us regain the balance of sympathetic-parasympathetic nervous system, right-left brain, the Ha-Tha of the energy, solar-lunar, loma-viloma, prana-apana and help us to enjoy our life and attain the optimum functioning of body and mind. A well balanced hatha yoga including kriyas, sun-salutations, asanas, mudra, pranayama and relaxation will help activate our muscles and nervous system, release stress and regain the ability to relax, restore and rejuvenate.

Isometric or gentle static Yoga Asanas will empower our parasympathetic nervous system and muscles to relax. So if we follow Asana, Kriya and stretching with conscious relaxation, we are not only increasing the muscles strength, mobility, and endurance but also inhibiting the over activation of the sympathetic nervous system or fight-flight-freeze responses and empowering the relaxation response.

This transition of the nervous system for healthy physiological functioning can be achieved through conscious relaxation. There are sensors in our body known as mechanoreceptors of different types of sensitivity within the fascial matrix (the connective tissue network that holds the body together). These are located in the tissues. These mechanoreceptors are found in the joints of the hip, knee, shoulder and the backbone. These sensors sense, communicate and respond to changes in movement, tension and temperature. These sensors also inhibit the stress response in the body. Releasing connective tissue within the joints through gentle stretches activates them. According to Kruger (1987) the Ruffini mechanoreceptors are especially responsive to tangential forces (linear motion) and lateral stretch. Van Den Berg and Capri (1999) explains that the stimulation of Ruffini corpuscles is assumed to result in a lowering of sympathetic nervous system activity.

These findings show that the gentle practice of postures or asanas with holding them for a little longer, will have a relaxing effect on the local tissues and the whole body as it acts on relaxing the nervous system and empowering the parasympathetic nervous system. This is quite amazing to see how Patanjali had realised the beautiful and most beneficial approach of Asana or Hatha yoga practice, with the understanding of Asanas as being able to be steady and at ease in a pose or 'sthiram-sukham-asanam'. According to Maharishi Patanjali, by mastering Asana, one attains peace, equanimity and the balance of duality; with the two opposites of liking and disliking, pain and pleasure, the sympathetic and parasympathetic remain in balance.

Our deep conscious breathing also plays an important part in activating the parasympathetic nervous system and relaxation response in the body. Following the Savitri Pranayama (Inhale 6 x hold 3 x exhale 6 x hold 3) will stimulate the vagus nerve. The vagus nerve is the longest nerve in our body and is associated with the parasympathetic regulation of the heart, lungs and digestive system. We can bring about a significant positive change in our nervous system response in the body by practicing isometric stretching or static poses for short periods of between 3 to 4 minutes, in combination with Sukha or Savitri Pranayama. This will cause myofascia release, relaxing our overactive sympathetic nervous system and helping release stress and trauma from the body. The myofascia is the dense tissue surrounding our muscles and bones; it is very strong and flexible. Under a microscope it looks similar to a net and runs throughout the body holding the body in form; when healthy it is relaxed and soft and helps maintain good posture and flexibility, but can become tight and restricted causing poor posture and reduced flexibility.

Dynamic Hatha Yoga Kriya, Vinyasa or active stretching has a very different effect on our nervous system. In these active flow hatha yoga practices, muscle tension can increase when the muscles are in in active contraction in a concentrically or shortening action or through the extending or eccentrically (lengthening) action. The active movement and stretching activates the Reciprocal Inhibition response in the nervous system. This response inhibits the antagonist when the agonist or primary mover is activated. Simply put reciprocal inhibition is the process in which a muscle must relax on one side of a joint to allow for a muscle on the other side to contract. The dynamic approach of Hatha Yoga practice simultaneously increases and releases the tension in the muscles and nervous system.

Therapeutic Hatha Yoga Kriyas should be designed with a balanced use of active stretching Asanas and passive relaxing Asanas. A simple example can be moving from relaxing Shashanka Asana to balanced Chatus-Pada-Asana and reaching to active stretch in Bhujanaga Asana and returning back to relaxation pose in Shashanka Asana. This approach tremendously benefits us in equally empowering and balancing our sympathetic and parasympathetic nervous systems to bring balance, harmony and homeostasis.

What is Isometric Yoga Exercise?

An isometric exercise is a form of exercise involving the static contraction of a muscle without any visible movement in the angle of the joint. The dictionary defines isometric exercise as "a type of strength training in which the joint angle and muscle length do not change during contraction." In Yogic terminology instead moving from Asana to Asana in a dynamic flow, you hold an Asana or stretch and apply pressure on those particular areas of body for physical, mental, and energetic benefits. Yogi Gheranda mentions in the Gheranda Samhita, "press your organs against your organs for healing your body and mind and awaken the kundalini or evolutionary life governing energy".

According to Physical Therapist Michelle Orefice-Thomsen, "Isometrics are extremely beneficial when incorporated into a complete strength and flexibility program. They help to overcome muscle imbalances while also improving body control, body awareness and core activation". A study by Takakazu et al. (2014) revealed that "Isometric yoga as an add-on therapy is both feasible and successful at relieving the fatigue and pain of a subset of therapy-resistant patients with CFS (Chronic fatigue syndrome)".

Benefits of Isometric Hatha Yoga

❖ Helps improve strength and enhances flexibility and mobility working through an entire range of muscle groups and pressure points

❖ They are safe and can be easily modified or manipulated for each and every individual to their level without having any negative impact or adding more stress and strain to the body

❖ The application of pressure on certain areas of the body in a static manner stimulates and strengthens connective tissue, tendons and ligaments

❖ Improves motor skills and enhances body awareness, enabling the body to respond much quicker and better to falls, slips, or exertions in day to day life

❖ Stimulates and activates various Nadis, Prana Vayus and Chakras as we apply pressure or stretch in associated areas of the body and muscles

❖ They are easily accessible and convenient for any one and can be practiced standing, on the floor, in a chair or on a bed

❖ Enhances our homeostasis or spanda-nispanda as we apply pressure and then let go through the stretch and relax

❖ Stimulates our neurotransmitter receptors to fire and communicate with our muscles to engage in the Asana. This improves the connectivity of our muscles and brain, which improves connectivity and co-ordination of body movements and improves balance

❖ Trains our body and skeletal-muscles to hold our posture better by improving muscle memory and response

❖ Burns calories, boosts metabolism and helps in reducing fat and weight

❖ Stimulates the parasympathetic nervous system and hence gradually helps in reducing blood pressure

❖ Helps in improving bone density, which will help in preventing or managing osteoporosis.

❖ The limited movement during isometric yoga practice gives the body the opportunity to focus on strengthening and improving the joints rather than stressing them

❖ These Yoga exercises have proved significantly beneficial in reducing or eliminating pain caused by arthritis

❖ Isometric yogic exercises can be great aid in rehabilitation and recovery from injuries as well as in pre and post surgeries

❖ These exercises can help overcoming our physical weakness as we can easily apply some pressure or stretching in any part of our body

This lesson has examined how yoga vyayama builds and strengthens flexibility, fitness and health. Our yoga sadhana increases our energy levels by increasing the delivery of oxygen and nutrients to the whole body through balancing our solar-lunar, prana-apana, loma-viloma, yin-yang, action-reaction, stretch-relaxation, sympathetic and parasympathetic nervous system.

References and resources

Dr Ananda Balayogi Bhavanani et al., Modulation of stress induced by isometric handgrip test in hypertensive patients following yogic relaxation training
Isometric exercise - Wikipedia, https://en.wikipedia.org/wiki/Isometric_exercise
https://www.ncbi.nlm.nih.gov/pmc/articles/PMC4269854/
"Relaxation Response" by Dr. Herbert Benson, professor, author, cardiologist, and founder of Harvard's Mind/Body Medical Institute.
Yoga Chikitsa By Dr Ananda Balayogi Bhavanani
Yoga Step By Step by Swamiji Dr Gitananda Giriji.
Various Articles by Dr Ananda Balayogi Bhavanai on Yoga Therapy.
Karger, Neuroscience of Exercise: From Neurobiology Mechanisms to Mental Health, www.karger.com/nps
Yoga Anatomy By Leslie Kaminoff
Science of Yoga: Understand the Anatomy and Physiology to Perfect Your Practice by Ann Swanson
Functional Anatomy of Yoga by David Keil
Yogabody: Anatomy Kinesiology & Asana by Judith Hanson.

Lesson 27.
Simple Ayurveda to Assist Yoga Therapy

In this lesson we will explore the Pancha-Koshas and the Pancha Mahabhutas. Pancha is 'five' and Kosha means 'sheath', in Yoga Philosophy there are five layers of awareness through which all experience is filtered. The Pancha Mahabhutas are the 'five great elements' that are said to be present in everything in the universe, including the human body.

The three bodies and five sheaths (Pancha- Kosha) concept of Yoga

Yoga Darshan explains that our living existential body is made up of three bodies or Sharira. These three bodies are:
   ❖ Sthula Sharira – Gross or Physical Body
   ❖ Sukshma Sharira – Subtle or astral body
   ❖ Karana Sharia – Causal or Karmic body

Within these three bodies are five sheaths (Pancha-Koshas):
   ❖ Annamaya Kosha – Food or physical body
   ❖ Pranamaya Kosha – Subtle energy or psyche (vital life force) body
   ❖ Manomaya Kosha – Mind Body
   ❖ Vijnanamaya Kosha – Wisdom or intellect body
   ❖ Anandamaya Kosha – Bliss or Spiritual body
   ❖ Sthula Sharira or Physical Body

This is our physical or structural body including skin, bones, organs, muscles and all that can be experienced by means of our senses. Our physical body is made up of Pancha-Mahabhutas or Primary five subtle elements:
   ❖ Prathvi – solid or earth matter
   ❖ Jala or Apas – liquid or water matter
   ❖ Vayu – wind or air matter
   ❖ Agni or Teja – fire or heat
   ❖ Akasha – ether, space or voidness

According to the Ashanga-Samgraha, an ancient authoritative text on Ayurveda, the different parts of the body have different predominance of Bhutas (elements) that make up our body constitution:

Body Constituent or dhatus in (Ayurveda)	Body Part	Bhuta
Rasa	plasma i.e. serum, white blood cells, lymphatic system	Jala
Rakta	red blood cells	Agni
Mamsa	muscle	Prithvi
Meda	fat	Jala + Prithvi
Asthi	bones and cartilage	Vayu
Majja	bone marrow, nerve tissue, connective tissue	Jala
Sukra	male/female reproductive organs	Jala

Sukshma Sharira or Astral Body

Our astral or subtle body is comprised of our mind and our senses, which enable us to experience pain and pleasure and are the source of all our cognitive processes. In total there are 19 elements making up our astral body:

❖ Jnanendriyas – Five sense organs- sight, hearing, smell, touch and taste
❖ Karmendriyas – Five subtle organs of action- the feet (pada) movement, the hands (pani) grasp and hold, the rectum (payu) elimination, the genitals (upastha) procreate and the mouth (vak) speech
❖ Pancha Prana Vayus – The five subtle energy currents, which are prana, apana, samana, vyana and udana
❖ Four Atahakarana – the four inner subtle instruments which are manas (the mind), buddhi (the intellect), chitta (the awareness) and ahamakara (the ego)

Karana Sharira or Causal Body

This is our seed body or blueprint of the gross and subtle bodies along with the life process. This body cannot be experienced by means of our sense organs. Yoga guides us to a step-by-step manner to experience this Karmic Body and then liberate the soul from the grip of this Karmic body to attain liberation. This body links us to our True Self or Atman. It contains all our previous experiences, memories, habits and information of not only this life but, all the previous lives we have lived. According to Upanishadic Wisdom our causal and subtle bodies stay together and depart the physical body at the time of death and move in to the next body at the birth.

Pancha Koshas or The five sheaths

- ❖ **Annamaya kosha** - The food or structural sheath, this is our anatomical body or structure made of food, this sheath belongs to Sthula Sharira
- ❖ **Pranamaya kosha** - The vital energy sheath, this is the subtle energy body that transform our anatomical body in to the physiological or functional body. According to Upanishadic wisdom this body is composed of nadis, prana vayus, chakras and Karmendriyas or organs of action
- ❖ **Manomaya kosha** - The mental sheath, this is our mind body comprised of manas (mind), chitta (awareness or consciousness) and jnanendriyas or sense organs. This transforms our anatomy and physiology in a living body, which has the ability to feel and experience
- ❖ **Vijnanamaya kosha** - The intellect or wisdom sheath, this sheath is related with the astral body. It contains all the intellectual information (Buddhi) related to life processes, growth and evolution. It has the ability to analyse the information we receive and governs the ahamkara or ego and iccha-shakti or will-power. Our choices, discrimination and decision making abilities are manifestation of this Vijnanamaya Kosha
- ❖ **Anandamaya kosha** - The bliss sheath, this is the all pervading and central aspect of the causal body. This sheath is our Jiva or Living being which experiences true wisdom, joy and bliss

Anatomy according to Ayurveda

Vedic teachings of ancient Ayurveda begin with the absolute concept of 'atha pinde tat Brahmande' meaning the individual jiva (living substance) and body represents the whole universe. This then is followed further with 'atha Brahmande tat Pinde', which means that the universe represents the individual life. So the individual life and universe are interconnected and interrelated. The Prakriti or creation is constituted of Pancha-Mahabhutas and so is our body. According to Vedic teachings the Pancha-Mahabhutas and the Atma, Jiva or Soul together form the body. One of the Sanskrita phrase mentions, 'shat-dhatvatmak Purusha' meaning the gross existence of the soul in the form of the body is made of the seven dhatus or body constituents.

The great Ayurveda master Charaka explains in the Charaka Samhita (6. II) "Tatra shariram naam chetanadhishtanabhutam. Panchmahabhutvikar samudayatmakam samyogavahi". This means that our Chetana (Consciousness) and the elements arising out of panchmahabhutas, the five essential elements of earth, fire, water, air, space or ether, form the body. Both Samkhya and Upanishadic teachings on creation explain that the body is constituted of Panchamahabhutas. Each of these five elements bring forth the qualities and abilities of cognition by means of Jnanendriyas or sense organs:

Bhuta	Quality or characteristic and Indriya or faculty
Akasha – space or voidness	Sabda or sound, ear
Vayu – wind, air	Sparsha or touch, skin
Agni or Teja, fire, heat	Roop or form, view, eyes
Aapa, Jala or water	Rasa or taste, tongue
Prathvi, earth or solid	Gandha or smell, nose

It is understood that the Panchamahabhutas (earth, water, air, fire and ether) constitute the body, and through the Jnanendriyas or sense organs the Jiva (living substance) perceives the qualities and characteristics of these elements.

The nature of the Mahabhutas in the organs of our body is as follows:

Prathvi Bhava (earthly or solid quality or nature)	Nails, bones, teeth, flesh, skin, excretion, beard, body hair, hair etc.
Jaliya Bhava (Liquid or watery nature or quality)	Fluids, kapha, pitta, urine, perspiration, and saliva.
Vayaviya Bhava (wind or air nature or quality)	Breathing, blinking and opening of the eyelids, speed, inspiration, dharana etc.
Agneya Bhava (fire or energy nature or quality)	Pitta, heat, the glow of the body, view, eyesight etc.
Akashiya Bhav (Nature and quality of ether or voidness)	All holes, hollow places, small and big throat, vocal system and ear system

Ayurveda mentions that 'shiryate tat shariram', meaning 'that which degenerates is known as the body'. Our body is a gradual accumulation of panchamahabhutas, as part of our growth as well also it gradually decomposes or degrades leading to old age, disease and death. In this process the panchamahabhutas meet back into their source. This process of the creation of the body and the decomposition of body carries on continuously.

We pick the elements from the surrounding environment knowingly or unknowingly and these are assimilated by the body. Due to access or lack of access, the dependence and toxicity of these subtle elements gives rise to desires, hunger and thirst and also gives rise to liking and disliking, or attraction and repulsion towards these elements. If you reflect in your own life on how we develop attraction or aversion towards food, drink, cold, heat, water etc. it is really a sign of access or lack of to particular elements or toxicities in our bodies.

According to the Ayurvedic text Sushruti, all the natural processes in our body may result in one of the three: Visarga, Aadan or Vikshepa.

Visargadanvikshepe somsuryanila yatha |
Dharyanti jagddeham kaphapitta nilastatatha || Sushrut ||

Visarg (giving strength), Aadan (taking away of strength) and Vikshepa (movement), behind these three outcomes, there are three strengths in nature: Chandra, Surya and Vayu (moon, sun and wind). In the body, these outcomes are governed or performed by Kapha, Pitta and Vata. These three principles or Doshas (Vata, Pitta and Kapha) are governing the integration and disintegration of the constituents in the body.

The Charak Samhita explains the Tridoshas as follows:

Kapha is a white coloured substance, which is of a cold, heavy, slow, sticky and glossy type; even if it is subtle or gross, it has these qualities. As per Ayurveda, kapha amounts to six palm full. That means it can be in liquid form too. Even if the oily part of the kapha is demonstrated through the organs, its other characteristics are according to its functions.

Pitta is hot, sharp, and has a little bit of an expansive property, with particular smell or strong smell. Even if these are demonstrated through organs, other characteristics are as per functions. Pitta is five palmfuls. This also is a liquid substance.

Vata is dry, less cold as compared with kapha, tiny and movable. This substance is of a moving nature and is not related to body organs. This is at some places gross and at most places subtle. It is called 'Avyaktovyaktakarma', which means "although it is not expressed on its own, it is expressed through actions".

Further Ayurveda explains that health or illness of the body depends on the balance or imbalance of the tri-doshas. Our body functions and movements are also dependent on these principles too. Even though the Pancha-Mahabhutas are constitutional elements of body formation, primarily the three elements (aap – liquid, teja – energy and vayu - wind) are the main elements of function. These elements seek the help of Prathvi (earth) and Akasha (space) elements to carry out their functions.

In this lesson we began with understanding the Pancha-Koshas, the concepts of the three bodies and five sheaths, which make up our living existential body. Our physical body is made up of Pancha-Mahabhutas or Primary five subtle elements, which have different predominance of Bhutas (elements) that make up our body constitution. In the body the three principles or Doshas of Vata, Pitta and Kapha, govern the integration and disintegration of these constituents in the body. In the next lesson we will examine the Tri-doshas.

Lesson 28.
Tri-dosha: Three Doshas (Vata, Pitta, Kapha)

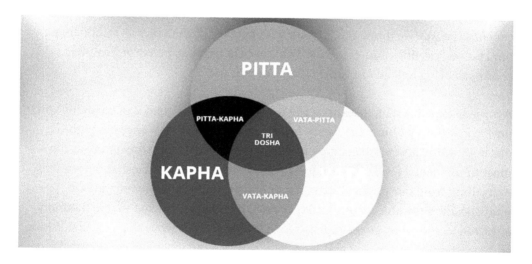

The Ancient Ayurveda science of herbal remedies, yoga therapy and naturopathy is the oldest known form of health care in the world, emanating from the Vedic Culture of Bharat-Varsh of great Rishis, Sages and Therapists in India around 5000 or more years ago. In Recent decades Ayurveda has become more popular and has been adapted with modern scientific research studies. Swami Ramdev's Yoga and Ayurveda movement has made Ayurveda available to wider communities in India now. Ayurveda offers us the potential to heal chronic diseases, cleanse our body-mind system and improve health and longevity.

Maharishi Patanjali offers us three healing aspects:

- ❖ *Ayurveda*- for purifying our body for health and evolution
- ❖ *Vyakarana* (grammer)- for purifying our language
- ❖ *Yoga Darshan*- for purifying our mind and attaining self-realisation

Ayurveda is a science of understanding our 'wholisitic' self and offers us many key concepts:

- ❖ *Sapta Dhatus*- Seven constitutional aspects
- ❖ *Tri-Doshas*- Vata, Pitta, Kapha
- ❖ *Tri-Gunas*- Sattva, Rajas, Tamas
- ❖ *Ahara-Vihra*- Life Style and diet
- ❖ *Samaskaras and Karma*- Genetic, Epigenetic, Birth and Mind
- ❖ *Pranaic Energy*- Prana Vayus or vital energy currents

Ayurveda Science provides these scientific tools to help us understand our individual self from gross to subtle, from our constitution to unique nature. It also explains the way we think and interact with people. This enables us to understand our choices, cravings and desires, which can help us make better or healthier choices to bring holistic transformation into our life.

Ayurveda explains that, diseases is the natural result of living out of harmony with one's constitution. Our constitution is the inherited balance of energies within our body, mind and pranic energy system. This describes our true nature at the most fundamental level. This unique constitutional science of Doshas determines everything from our physical structure of bones, muscles, tissues etc. to our predisposition toward various health threats. It also defines what we are naturally attracted to and what we are repelled to. It further details what helps in establishing and maintaining our nature and inherited qualities and what will cause imbalance and result in diseases or sickness. Because we are different in constitutional energy, the path of optimum health and wellbeing will be different for each individual depending upon our own constitution.

The Ayurvedic Science of understanding our true nature, and energy constitution is known as the Science of Tridoshas. Tri-Doshas are defined as three fundamental energy principles, which govern the function of our bodies on physical, mental, emotional and intellectual level. These three energy principles are known as Vata, Pitta and Kapha. Each individual has a unique balance of these three energies; many of us can be predominant in one of the three, or mixture of two or more.

On the most fundamental level, pitta is our metabolism, kapha is our structure, and vata is the mobility that brings action and life into creation. Without all three energies, we simply could not exist.

To determine a person's constitution, a Clinical Ayurvedic test of consultation with an Ayurveda specialist is necessary. This physical, emotional and spiritual evaluation identifies the balance of energies in a person's body as well as areas of imbalance. Once the nature of the person and the imbalance are identified, we can design a yoga therapy plan according to our 12 point model including diet, life style, hatha yoga, pranayama, relaxation techniques, yogic attitude, contemplations etc. to restore and maintain the balance.

The Vata Dosha

- Elements – Vayu and Akasha

- Qualities- light, cool, dry and mobile

- Body- light, bones are thin, and dry skin and hair

- Personality - talkative, enthusiastic, creative, flexible and energetic

- Issues with Imbalance- worry, fear, anxiety, constipation, instability, nervous system disorders, arthritis

vata

Vata Dosha is known to be made of the wind (Vayu) and the ether or space (Akasha) elements. The Vata Dosha contains similar qualities to Vayu and Akasha Bhutas. Vata has the similar qualities to the wind, which are light, cool, dry and mobile. People with Vata qualities experience these characteristics. Their bodies are often light, their bones are thin and they can have dry skin and hair. They tend to move and talk quickly. When people with Vata Quality are out of harmony they may lose weight, suffer with constipation and weak immunity and nervous system.

Those with Vata Qualities tend to be talkative, enthusiastic, creative, flexible and energetic in their personality. When they are out of balance they may easily become confused and overwhelmed, finding it difficult to focus and make decisions and may also suffer with sleep disorders. Stress is a strong triggering point for people with Vata quality; emotionally they suffer with worry, fear and anxiety.

Common health issues associated with Vata include anxiety, constipation and insomnia, arthritis, chronic pain, or Parkinson's disease. To establish balance within the Vata quality, we need a program emphasising the opposing qualities of warmth, heaviness, nourishment, moistness and stability.

Ayurvedic programs also include colour and aroma therapies, detoxification, yoga, and meditation.

Diet should include-

- ❖ Cooked grains like rice and lentils, cooked vegetables and intake of warm milk and spices
- ❖ Fruits - Sweet fruits such as bananas, coconuts, apples, figs, grapefruits, grapes, mangos, melons, oranges, papayas, peaches, pineapples, plums, berries, cherries, apricots, and avocados. Dried fruits can also be eaten, but not too much. The following general rule applies to fruit consumption: at least one hour before or after meals, but not in the evening
- ❖ Vegetables- Cooked: asparagus, red beets, carrots, sweet potatoes, radish, zucchini, spinach (in small quantities), sprouts (in small quantities), tomatoes (in small quantities), celery, garlic and onions (only steamed)
- ❖ Herbs – Pungent herbs like oregano, rosemary and sage and all the kitchen spices like ginger, coriander, cumin or cayenne are recommended to increase the digestive fires and are stimulating, warming, drying and dispersing

Hatha Yoga recommendations for Vata Balance

- ❖ Asanas engaging lower body (lower back, hips and legs) in gentle and static approach (Isometric) like Vriksha-Asana, Meru-Asana, Veera-Asana Variations, Veera-Bhadra-Asana Series can help us grounding our feet and stabilising our energies. All variations of Pawan-Mukta Kriyas are few of the best kriyas to release any trapped wind and balance Vata Quality.
- ❖ Pranayama for Vata Balance:- Anuloma-Viloma, Nadi Sodhana and Savitri Pranayama.
- ❖ Mudra – Prathvi Mudra – For Prathvi Mudra join the tip of ring finger and thumb with keeping other three fingers straight.

The Pitta Dosha

- Elements – Agni and Jala

- Qualities- hot, sharp and penetrating

- Body- moderate weight and good physique

- Personality - focused, competitive, courageous, energetic

- Issues - diarrhoea, infections, skin rashes and problems related to liver, spleen and blood, anger, short temper

pitta

The Pitta Dosha is constituted from Agni (fire or energy) and Jala (water or liquid) where fire is more predominant. People with Pitta qualites tend to have the qualities of fire, hot, sharp and penetrating. This is also volatile and oily due to the water element. People with Pitta Quality tend to feel warm with oily skin, penetrating eyes and sharp features. These people tend to have moderate weight and a good physique.

When out of balance, pitta dominated people suffer with diarrhoea, infections, skin rashes and problems related to liver, spleen and blood. Pitta Personalities tend to be highly focused, competitive, courageous, energetic and clear in communication. These people like finding and solving problems and thrive under stress. They can also be intense and speak sharply. These people are good at making friends and fear making enemies. Emotionally Pitta people are challenged by the heated emotions of anger, resentment and jealousy. Pitta quality people can be well-structured, good in managing projects and concentrating. They can be good teachers and their lessons are logically organised, which make them easy to follow. The Pitta types tend to spend money more systematically and prudently.

To bring balance to Pitta qualities, we need to design a program emphasising the opposing qualities of coolness, heaviness and dryness. They can be soothed by a predominantly vegetarian diet, bitter vegetables are recommended. The food should not be too spicy, salty, or sour and recommended to be cool in summer and hot in winter. A Clinical Ayurvedic program may also include aromas, colours, massage, detoxification, yoga and meditation.

Diet should include-

- ❖ Fruits - Sweet fruits like: apples, avocados, coconuts, figs, melons, oranges, pears, plums, pomegranates, and mangos are recommended to balance Pitta Quality. Avoid dried fruits
- ❖ Vegetables - Sweet and bitter: asparagus, cabbage, cucumber, cauliflower, celery, green beans, lettuce, peas, parsley, potatoes, zucchini, sprouts, cress, chicory, and mushrooms
- ❖ Grains - Barley, oats (cooked), basmati or white rice, and wheat
- ❖ Spices - cilantro, cinnamon, turmeric, cardamom, fennel, and some black pepper
- ❖ Milk Products -Butter (unsalted), ghee, goat milk, cow milk, pans, and cheese. Soy milk and tofu as a vegan substitute

Hatha Yoga for Pitta Balance

The seat of Pitta is our stomach and digestive area. Backbends, and twists and highly recommended hatha yoga practices for balancing Pitta. Dhanurasana, Ustrasana, Chakrasana, Ardha Matsendrasana and Brahma Danda Asana Series are some of the typical Asanas for Pitta Quality. A gentle, effortless, conscious and mindful flow or Kriya Yoga to rejuvenate, relax, develop patience, calmness and become receptive
Pranayama for Pitta - Shitali, Shitakari and Kaki Pranayama
Mudra for Pitta - Prana Mudra

The Kapha Dosha

kapha

- Elements – Jala and Prathvi

- Qualities- cool, moist, stable and heavy

- Body- dense, heavy bones, lustrous, supple skin, low metabolism with large stocky physique

- Personality – heaviness, stable nature, resilience to quick fluctuations.

- Issues – depression, obesity, lethargy and diabetes

The Kapha Dosha is constituted of Jala (water or liquid) and Prathivi (earth or solid) elements predominantly. Kapha is cool, moist, stable and heavy in quality. In our body these qualities manifest as dense, heavy bones, lustrous, supple skin, low metabolism and large stocky frames. People with kapha quality tend to feel cool. People with Kapha quality like regularity and routine in their life, which is something natural in them. They also carry tendency of overeating, insufficient exercise and excessive sleep.

Kapha People also carry the ability to hold onto things, money and people, coupled with water retention, makes their life difficult for them in respect or relationships, but financially, this leads them to wealth and possessions. When Kapha people are out of balance, they are prone to weight gain, and health problems associated with respiration and sinuses due to accumulation of mucous. People with Kapha quality are also prone to non-insulin dependent diabetes mellitus.

The Kapha quality can be also seen in our personality in the form of the heaviness, stable nature and stable personality, they show resilience to quick fluctuations. People with a Kapha nature are able to deal with stress efficiently with ease. However they don't like change and are comfort seekers, which can lead them to a lack of motivation and feeling of becoming stuck in life. When Kapha is out of balance, people suffer with the heavy emotions of depression, obesity and lethargy. To bring balance to a Kapha personality, we need to offer a program with the opposing qualities of lightness, dryness and warmth.

Diet should include-
- ❖ Eat less than you feel hungry for or are craving.
- ❖ Good foods are spicy or well-seasoned, dry, and anti-oedema
- ❖ Fruits - Apple, berries, cherries, mangos, peaches, pears, and raisins are recommended. Dried fruits other than figs and plums should be avoided
- ❖ Vegetables - Spicy and bitter: red beets, cabbage, carrots, cauliflower, celery, eggplant, garlic, lettuce, mushrooms, onions, parsley, peas, radish, spinach, sprouts, fennel, and Brussels sprouts
- ❖ Grains - Barley, corn, millet, oats, basmati rice (small quantities)
- ❖ Spices - All Spices specially pungent herbs like cloves, guggul, ginger, turmeric
- ❖ Milk and Milk Products - Reduced-fat milk in small quantities; avoid fatty cheeses and curd (quark). Vegan milk options are preferable in general.

Hatha Yoga for Kapha Balance

❖ The seat of Kapha is our upper digestive tract and chest area. Dynamic Practices like Vinyasa, Surya Namaskars, stronger yoga poses can help detoxifying ama or toxic build-up and boost metabolism. They need to feel full energy, lightness, letting go and forgiveness, clarity and illumination through the yoga practice

❖ Pranayama - Bhastrika and Anunasika Pranayama

❖ Kapha Nasaka Mudra - This mudra is performed by placing the ring and the little fingers on the base of the thumb and then bringing gentle pressure of the thumb upon these fingers. Keep the other two fingers straight.
This mudra increases the Pitta quality and decreases the Kapha quality.

❖ Samaan Mudra – can be used to balance the three Doshas

Lesson 29.
Dosha, Dhatu and Malas

Ayurveda teaches us that the body is made up of three components, Doshu, Dhatu and Mala. When the tri-doshas of vata, pitta and kapha are balanced they support each other's functions and maintain state of health and wellness in the body. So as we study the body, health and ill health, it is important to understand and analyse doshas.

❖ **Doshas:** The tri-Doshas of Vata, Pitta and Kapha are defined as the fundamental energy principles, which govern the function of our bodies on physical, mental, emotional and intellectual level. Tissues form a living place for the doshas, they are the structural component for the function of the doshas. The doshas carry out functions such as circulation of blood, oxygen, nerve conduction and they carry away the body's waste.

❖ **Dhatus:** There are seven types of dhatus including plasma, blood, muscle, fat, bone, marrow and reproductive fluid. When the doshas are in balance they are dhatus or tissue like, forming the anatomical tissues that make up the body. In a symbiotic relationship when in balance they support the tissues, but if imbalanced they can damage the tissues. They are part of the immune system and protect us when in balance but if weak can be part of pathogenesis.

❖ **Malas:** These are the metabolic waste or excreta, which need to be expelled from the body in order for the body to be clean and healthy. The accumulation of excreta leads to the manifestation of disease.

The amount of each dosha in the appropriate proportion is known as doshasamya. If it increases or decreases it is known as doshavaishamya. 'Doshadhatumalamulam hi shariram' means dosha, dhatus or tissues and mall is the waste product that make up our body and health.

Dhatus

Through Vakbhata one of the most influential writers on Ayurveda, we understand that there are seven fundamental elements that constitute the body, Rasa, Rakta, Mamsa, Meda, Asthi, Majja and Shukra; these are the seven dhatus.

Vayuh pittam kaphascheti trayo doshah samasatah (V S 1.6)
Vikruta vikruta deham ghananti the vardhayanticha (V S 1.7).

❖ Rasa (chyle or plasma)- is a flowing dhatu, a liquid or digestive fluid containing essential nutrients and minerals for the body. Within Panchmahabhootas and Ayurveda philosophy our diet should include six rasas (tastes or flavours), twenty characteristics and all types of viryas (energies) in balance. Additionally when the food is digested properly with the help of the digestive fire in the stomach, the nutritious substance generated has the subtle essence known as rasa. Its place is in the heart and it is circulated through all the vessels with the support of the Vyana Vayu all through the body. When rasa is absorbed into the body it becomes part of the blood or Rakta.

❖ Rakta (Blood) - When the rasa rich with Jala or water reaches the liver and the spleen, it is converted to Rakta or Blood which is red in colour due to the Ranjak Pitta. The blood within Panchamahabhautic understanding exibits the characteristics of Prithvi (smell), Aap (liquidity), Tej (red colour), Vayu (flow) and Aakash (voidness). When blood is washed away from a cloth and does not leave any stain on the cloth, it is termed as healthy blood (defectless). As it is absorbed and utilised by the body it is condensed into mamsa or tissue.

❖ Mamsa (Muscular Tissue or flesh) - With the supporting blood, the fire (agni) in the muscular tissue operates in the mansvah strotra (channels) and mamsa dhatu is produced. The warmth or heat of the Vayu and Tej is mixed up in the blood becoming thick and ripened and taking the form of mamsa. The cells and the muscles in the body are also various forms of tissue. The muscles protect the organs and support their functions, bearing the weight of the body; the joints articulate movement and all these movements are operated by the Vyana Vayu.

- ❖ Meda (Adipose Tissue or fat)- With the support of mansa (flesh), the fire in the meda operates in the medovah strota and the dhatu meda is created. It provides strength and lubrication to the muscles and bones and is also responsible for generating energy and warmth within the body.

- ❖ Asthi (Bones) – We understand from the Panchmahabhutas that the supporting elements, the fire (agni or tej) in the asthi dhatu operates and creates toughness. This creates bones, which are responsible for the upright structure of the body. Due to the Vayu, they can be porous. This function is carried on in the asthivah strota.

- ❖ Majja (Bone Marrow) – The asthidhatu supporting majja gets operated upon by the fire in the majja in the majjavah strota (channels) and the majja dhatu is created. This resides in the cavities in the bones and makes the bones stronger and less susceptible to fractures. It is the storehouse for blood cells and essential fats and is also associated with the nervous system including the brain, spinal cord and central nervous system.

- ❖ Shukra (Generative Tissue gametes, sperm and ovum) - Shukra dhatu is produced from majja with the union of tej or fire. The origin of the shukra dhatu is in the shukradhar kala in the shukravah strota all over the body. Although the testicles and the ovaries are the main origin, the shukra dhatu are produced all over the body in a miniscule form. The shukra dhatu originating in the female body is known as Aartava, which are of two kinds: firstly the Bahihpushpa, the monthly aartaya which is produced in the uterus (Garbhasaya) each month. This is not useful for conceiving (Garbha-Dharna), but very much necessary for purification of the uterus (Garbha-Suddhi): and secondly the Antarpushpa, which is the second form of aartaya produced in uterus in a very tiny amount each month takes part in conception by absorption of Shukra (semen).

- ❖ Ojas (vitality) –This is the brilliance or subtle excellent glow or energy in the Shukra Dhatu of all the seven Dhatus. The seven dhatus each support one another and develop the subsequent dhatus. Ojas is the subtle vitality and the heart is the seat of Ojas, it pervades the whole body. It is the fundamental energy principle in all living beings and our state of health and well-being depends on it. Prana dwells through this energy; this is can be considered as the eighth Dhatu or spiritual subtle energy field.

Upadhatus

There are upadhatus for all of the sapta dhatus, these are secondary building blocks of the body.

- ❖ Rasa - Stanya and Raj (breast milk, menstrual blood, ovum)
- ❖ Rakta - Kadara and Shira (blood vessels, veins, tendons)
- ❖ Mamsa - Vasaa and Twacha (muscles, fatty material, skin)
- ❖ Asthi- Daat (bone, teeth)
- ❖ Majja- Kesh (bone marrow, hair)
- ❖ Meda - Snayu, Sandhibandha, Shira (ligaments, nerves, bone joints)
- ❖ Mala – waste products, which are three (faeces, urine, perspiration

Mala

Equally important is the excretion of waste matter. Urine, stool and sweat are known as mal. They are also substances and can be affected by the doshas. There are two types of mala: sharira mala or waste products of the physical body; and dhatu mala or waste products from the metabolism of tissues.

- ❖ Purish (faeces) - Once the food has been fully digested, at the time of division of Sarkitta, Purish is produced by Purishdharakarla in the Purishvah Strota. According to the Charaka Samhita, the measure of it is 7 handfuls. Vayu and Agni are outcomes and also governing principles (dharana).
- ❖ Mutra (Urine) - According to the Charaka Samhita, the measure is 4 handfuls.
- ❖ Sweda (Perspiration) - This is mal of meda and is released through the skin. It plays important role in keeping skin and hair moist and maintains the body's temperature.

Ayurveda and fertility

Ayurveda Explains Conception and Body Development. Once we understand the principles of tridosha (vata, pitta, kapha), saptadhatu (the seven body tissues) and Malas (waste products), lets now try to understand the concept of fertility and the physical body according to Ayurveda.

Vayu provokes the teja in the body due to the friction caused between male and female genitals during the coitus. Due to the union of male and female Tejas and Vayu, the male shukra begins flowing and gets dislocated from the testicles and enters the vagina through the penis. The semen or shukra gets united with the aartaya or egg there.

From the union of Raj in the form of fire or Tejas and shukra in the form of soma, the fetus is formed and moves into the uterus and grows there until the time of birth. Vayu separates from the fetus in the form of Chaitanya, doshas, dhatus, Mala and other organs. Teja or fire governs the digestion. Gradually the foetus develops hands, legs, tongue, ears, nose and other organs and takes form as the body. Ayurveda describes the body development in womb in four states as follows-

- ❖ In first stage the shape of body is developed with Asthi (bones) and Mansa (muscles) dhatus.
- ❖ In second phase Prakriti or nature of body is developed, which includes inner organs and internal process. Rasa, Rakta, Meda, Majja and Shukra development takes place in this phase.
- ❖ Vikriti or disturbance in doshas, dhatus, and malas may develop in phase three.
- ❖ Nishkruti means the process of examining the body with the respective Vikriti happens in forth phase. (Note- third and fourth phase are to be studied as an Ayurveda Specialist Practitioner Courses)

In this lesson we have examined the Ayurveda concepts of Doshu, Dhatu and Mala. When the tri-doshas of vata, pitta and kapha are in balance they support each other's functions and maintain state of health and wellness in the body. In a symbiotic relationship when in balance the Dhatu support the tissues of the body and through the Malas, the metabolic waste or excreta are expelled from the body in order for the body to be clean and healthy.

References and resources

Halpern, M. (2020). Majja Dhatu: A closer look at the nervous system from the ayurvedic perspective.

Pakhare, N. Dosha, dhatu and mala: The fundamentals of the human body.

Raghuram, Y.S. Role of Doshas as tissues and waste products: Dhatu and malaroopa of doshas.

Lesson 30.
Asthi Dhatu: Ayurveda and Yogic Perspectives

Asthi means bone or structural support. The asthi dhatu gives solid structure to the body. As the part of annamaya Kosha or physical body, the asthi dhatu is formed as posaka (unstable) medas dhatu, which flows into the purisha dhara kala and is digested by the Asthi-Agni. In addition to the formation of the bones, teeth and the upasthu or secondary tissues are formed through this process. The hair and nails are described as the waste products (malas) of this metabolic process.

The purisha dhara kala is the membrane that holds the asthi agni. Purisha means 'faeces. The term is also used to describe the large intestine as in the purishavaha srota. This establishes a connection between large intestines, bones and health. The large intestine is the primary seat of Vata dosha. The close relationship between these two tissues enables us to understand the connection of the healthy Issues of the bones and muscles to vata dosha imbalance. When there is a health issue in the large intestine (gas, constipation, lack of healthy gut bacteria), this can lead to bone and muscle problems like osteoporosis, arthritis, and bones may become more porous and air filled.

Bones are primarily made up from solid structure known as Prathvi Bhuta. Space between the solid matter is filled by the Vayu or wind element. This helps bones to be solid and structurally strong but also light to support the easy movements. Long and hollow bones are filled with hematopoietic tissue known as bone marrow or Majja Dhatu. The low asthi agni leads to excess production of asthi dhatu. This results in production of denser tissues. In those with excess of Kapha, having a low agni, can result in producing thicker and denser bones.

People with pitta nature will have high agni, which results in producing less dense asthi majja which are metabolically more active. This may lead to narrow and weak bones, as well as lessened inflammation.

Vata nature leads to a variable agni which causes the lesser production of asthi dhatu. This results in poorer quality of bones, which can be thinner and more fragile.

Ayurveda recommends that to produce healthy asthi dhatu, one must consume adequate amount of prithvi and vayu bhutas through a balanced diet. Prathvi is present in abundance in sweet foods (madhuriya ahara) such as grains and nuts as well as astringent foods like beans and lentils. Vayu is present in bitter and pungent foods like most vegetables.

Most us may be consuming these foods as part of a healthy diet already, however Ayurveda mentions that consumption alone does not guarantee production of healthy asthi. These two elements must be properly digested so that their qualities can lead to production of healthy bones. The jatharagni (the primary digestive fire) must be healthy and balanced. If the jatharagni is out of harmony even healthy food will lead towards production of ama, which causes toxicity of the body and mind.

Asthi Dhatu and Health Issues

Having over active Vata leads to weak and fragile bones, that can become osteoporotic and easily result in fractures.

Pitta over activation leads to bone infections (osteomyelitis) and inflammation. Over active Kapha leads to excessively thick and dense bones.

Osteoarthritis is combination vata-kapha imbalance condition in which vata (motion, stress and ageing) causes irregular growth in an unhealthy manner leading to bone spurs.

Rheumatoid arthritis is a Sannipatika condition, where Vata irritates Kapha to cause irregular bone growth. Vata blows the wind to the Pitta causing inflammation and bone deterioration. Ama or toxins work as a supporting aid to this situation.

The Asthi Dhatu and Manas or Psychology

Ashti Dhatu plays an important role in the structural composition of our body, but it also plays an important role in to our mental and emotional composition. The way we stand, walk, sit and hold our posture is the physical expression of our mental and emotional states. Ones posture or Asana is not just the gesture of our physical nature, but also the quality and state of our mind and inner self.

Maharishi Patanjali refers to Asana or Gestures as 'sthirum sukham asana', which means the state of being at ease and stable with and within ourselves and also our composure. This statement clearly refers to connection between our structural posture, gestures and the state of our inner selves.

If our asthi dhatu is weak and fragile, there will always be a struggle in standing firm and composed in the face of adversity or controversy. There will be a lack of steadfastness.

When the asthi dhatu is healthy and strong, there is a sense of healthy confidence, stability and the ability to make clear decisions and follow one's own beliefs and ideas.

If there is excess of asthi dhatu, the quality of prathvi element is increased, which leads that individual to become overly attached, obstructive and stubborn. For these people it is very difficult to move forward or change their life direction.

When there is deficiency of asthi dhatu, the qualities of Prathvi element is decreased and there will be a very little attachment or stability in their life activities and choices. These people can be easily persuaded by others and lack conviction for their own will.

Kapha dosha causes excess in asthi dhatu, Vata dosha leads towards deficiency in asthi dhatu. In the long term Pitta Dosha burns down asthi dhatu resulting in a weak and fragile body and mind.

Asthi Dhatu and Chakras

In the Pranamaya Kosha, the health of the asthi dhatu relies on a healthy prana flow through the Mooladhara Chakra. Prana flowing through this chakra is associated with the qualities of the Prathvi element in the pranamaya kosha and manifests in solidarity, stability, strength and endurance of body and mind. This develops a solid sense of Self (Atma-Nistha).

The Manipura Chakra is associated with Agni element, the Anahata Chakra is associated with the Vayu element, while Vishuddha Chakra is associated with qualities of the Akash element. Through these Chakras qualities of respective elements and prana vayus are circulating or governed. If there is excess of flow of pranic energy currents through these chakras, it will also increase the qualities of respective elements, which in excess will cause weakening of asthi dhatu in both physical and mental bodies.

Asthi Dhatu and Health Assessment

Assessment of ashti dhatu (skeletal system) directly is not possible as it covered by mansa dhatu (flesh and muscles) and tvacha (skin). But we can assess the asthi dhatu by means of upadhatus (sub-tissues) and malas (waste products). By examining the hair, nails, and teeth a Yoga Practitioner can determine the state and health of asthi dhatu.

If there is deficiency and weakness of asthi dhatu, hair density becomes scant, and weak. Hair loss, and scalp irritation may be distributed throughout the scalp or in patches. Also, nails will become weak and break easily. The teeth will also become crooked, darker or grey compared to usual. These findings are also associated with the Vata Dosha.

When there is excess of asthi dhatu, hair density becomes full and crowded. The nails will be thick, and the teeth become large, straight and whiter. These are signs of Kapha Dosha in the asthi dhatu. Kapha disorder also leads into sluggish digestion and a stubborn mind. When these both can be seen in the care seeker, then Kapha dosha has entered into ashti dhatu too.

When the Pitta dosha has affected the asthi dhatu, the teeth and nails will become pale in shade of yellow and the hair will lose the colour and turn grey. Gradually this will lead to weaker nails and hair falling out.

Prevention, and Healing of Asthi Dhatu

Preservation of Asthi Dhatu and its wellness is easier than healing. Panchamahabhuta therapy (Naturopathy in Indian Ancient Therapies), Hatha yoga, healthy diet and maintaining a balanced polarity and chakras can be key practices in prevention and healing of asthi dhatu.

Healing of asthi dhatu will need restoring of the balance of Pancha-Mahabhutas especially between Prathvi and Vayu as well as a balanced flow of prana vayus of Mooladhara, Manipura, Anahata and Vishuddha Chakra. The appropriate quantity and ratio of these subtle elements varies with the each individual's constitution. Individuals with Kapha constitution will naturally have a strong asthi dhatu. In these people deficiency of asthi dhatu is less likely, compared to the likelihood of excess.

Those with Vata constitution will naturally tend to have a lower amount of asthi dhatu and are more susceptible to deficiency of asthi dhatu.

Individuals with Pitta constitution tend to have a moderate quantity of asthi dhatu and are prone to deficiency only when exposed to excess agni or heat for an extended period. In these individuals asthi dhatu is affected adversely by vata imbalance too.

Asthi Dhatu and Diet

When the Vata Dosha is affecting the asthi dhatu, one need to increase the quantity of Prathvi elements in the diet. Prathvi is found in large amounts in sweet foods like grains, nuts, lentil and beans and lesser amounts in root vegetables. Fruits and leafy vegetables carry the least amount of the Prathvi element. In naturopathy having a mud bath, or a steam bath and hot and cold showers are highly recommended.

People with the Kapha Dosha affecting the asthi dhatu must decrease the quantity of the prathvi element in the diet and increase the vayu element. Fruits and leafy vegetables and salads carry an excess amount of the vayu element. It is also recommended that excess of fruit may aggravate the Jala aspect of Kapha and hence caution should be taken in the quantity of fruits and vegetables. However pungent and bitter foods are highly recommended to increase the quality of Vayu element and an increase in use of spices and a comparatively light diet is advisable.

If Pitta is affecting the asthi dhatu, it is advisable to decrease the quality of the Agni element. The recommended diet should be cooling and contain reduced quantities of hot spices and cooked oils. Whole milk, wheat and other grains are recommended in moderate amounts. Beans and lentils are also recommended if they are easily digestible and not causing wind related issues in individuals.

Hatha Yoga, Yoga Vyayama and the Asthi Dhatu

Any form of healthy exercise increases the asthi dhatu, which supports formation of high quality bones and supporting tissues. We need to be very careful with people with weak asthi dhatu as their bones and supportive muscles are weak and easily prone to fractures and damage due to lack of endurance and strength. For people with weak bones and structural issues like various types of arthritis, a gentle and slower form of hatha yoga or yoga vyayama should be considered as a healing practice and vigorous and weight bearing exercises should be avoided.

Walking in nature is one of the healthy exercise as well as Panchamahabhuta
therapy, as you will be exposed to all the healthy elements of nature. Also water
based exercises can be a great way to start for people with more severe health issues
related to bones and supportive tissues.

Short sessions of gentle hatha yoga vyayam suitable to each individual several times
a day can be highly beneficial, especially isometric or static stretches (held between
10 seconds to 3 minutes): these can be a great way to stimulate the muscles, increase
blood circulation and activate nerves to stimulate the healing process and reduce
the pain. Some of these yoga based exercises can be very simple, here are few
examples:

❖ Press your hands against each other in Namaskar Mudra and hold for few
   deep breaths
❖ Clasp your fingers and pull them against each other and hold the tension and
   hold for few deep breaths
❖ Stretch your feet away from body and raise your arms over your head and
   stretch the arms upward and hold for few deep breaths
❖ Press your shoulder against the wall and breath deep into your shoulder
❖ Press both your arms against the wall and hold it for several deep breaths
❖ Come to half plank or full plank and hold for few breaths
❖ Perform janusirasana and hold the gentle stretch for few breaths
❖ Join the soles of your feet together in baddha konasana with knees pressing
   down, bring your hands in garuda mudra and hold the stretch for few deep
   breaths

Further gentle hatha yoga kriyas which can be introduced to support further
healing, enhanced blood circulation, cleansing, healthy pranic energy flow and
activating the healing response include:

❖ Plavini Kriyas for legs, arms and neck along with neuroplasticity and healthy
   pranic flow
❖ Brahma Mudra Kriyas for neck and shoulders
❖ Setu Bandha and Kati Chakra Kriyas for spine, hips, abdominal and pelvic
   areas
❖ Rishikesh Suriya Namaskar for healthy body, mind and pranic energy

A healthy pressure on joints, bones and muscles in an appropriately designed yoga
session for care seekers can be a great aid to enhancing their health and wellness.
An appropriate pranayama and yogic relaxation should be followed by the hatha
yoga or yoga vyayama for optimum benefits.

Mantra Chanting, and Meditation for Healthy Asthi Dhatu

Meditation, mantra chanting and spiritual contemplations enhance the coherence between pancha-koshas, pancha-bhutas, pancha-prana-vayus and chakras and hence develop a healthy body, mind and psyche. If possible sadhakas should follow meditation and mantra chanting closer to earth compared to being on a chair as it brings us closer to earth and enhances the qualities of the Prathvi element. Mantras can be chanted out loud, softly or mentally.

Focussing on the mooladhara chakra and its connection with the earth element also helps enhancing the health and wellness of the asthi dhatu. One can follow Sukha Purvaka Pranayama (inhale for 6 x hold in for 6 x exhale for 6 x hold out for 6 counts; it can be followed in counts of 4, 6 or 8) for enhancing the qualities of the earth element and root chakra.

One can also meditate on the earth mandala, which is a square or cube from the mooladhara chakra. This mandala is vibrant yellow in colour and can help with developing a greater sense of feeling clarity, grounded and stable which will support the asthi dhatu.

We can chant the bija mantra LANG for the mooladhara chakra, or the pranava OM for the complete physical, mental and psychic bodies and OM SHANTI SHANTI SHANTI OM for inner peace and tranquillity.

If the asthi dhatu is in excess, then dharna (concentration) and dhyana (meditation) can help enhance the qualities of Akasha (voidness or ether) and Vayu (wind) and hence will help purify an excess of asthi dhatu. Further meditation on the Anahata Chakra and Vishuddha Chakra can help cleanse and reduce the excess of asthi dhatu. Chanting of Bija Mantras for Anahata (YUNG) and Vishuddha (HUNG) can be a great aid to enhance the qualities of Akasha and Vayu and reduce excess of asthi dhatu.

Lesson 31.
Ayurveda and the Skeletal System

Ayurveda describes skeletal system as the main basis of the human body, which includes the skeleton and all of the bones. It states that all the parts, organs and functions are supported by the Asthi (bone). Bones primarily belong to the Parthiv or solid element and described as hard and durable. Even when the body is burnt on a cremation pyre, the bones do not burn easily.

The ancient Rishi and Ayurveda pioneer Sushruta in traditional and Sanatan anatomy study, describes the human body in six aspects. The torso and head are considered as the main (mukhya sarira bhaga) while the two hands and two legs are considered as the four branches. Sushruta goes on to describe the hands and legs as only branches just the like the branches of a tree; even if the branches are cut, a tree stays alive as long as the main trunk and roots are there and so does our body stay alive even if the hands and legs are removed.

The upper and lower part of body have 30 bones each. The middle part of the body which contains the spinal cord is considered primary. The spinal cord is composed of 33 vertebrae, which are joined with each other. The seven vertebrae in the upper part of spine are considered as part of the neck, followed by 12 vertebrae which are part of the chest. These are also known as ribs and termed as Parshuram or Varki in Sanskrit. The spinal cord is described as like bamboo, thick at the base and narrowing as it grows upwards, hollow inside through which the cord or Nadis pass through.

In the skull or head (kapal) there is a cavity made of eight flat bones. The brain is placed safely in this cavity where it is very well protected. The bones below the skull are known as Shankasthi. They are thin and beneath them there is large number blood vessels supplying blood to brain. In front of this cavity, there are 14 bones in the face. The cavity of the ears has a chain of small bones and hearing is carried through this chain of bones and nerve fibres.

According to Sushruta there are 300 bones altogether and according to Charaka there are 360 bones. In a way this can be understood because of the way the bones are counted or considered; our modern anatomy and physiology considers 206 bones all together in a full-grown adult. These bones are grouped into six categories:

- ❖ *Nalikasthi* - These are long like tubes and hollow from within, they are filled with majja(marrow). Until the age of 20 years, the colour of this is red, then it turns yellow. These types of bones are in the hands and legs.
- ❖ *Kapalasthi* - These are flat in nature. The above and below layer is separated and hollowed parts are made and filled with red majja.
- ❖ *Valayasthi* - These are round in shape for example the ribs of the chest.
- ❖ *Tarunashthi* - These are soft in nature and are mainly in between the joints in the vertebrae, between two vertebrae there is a circle of tarunasthi, which cushions any jolt to the body, until it reaches the brain.
- ❖ *Ruchakasthi* - The teeth, which are different from all the other bones in the body, are covered in this and number 28 or 32 in all.
- ❖ *Aanvashti* - These bones are smaller and irregular in size and do not fit under any of the above categories; they contain fat and blood.

The entire bone system is divided into two main parts: firstly Bahyakankal, the nails and teeth are considered as external bones as they don't have outer layer of flesh and skin (mansa and tvach). These bones can be used as part of diagnosis by consideration of the colour and structure of nails and teeth; secondly Antahkankal, these are internal bones covered by flesh and bones.

All the bones are joined with each other and these joints are known as Sandhi. Sadhis are classified in two categories: firstly Sthir or Achal Sandhi, these are fixed joints for example in the skull, jaw and teeth and secondly Chala or Cheshthavanta that have limited movement against each other and are covered with tarunasthi which is elastic in nature and can withstand the pull and pushes of aticulation. The Sandhikosha is another layer above the tarunasthi, which covers the joints like a bag. Inside these bags rests the grease like substance known as shleshak and shleshma (like synovial fluid) which supports the smooth movements.

Ayurveda describes eight types of sandhis and 210 joints altogether:
- ❖ Kor - Joints in finger, wrist, ankle, elbow
- ❖ Ulukhal - The joint of the thigh and joints at the roots of the teeth
- ❖ Samugad - Joints near the shoulder, anus, reproductive organs, hips
- ❖ Pratar - Joints like the neck and the vertebrae of the back
- ❖ Tunnasevani - Joints of the kapalashthi at face, waist
- ❖ Vaayastund - Joints near the chin on both sides
- ❖ Mandal - Round joints at the heart, eyes
- ❖ Sankhavarta – Joints in shape of circles, ears, shankha (inner ear)

Muscles and Ayurveda in Summary

Muscles join all the bones with each other and the movement is made with expansion and contraction of the muscles.

The muscles are of four types:

- ❖ Pratanvarti Muscles - Four branches and in all joints
- ❖ Vruta - Kandara - All round muscles
- ❖ Sushira - Contracting muscles in the large intestine
- ❖ Pruthul - Flat muscles - muscles at side, chest, back, head etc.

In this lesson we have considered how Ayurveda describes the skeletal system and the importance of it as the supporting structure for all of the bodies organs and functions.

Lesson 32.
Yoga, Ayurveda and Digestive Health

In the Ayurvedic principles of health, the understanding of diseases and therapeutic processes, our digestive system plays a very important role. Ayurveda explains that the food we eat, the digestive process, distribution and metabolic processes are considered very important. Also within Yogic principles our mind, emotions and sense of well-being is connected with our solar plexus and sacral chakra. We all are aware of sensations of upset and churning of the stomach during stressful, anxious or fearful times. Yoga and Ayurveda give an immense amount of importance to our digestive health. It is said that being able to enjoy the meals you like itself is a blessing.

According to Ayurveda, there are seven constitutional tissues or aspects in the body:

1. Rasa Dhatu: Plasma and fluid
2. Rakta Dhatu: Blood
3. Mamsa Dhatu: Muscles
4. Medhas Dhatu: Fat
5. Asthi Dhatu: Bone
6. Majja Dhatu: Marrow and nervous tissue
7. Shukra Dhatu: Reproductive tissue

Ayurveda explains that our body follows the above chronological order in the process of assimilation or development of our body. It is said Rasa is the first to be formed during the digestion of food. Rasa dhatu further helps formation of Rakta Dhatu. Rakta forms the Mamsa and thereafter, Medhas, Asthi, Majja and Shukra are formed in order. It is said that proper formation of first dhatu will lead healthy and vital formation of subsequent dhatu. Hence it is important that all these metabolic process are in a healthy order in each of these seven stages.

There are several stages of digestion. According to Ayurveda digestion is not only happening in the digestive tract but also in the Dhatu or tissues in each part of the body. Ayurveda clearly connects the body in this way. Prapaka is the first part of food digestion including ingestion, digestion, absorption of food and nutrients. Vipaka is the second phase of digestion where the nutrients are processed for the formation of Dhatus. Ayurveda also explains Agni as an important aspect of digestion, Agni literally translates as the fire, heat or energy. In the context of digestion it is known as the digestive fire (Pachan-Shakti). Agni is also associated with the biological energy or heat that is governing the output of metabolism, which sustains psycho-physiological life process. Agni is associated with the digestive enzymes and the metabolic and digestive process that are taking place as part of breaking down the food within the digestion, absorption and assimilation of food.

Ayurveda states that a living being is as old as his 'Agni' or digestive fire. As long as the digestive fire is strong and at it's full potential, AMA or toxins cannot be formed and the person remains healthy. All the seven elements of the body have their own Agni to metabolise the nutrient materials supplied them through their own strotas-

- ❖ Jatharagni – Present in the Rasa Dhatu
- ❖ Rastagni- Present in the Rakta Dhatu
- ❖ Mamsagni- Present in the Mamsa Dhatu
- ❖ Medhagni- Present in the Meda Dhatu
- ❖ Ashthigni- Present in the Asthi Dhatu
- ❖ Majjagni- Present in the Majja Dhatu
- ❖ Shukragni- Present in the Shukra Dhatu

A healthy and normal digestive process in our body follows the following steps: ingestion after proper chewing; breaking down and digestion; absorption of nutrients; and excretion of toxic waste. Due to various physical, mental and emotional stress, as well as indigestible food, our digestive system cannot follow the proper or full digestion. Ayurveda explains following causes of unhealthy digestion: inappropriate food; unhealthy eating habits; weak digestive fire; and the stress and strains of life.

When the body is not fully digesting the food and processing it in a natural manner, the food cannot be identified by intestines or the Dhatus and leaves the waste or toxic elements in our digestive system and body known as AMA (a Sanskrt word meaning undigested). This half processed food in the digestive system contains un-metabolised by-products, which circulate in the body as toxins leading to various health problems (roga-karana).

The Four Types of Agni-

Sama-Agni - A Balanced Digestive Fire

- ❖ Digestion, absorption, and elimination are all at their best and healthy
- ❖ Food is easily digested without losing or gaining of weight
- ❖ Feel full of energy and vitality
- ❖ Clear, sharp, attentive senses
- ❖ Easy elimination of faeces or stool, not too dry or watery
- ❖ Tongue is pink, soft, smooth and moist with little to no white coating in the morning
- ❖ No gastric, and flatulence issues

Vishama-Agni - Irregular Digestive Fire

- ❖ Vata excess digestion
- ❖ Fluctuates between lack of hunger or excess of hunger and very random timing
- ❖ Erratic behaviour
- ❖ Irregular eating patterns and craving for spicy, sweet and salty foods
- ❖ May suffer with gas, bloating, gurgling, distention, or constipation
- ❖ Underweight or overweight
- ❖ Stool tends to be small, dry, or hard

- ❖ Brownish-black coating on tongue, which may also be dry, or may has scalloped edges
- ❖ Low energy, get tired easily
- ❖ Tends towards feeling ungrounded, fearful, anxious and insecure

Teekshna-Agni - Sharp Digestive Fire

- ❖ Pitta excess type digestion
- ❖ Hunger is sharp, fierce, intense and strong
- ❖ May suffer with anger and irritation if no food available when hungry
- ❖ Hypoglycemic or blood sugar level issues
- ❖ May suffer with acid reflux, heartburn, hot flashes, acid indigestion
- ❖ Stool is more often soft, loose, may have tendency towards diarrhoea
- ❖ Faeces may be rusty/orange in colour, falls apart, or contain undigested pieces of food in it
- ❖ Yellow coating on tongue with red patches or red spots, or a bright red tongue
- ❖ Easily gets tired often feel hungry
- ❖ Judgemental and critical attitude, anger, self-centredness

Manda-Agni - Slow Digestive Fire

- ❖ Kapha excess type digestion
- ❖ Slow, weak, dull, and sluggish digestion
- ❖ Low hunger and easily feel full
- ❖ Often skip meals, but may eat in access when bored, depressed, or comfort eating
- ❖ Easily gains weight
- ❖ Often suffer with mucous, cough or congestion
- ❖ May develop oedema, water retention, nausea, loss of appetite, allergies or obesity
- ❖ Stool tends to be soft, dense and heavy, dark brown or black, possibly with mucous
- ❖ White coating on tongue, more moisture, excess saliva or slimy coating
- ❖ Gets tired suffer with feeling heavy after eating
- ❖ Tend to suffer with depression, attachment, greed, lethargy and dullness in mind

Simple Ayurvedic Recommendations

1. Regular Use of some digestive and cleansing herbs like ginger, turmeric, cumin seeds, coriander, mint, Himalaya rock salt and tulsi in herbal teas or warm drinks.

2. Warm food and warm drinks, warm water improves our digestive fire as well as warm food compare to cold or raw food also improves digestion. Ayurveda uses the term Agni or Fire with digestion and mentions that cold food and drinks extinguish the digestive fire.

3. Prepare and eat your meals with love and gratitude and try to connect with the food.

4. Eat mindfully, chew your food properly and avoid other destructions while eating.

5. We eat to live and grow and hence it should be a sacred practice. Avoid eating on the go if possible and try to make time and sit quietly with your food even for a moment and follow a prayer, at ashram we follow the prayer- 'aum tat-sat krishnat panamastu', which means 'I offer my gratitude to divine for this nurturing food'.

6. Enjoy your meal and try to connect with each of the elements (Pancha-Mahabhutas).

7. Eat healthy, fresh, nutritional and easily digestible food.

8. Cook meals with Ayurvedic herbs like cumin, turmeric, fenugreek, asafoetida, coriander, ajwain seeds are highly recommended.

9. Create a healthy gap between meals and avoid snacking between meals. Ayurveda recommends that we should fast between meals and not eat anything until the last meal is fully digested.

10. Signs of good food and healthy digestion are feelings of physical lightness, enthusiasm, genuine hunger and a sense of comfort in body.

11. Avoid Comfort eating when you are feeling emotional, or distressed.

References and Resources

1. *Yoga Therapy By Dr Ananda Balayogi Bhavanani, www.icyer.com*
2. *Yoga Step by Step by Swamiji Dr Gitananda Giriji, www.icyer.com*
3. *Anna Selby; Home Ayurveda Kit; C&B Collins and Brown Publication.*
4. *Yogacharini Anandhi, Activated Vegan Food, https://activatedveganseminars.com*
5. *Dr Marc Halpern; Tridosha: The Science Of Ayurveda and the Three Doshas (Vata, Pitta, Kapha); https://www.ayurvedacollege.com/programs/certification-courses/ayurvedic-health-counselor-1/*
6. *The Dosha Types in Ayurveda and Reccomendations; https://www.euroved.com/en/ayurveda/test/vata/#eggs*
7. *Kristen Schneider, Yoga for Three Doshas; https://www.banyanbotanicals.com/info/blog-the-banyan-insight/details/yoga-for-the-doshas/*
8. *Charaka Samhita — PV Sharma Translator, Chaukhamba Orientalia, Varanasi, India, 1981, pp. ix-xxxii (I) 4 Volumes*
9. *Sushruta Samhita — KL Bhishagratna Translator, Chaukhamba Orientalia, Varanasi, India, 1991, pp. iii-lxvi (I), i-xvii (II) 3 Volumes*
10. *Ashtanga Hridaya — Shri Kanta Murthy Translator, Chaukhamba Orientalia, Varanasi, India, 1991, pp. ix-xxvi 3 Volumes*
11. *Sharngadhara Samhita — Shri Kanta Murthy Translator, Chaukhamba Orientalia, Varanasi, India, 1984, pp. iii-xvi*
12. *Madhava Nidanam — Shri Kanta Murthy translator, Chaukhamba Orientalia, Varanasi, India, 1993, pp. iii-xv*
13. *Bhava Prakasha — Shri Kanta Murthy translator, Chaukhamba Orientalia, Varanasi, India, 1998, pp.vii-xii 2 Volumes*

Lesson 33.
A Yogi, Bhogi, Rogi and Drohi

Lord Krishna stated that "A Yogi is the one who has the senses under control and is able to withdraw the mind from objects of senses or focus outward at his own will, just like a tortoise is able to extend or withdraw its limbs". (Bhagavad Gita, 2:58).

Our first self-enquiry is to find out if we are a Yogi, Bhogi, Rogi or Drohi?

- ❖ *Yogi*- One who has mastered the mind and remains in inner balance or Tranquillity.
- ❖ *Bhogi*- One who lives life for worldly consumerism, a passionate, goal oriented person with strong opinions and often strong ambitions. They carry a great desire to succeed in life for material possessions, recognition, pride and wealth. Material satisfaction and validation through others is very important for these people.
- ❖ *Rogi*- One who suffers some form of health issues, sick, diseased or someone who is a patient. Even if they do not realise it, they are burdened by disease in their life and cannot experience happiness because the health of the body and mind are the first steps to happiness.
- ❖ *Drohi*- One who is against all the appropriate life habits, someone who carelessly desire for materials, power and ego-centric recognition which can be deadly and toxic. This will not only destroy his life but end up distressing others around him as well.

These days the word Yogi or Yogini is quite often used as a title for anyone who practices yoga in some form and they may even have no idea of what yoga really means other than a form of exercise.

The Himalayan yogis say that "Three people can occasionally sleep at night, they're: Yogi, Bhogi, and Rogi". The Yogi, because he is steadfastly engaged in Yoga Sadhana; the Bhogi because being addicted to some or the other kind of material pleasures is ever engrossed in pleasing his senses; and the Rogi (once a Bhogi) who has abused his body and mind so much that it has resulted in pain and health issues, suffering and miseries and is therefore unable to sleep.

Only a true Yogi knows that material objects can only bring temporary joy. With mastery of Ashtanga Yoga, our mind and senses can be well established in self and united with the divine; this is the only source of absolute bliss known as Satchitadananda. This process of following the yogic path is known as Yoga Sadhana and the follower of Yoga is known as Yoga Sadhaka or Sadhaki and not a Yogi or Yogini.

Ayurveda describes four categories of people: the one who eats once a day is a Yogi (mastered one); the one who eats twice a day is a Bhogi (living for pleasure and consumerism); the one who eats three times is a Rogi (one with ill-health); and the one who eats four times is a Drohi (destructive or troublemaker to society). This ancient concept Ahara or Food consumption is not merely about the food itself. Yoga teaches us that worldly people who have an attitude of a Bhogi (consumerism) are living to eat and consume for pleasure, while a Yogi only eats and consumes what is necessary to live. This idea of Yogi, Bhogi, Rogi and Drohi in a true sense is about attitude, mind-set, habits and desires. We are not only hungry for food, but there is stronger hunger for other pleasure seeking activities like sex, entertainment, social media, self-appraisal, attention, reward, ego, success, money, etc. leading us to all sorts of physical, mental, emotional, social and economic problems. The quality of inner consumerism, media, information, associations, and so many other such activities we are taking part in, can be easily looked at from the four types of personalities.

The innate appetite to gratify our senses and pleasure principles are very strong in all of us and they can easily take over our Buddhi and Viveka. Our desire to feast our eyes with certain visions, our ears with certain sounds or music, our taste buds with certain flavours, our brain with certain intellectual ideas are unique and deep. We get cravings for certain touch and smell sensations, our muscles can overindulge in regimes of extreme exercise and our minds can be captivated by certain ideas, thoughts and words.

Many of us suppress or over consume unhealthy emotions such as resentment, revenge, jealousy, guilt and fear. Many people use harsh language, words and emotional torture to harm other people. Over consumption in social media, endless obsession with various conspiracy theories and negative attitudes are all part of Drohi or the destructive nature. Our body and mind flourish on a balanced approach to fulfilling our innate needs and desires, whilst our health and balance is destroyed when we overindulge them, regardless of the object and because of our enchantment. Even excessive exercise, nutrition, or hatha yoga etc. can also become an addiction. The excess of any type of activity and lack of time produces an inordinate amount of stress on the body and mind as well taking away time to withdraw our senses inwards, to digest food, process information, rest, sleep and meditate. Compulsive impulses raise our stress hormones and are destructive, over activating our sympathetic nervous system and destroying our peace of mind, equanimity, homeostasis and the healthy balance between the sympathetic and parasympathetic nervous systems.

Scientific research by Harvard Medical School shows the result of stress and overconsumption on our hippocampus, which is smaller in depressed people because stress can suppress the production of new nerve cells needed for its regeneration. Even our obsession and excessive focus on physical health can lead to ill health and allow no time to enjoy or live to our full potential. A healthy body (Swasthya) is very essential for our day-to-day life and spiritual quest, but still our attitude and mind matter the most. We understand that pain may or may not exist in our lives, it is not always in our control, but suffering is optional, we chose to suffer with a problem or deal with it and thrive towards better things.

The **Yoga Vashistha** finds that a person who either eats too much or too little, who engages stubbornly in bodily pleasures and is extreme in his emotional inclinations can rarely be a Yogi. A Yogi refines and disciplines his cravings and passions, following the path of moderation (madhyam-marga or mitahara) in sensory gratification, no matter how delightful or tempting the experience in front of him. He eats just enough to live and does not let his cravings overwhelm him. He takes what is absolutely necessary to live. He doesn't hold on to anything for the sake of future use and lives fearlessly in abundance.

We become Rogis when we chase a desire, hunger, thirst, goal, person, emotion or experience without restraint and exert ourselves beyond our capacity desiring to attain them at any cost. This excessive single-mindedness usually is a result of some deep-seated psycho-emotional pain or blockage that we are unable to process and also maybe are unaware of. These emotions and desires urge us forward or hold us back and seem to have a life of their own. Our compulsions lead us to self-destructive behaviours that demolish our peace of mind and fuel further negative cravings. According to Shawn Achor, the author of **Scientific Proof that Happiness is a Choice**, every time we have a success, our brain moves the goalpost of where success is.

In spiritual terms (adhyatmik) a yogi lives free from material attachment, a bhogi is the one who lives for material objects, a Rogi is one who solely identifies with the body and the health of our body (we are Rogi's when we identify solely with the body) and a Drohi is the one who identifies the self as a victim and opposes divine principles.

References and Resources:

https://www.health.harvard.edu/mind-and-mood/what-causes-depression
https://www.shawnachor.com
http://www.yogayuktalife.com/articles/2015/4/9/are-you-a-yogi-bhogi-or-rogi
https://www.vedic-management.com/yogi-bhogi-rogi/
Yoga Chiktisha By Dr Ananda Balayogi Bhavanani
Yoga Step By Step by Dr Swamiji Gitananda Giriji
Charaka Samhita -- PV Sharma Translator, Chaukhamba Orientalia, Varanasi, India, 1981, pp. ix-xxxii (I) 4 Volumes

Lesson 34.
Adhi Vyadhi Concept of Diseases and Yoga Chikitsa

This concept of Adhi-Vyadhi from Yogic drishti explains that the loss of mental balance, equanimity and peace is the result of physical health problems caused by the dysfunctional relationship between the body, mind and energy.

Ancient Yogis realised that self-realisation or samadhi where the Purusha or self becomes one with the Parmatman or higher self, is the way to access and experience the cosmic bliss or true Swasthya known as Sat-Chit-Ananda. We need to free our mind from all the subjects of sensory disturbing objects and information.

The Yogic scriptures and Vedic wisdom teachings explain that the Purusha or soul is always eternal and free from all suffering and not subject to change. The Upanishads teach us that at the subtlest sheath or body of our existence, the Anandamaya Kosha we are in the healthiest, holistic state of blissful harmony and balance. In our second body the Vijnanmaya Kosha, there are some changes or movements, but these are channelled at subtlest level in right direction with creative, dynamic and effortless life functions.

Our imbalances start at the Manomaya Kosha, according to the Yoga Sutras these are mental imbalances known as Adhis. Adhi means disturbed state of mind or mental illness, at this stage there are no physical symptoms in our body. These mental problems can deteriorate due to Avidya (ignorance), Vasanas (desires), Kaam (lust for sensual pleasures), Krodha (anger), Lobha (greed) and Moha (attraction): this causes further imbalance in our Pranamaya Kosha. This imbalance of our energy and polarity is described as the concept of Nara by Swamis Dr. Gitananda Giriji and we will go into further detail on this when we come to concept of yogic polarity.

Avidya or Ajnana, which we can understand as not knowing our true self and state of absolute bliss, leads us in ignoring the activities that lead us to health and wellness. We eat unhealthy food, consume alcohol, smoke, take drugs, live a sedentary life and make unhealthy associations: this lack of healthy life routine gradually result in Vyadhis or physical illnesses. So in this way Adhija is the primary, mental suffering or imbalance and Vyadhis is the physical or secondary diseases.

The Adhis are classified into two categories:

Samanya or Ordinary:- These mental problems and conflicts are the incidental cause to the physical ill-health. These are caused by our interactions within ourselves and with the rest of the world, which are known as psychosomatics according to modern science. Through Jnana Yoga, Yogic life philosophy and wisdom, Hatha yoga and Pranayama we can remove these mental illness and disturbances and avoid, heal and maintain our physical and mental wellness.

Sara or Essential:- These mental problems are responsible for our state of rebirth. These subtle Adhis can be removed or healed through the realisation and experience of higher states of mind and living in harmony with the Vijnanamaya and Anandamaya Kosha. Many people these days are living in Annamaya Kosha or Manomaya Kosha.

In this concept there are two types of diseases:

Adhija Vyadhi:- these are known as psychosomatic health problems and one of the primary cause is stress.

Anadhija Vyadhi:- These are somatic or physical problems caused by infections, injury, toxins, etc. The Anadhija Vyadhi is sub-categorised in two types: firstly the Sara Adhija Vyadhi which are influenced by our Samaskaras, past karmas and heredity; and secondly Samanya Adhija Vyadhi which are what we acquire or accumulate through life experiences and situations.

In the Yoga Vashistha when Lord Rama asked Sage Vasistha about the causes of illnesses he replied that the Adhi and Vyadhi are the root cause of sorrow or pain; by avoiding them we can attain happiness, completely freeing ourselves from them is liberation. Sage Vasistha explains further that sometimes they arise together, sometimes they cause each other and sometimes they follow each other.

All physical health problems are known as Vyadhi and mental and psychological problems are known as Adhi. Both these are rooted in Avidya (ignorance), bhaya(fear), kshal (deceit) and kapat (treachery). We can be free of all these by attaining true knowledge of atma (soul), Jeevan (life), Parmatman (the divine) and through atma-sakshatkar (self-realisation). Ignorance gives rise to likes and dislikes, desires, ego, I-ness, greed, jealousy, anger, self-centredness and we lose the ability to use our intelligence and reasoning (Buddhi and Viveka). This intensifies our delusion and psychic disturbances, and our mental and emotional imbalances.

Sage Vasistha goes on to explain that many physical health problems are caused by ignorance, as ignorance causes absence of mental discipline, improper or unhealthy eating habits, irregular life activities like not eating at right time, not going to sleep at appropriate time, or sleeping too much, not eating enough or eating too much and other unhealthy life habits.

The Yogic Concept of Health Diseases based on Adhi-Vyadhi

The Yogic concept of health and disease enables us to understand that the cause of physical disorders stems from the seed in the mind and beyond. Adhi (the disturbed mind) is the cause and vyadhi (the physical disease) is only the manifested effect in the Yogic scheme of things. By paying careful attention to personal history, one can nearly always trace origins of psychosomatic disease back to patterns of mental and emotional pressures.

From the Yogic viewpoint of disease it can be seen that psychosomatic, stress related disorders appear to progress through four distinct phases. These can be understood as follows:

1. Psychic Phase: This phase is marked by mild but persistent psychological and behavioural symptoms of stress like irritability, disturbed sleep and other minor symptoms. This phase can be correlated with vijnanamaya and manomaya koshas. Yoga as a therapy is very effective in this phase.

2. Psychosomatic Phase: If the stress continues there is an increase in symptoms, along with the appearance of generalized physiological symptoms such as occasional hypertension and tremors. This phase can be correlated with manomaya and pranamaya koshas. Yoga as a therapy is very effective in this phase.

3. Somatic Phase: This phase is marked by disturbed function of organs, particularly the target, or involved organ. At this stage one begins to identify the diseased state. This phase can be correlated with pranamaya and annamaya koshas. Yoga as a therapy is less effective in this phase and may need to be used in conjunction with other methods of treatment.

4. *Organic Phase:* This phase is marked by full manifestation of the diseased state, with pathological changes such as an ulcerated stomach or chronic hypertension, becoming manifest in their totality with their resultant complications. This phase can be correlated with the annamaya kosha as the disease has become fixed in the physical body. Yoga as a therapy has a palliative and quality of life improving effect in this phase. It does also produce positive emotional and psychological effects even in terminal and end of life situations.

In this lesson we have considered the concept of Adhi-Vyadhi from Yogic drishti that the loss of mental balance, equanimity and peace is the result of physical health problems caused by the dysfunctional relationship between our body, mind and energy.

Lesson 35.
Shavasana (Yogic Relaxation) and stress management

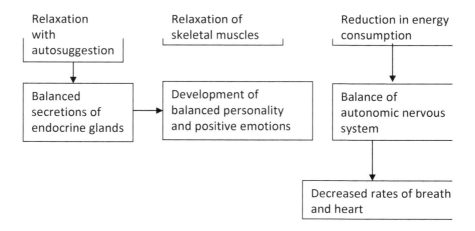

A process of relaxation

The shavasana is the yoga technique which releases physical, mental and emotional tension and to develops steadiness in the body. The basic purpose of shavasana is to develop awareness of the real-self apart from the body, without attachment, apart from the emotions and excitement.

The two necessary conditions for shavasana are-

(i) The total cessation of voluntary movements, maintaining a relaxed condition of all skeletal muscles
(ii) The slowing down of the rate of respiration as if the system has stopped working

The meaning of shavasana is complete relaxation with self-awareness; the shavasana is an effective, harmless and easily learnable technique for releasing tension so that we can enjoy a healthy and happy life. One who practices relaxation for 30 to 45 minutes daily in life, would remain relaxed and able to maintain equanimity in any situation.

Gaur, Saini and Srivastava (2001) have explored the effective role of Preksha meditation in releasing the tension and anxiety and refinement of emotions of the prisoners in Central Jail, Jodhpur. The goal of Preksha meditation, meaning perception, is to bring about integration of our existential being through keen perception of the body, breathing and physiological processes.

The shavasana is a better process of resting and relaxation in comparison to sleep. During muscular and physical activity, there is a high flow of electromagnetic current within the muscles, while during deep-sleep a weak magnetic current flows. During the relaxation of shavasana, this flow is minimized and at its perfection, it is completely stopped, hence energy is also conserved.

Shavasana and therapy

Shavasana is the effective stress management therapy of the following physical and mental problems-

- ❖ Mental weakness
- ❖ Physical weakness
- ❖ Insomnia
- ❖ Weak memory power
- ❖ Hypertension
- ❖ Heart troubles
- ❖ Respiratory problems
- ❖ Epilepsy
- ❖ Lack of concentration
- ❖ Emotional imbalance

All these problems are more prominent in cases of excess stress. Through regular practice of the shavasana, we can release the stress and attain the relaxation of the mind and muscles. As the energy is conserved by the practice of the shavasana, the energy flow is directed towards the brain and the nervous system. The nervous system is activated now and thus the neuro-endocrine control system is also activated. The immune system and our immunity power are developed by the regular practice of shavasana.

The secretions of the endocrine glands are also balanced by regular practice of the shavasana. There can be excessive secretions of the adrenal hormones by the adrenal glands, which are responsible for the fight and flight response. The regular excessive secretion of epinephrine may contribute to developing problems of hypertension, heart troubles, emotional imbalance, negative irrational thinking, etc. The secretions of the endocrine glands are balanced by refinement of thoughts, emotions and mind, and by releasing the stress. Thus the shavasana is an effective technique of health promotion.

Physiological changes by shavasana include-

- ❖ Relaxed muscles
- ❖ Decreased breathing rate
- ❖ Decreased heart rate
- ❖ Decreased blood pressure
- ❖ Decreased secretions of lactic acid
- ❖ Decreased metabolic rate
- ❖ Balanced automatic nervous system
- ❖ Balanced hormonal functions

Mental and emotional changes by shavasana include-

- ❖ Development of mental and emotional balance
- ❖ Refinement of negative thought and emotions, i.e., frustration, fear anxiety, jealousness
- ❖ Increased memory
- ❖ Development of happiness and joyfulness
- ❖ Better sleep
- ❖ Development of rational thinking

Technique of shavasana

Step-1 Stretch the whole body and than relax the muscles completely; three times in standing posture and three times in the lying posture.

Step-2 Lie on the back, there should be one to two feet distance between the legs, hands should be in comfortable position apart from the body, palms in an upward direction. Feel the heaviness in the complete body. Feel the lightness in the whole body (three times for each).

Step-3 Focus on each part of the body, one by one from toe to head and suggest for the relaxation and then feel the relaxation with the awareness. (Autosuggestion with complete awareness)

Step-4 (For spiritual development) Concentrate on body as a whole and visualize the cool white colour around the body like moonlight. Feel the coolness and peace of the white colour of the aura.

Step-5 With two or three long deep breaths feel the activation and energy in the whole body.

This lesson has focussed on shavasana for the reduction of stress and as a pro-active preventative health therapy. It is an important resource in restorative yoga that can rejuvenate the body, mind and spirit.

Yoga Therapy Lesson on Stress by Jyoti Vora, Physiotherapist

Dr Hans Selye was an endocrinologist, who first gave an explanation for biological stress. He explained the three stages alarm response, resistance and exhaustion and also explained about the HPA axis.

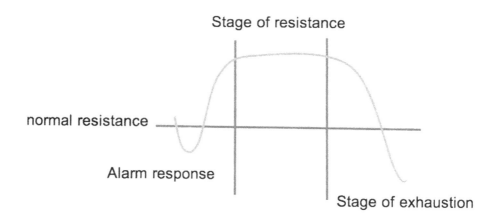

In the animal kingdom, sustained psychological stress is a recent invention, limited mostly to humans and social primates. Two individuals sitting facing each other, could be doing nothing more strenuous or exciting then moving a piece of wood from time to time, or signing a piece of paper; yet this can be an emotionally taxing event.

A stressor is anything in the outside world that can knock us out of homeostasis. And the stress response is what your body does to re-establish homeostasis. A stressor can also be the anticipation of that happening. Sometimes we are smart enough to see things coming and based only on the anticipation, this can turn on a stress response as robust as if the event had actually occurred.

Stress/ or repeated short-lasting stress responses directly do not make us sick. Sustained stress puts the body out of homeostasis for prolonged periods. So, it will be appropriate to say that stress increases the risk of developing diseases that makes one sick. It is the chronic activation of the cardio-vascular system that poses a risk of developing heart diseases; the constant mobilizing of energy at the cost of energy storage, causes fatigue/exhaustion and puts one at risk of developing diabetes. Constant stress on the body affects digestion, growth and reproductive functions.

Our brain is over 7 million years old and it is split into 3 smaller brains. The reptilian brain, the monkey brain and the leadership brain.
The reptilian brain (amygdala) has a primary focus to survive and when you perceive a threat it fires off your patterns of fight or flight.

The monkey brain (limbic) is our relationship brain and it looks for connections but gets easily distracted and struggles to focus on any one thing. It is constantly chattering away to itself and if it asks questions that create doubt, it will feel threatened and call upon the reptilian brain to get ready to run or fight.
The leadership brain (neo-cortex) visualises into the future, creating and building a better world for itself and others, it is our logical brain that can also solve problems in creative ways.

Successful people live in their leadership (neo-cortex) brain and know how to control their monkey brain while keeping their reptile (amygdala) asleep. However, if you are carrying around unresolved issues in your personal or professional life (baggage) it is hard to do, as your monkey chatter keeps on waking up your reptile brain and SHUTS DOWN the neo-cortex (leadership brain).

Thinking About Thinking

Our minds are always working away in the background. They try to make sense of what's going on around us and how we feel about things. We use what we know from the past to work out how we feel about things now. We also use what we know to make predictions about what will happen in the future. Most of the time our mind is very helpful. For example, your mind helped you to take all the necessary steps to get out of bed this morning. It can also help you to think about all of the things you need to do tomorrow. But sometimes our mind can be less helpful, and can even become a negative influence on how we feel and what we do.

Unhelpful thinking: when a person experiences an unhelpful emotion (e.g. anxiety or depression); is usually preceded by a number of unhelpful self-statements and thoughts. Often there is pattern to such thoughts, and we call these 'unhelpful thinking styles'. It has been observed that people use unhelpful thinking styles as an automatic habit. It is something that happens out of our awareness. However, when people use these patterns consistently and constantly; they can cause themselves a great deal of emotional distress.

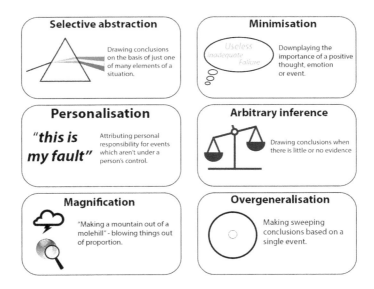

Cognitive Behavioural Therapy is based on the idea that unhelpful thoughts and behaviours can make problems worse. By recognising unhelpful thoughts and behaviours, a person can improve how they feel. They can also improve areas of their life that have become difficult. CBT does not spend time looking in the past. It looks at the 'here and now' and focuses on solving a person's current problems.

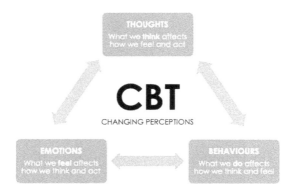

Neuroplasticity

'What fires together, wires together' is the famous abridged version of the Hebbian rule. It states that neurons in the brain adapt during the learning process, a mechanism which is called neuronal plasticity. Hebb's theory dates back to the 1940s and subsequent research in neuroscience has further corroborated it.

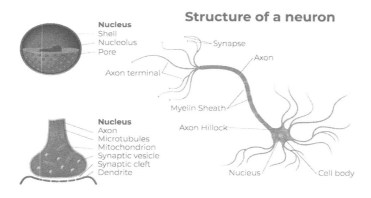

It can be beneficial to have neurons wired together. The neural network helps us learn, store and recall information in an effective way. For example, when you're getting to know an acquaintance, the neural network helps you to remember the person's name through many subtle triggers. However, the network can go awry when we try to unwire or rewire neurons to respond to a situation in a new way. A tragic example would be a child who has suffered abuse. Physical contact of any kind might be enough to trigger a fight, flight or freeze response, even when it isn't appropriate.

We can use neuroplasticity to help our way out of stress and negative events. Each time we go through the trail of negative thought patterns, that same pathway becomes activated and gets stronger with repeated thinking. However, each time we have that thought pattern, if we can build onto another thought which might be different to those negative thoughts (it does not have to be positive but different to those negative thoughts); then we create new pathways. And then repeating the same each time we strengthen the new pathway, which helps us deactivate the original negative thought pattern.

Exercise benefits

The mental benefits of aerobic exercise have a neuro-chemical basis. Exercise reduces levels of the body's stress hormones, such as adrenaline and cortisol. It also stimulates the production of endorphins, chemicals in the brain that are the body's natural painkillers and mood elevators. Endorphins are responsible for the 'runner's high' and for the feelings of relaxation and optimism that accompany many hard workouts — or, at least, the hot shower after your exercise is over.

Behavioural factors also contribute to the emotional benefits of exercise. As your waistline shrinks and your strength and stamina increase, your self-image will improve. You will earn a sense of mastery and control, of pride and self-confidence.

Your renewed vigour and energy will help you succeed in many tasks, and the discipline of regular exercise will help you achieve other important lifestyle goals. Exercise and sports also provide opportunities to get away from it all and to either enjoy some solitude or to make friends and build networks. "All men," wrote St. Thomas Aquinas, "need leisure". Exercise is play and recreation; when your body is busy, your mind will be distracted from the worries of daily life and will be free to think creatively.

Yoga provides us with the tools and techniques to lead a stress-free and tension-free life. Yoga therapy can help people in stress manage their lives in a holistic way. Education and advice on healthy living, eating and regular exercise including asanas, pranayamas, yoga nidra etc. is all useful in managing acute and chronic stress.

References and resources

https://www.interaction-design.org/literature/article/our-three-brains-the-reptilian-brain
https://youtu.be/n6pMbRiSBPs
https://www.webmd.com/balance/stress-management/stress-symptoms-effects_of-stress-on-the-body#2
https://www.health.harvard.edu/staying-healthy/exercising-to-relax
https://www.supercamp.com/what-does-neurons-that-fire-together-wire-together-mean/
https://www.getselfhelp.co.uk/docs/UnhelpfulThinkingHabitsWithAlternatives.pdf
https://www.nhs.uk/conditions/stress-anxiety-depression/reduce-stress/
*https://books.google.co.uk/books?id=EI88oS_3fZEC&pg=PA21&source=gbs_selected_*
pages&cad=3#v=onepage&q&f=false zebra don't get ulcers e-book
https://www.cci.health.wa.gov.au/-/media/CCI/Mental-Health-Professionals/Depression/Depression---Information-
Sheets/Depression-Information-Sheet---11--Unhelpful-Thinking-Styles.pdf

Lesson 36.
Pancha Kosha – Yogic Principles of Existence and Yoga Therapy

To understand the therapeutic applications of holistic yoga, we have to understand the multi-layered concept of our existence as described in yoga. Our modern sciences deal with our existence in the form of our anatomy, physiology and psychology. Yogic science takes it to further subtler forms, which explain our holistic health as well as our life evolutionary processes. Working with people in a therapeutic sense, is transformative for us in each role that we take, from being a Hatha Yoga Instructor, to a guide, therapist, counsellor, supporter, listener, facilitator and much more.

In Yoga Therapy, there are many paths to choose from like Hatha yoga, pranayama, meditation, yoga nidra, meditation, supporting a healthy diet, cleansing practices, etc. Thanks to Ammaji, Swamji and Dr. Ananda Balayogi, we are introduced to the Pancha-Koshas as our multi-layered concept of existence, which explains the need and importance of the different holistic paths of yoga as a tool of an integrated and individual therapeutic approach.

In this next lesson we will look into the therapeutic concepts of Ashtanga (eight limbs), Adhi-Vyadhi, Pancha Prana and the Tri-Doshas. I personally feel that starting this with Pancha Kosha will help us understand why we need to learn so many paths and approaches of yoga in developing WHOLISTIC HEALTH.

A Health Problem
We may or may not have a health problem; we will have people coming to us with various health problems, injuries, traumas etc. As a Yoga Therapist, what is our intention and role to help that person in the healing process?

In our modern health system, 'curing is seen as a singular solution to a single problem'. You can prescribe a medication for hypertension, which you will never use for hypotension. According to Northrop (1998) "Curing is a mechanism requiring medication or surgery to mask or eliminate symptoms". If someone suffers with migraine, a doctor will prescribe a painkiller. If there is an injury, a doctor will apply supporting aid to heal the injury.

Healing is actually far more than curing, it a journey, it is a process of letting go, it is process of re-structuring our mind and body. On this journey, we face all sorts of ups and downs, obstacles and motivational forces. On this path of physical, mental, emotional and spiritual healing, as a yoga therapist, we must be able to distinguish between curing and healing, preventing and managing, rehabilitation and optimum living. The curing and healing are dynamically different process and involve different tools and practices. According to Northrup (1998) "Healing, after all, is a process generated from within and a process that journeys far beyond the physical. It is a process that is much deeper than the cure".

Our health system provides the medication for curing processes, but the issue here is, when a health problem occurs at physical, mental and emotional level, it leaves a trauma, or pain memory as an imprint in our brain as well as at the level of cellular memory. These painful trauma memories carry a residue of pain and discomfort, which carries a stress triggering, reflex response. This results in disconnection, or misalignment between the psyche, the body and the mental story associated with the health issue. Swamiji Dr. Gitananda talks about the concept of Nara as Pranic energy dissociation with our physical and mind body. This disturbs the balance of our body, the instrument with which we are to live and enjoy life. Our spirit is also disturbed.

Van der Kolk (2007) explains that "trauma robs you of the feeling that you are in charge of yourself". The loss of optimal health causes a struggle to adapt to necessary changes and a desire to thrive in order to engage in the life process that we used to enjoy before the health problem. Gradually we also adapt our limited perspective on our own life and health. This results in negative changes in our relationship with ourselves and with others. This is the end result where the seed of health problems gets imprinted deeply within us at the subtlest levels. Remember this imprint can never be removed by cure or medication: this requires a holistic healing process at subtle psyche, energy and mind fields.

In a way, this is why I feel, our first model of therapeutic level, has to be Pancha Kosha System or the five-body system of our existence and a multi-path yoga therapeutic approach.

The Pancha Kosha Model of Yoga

Pancha is Sanskrit word meaning five, while Kosha means body, layer or sheath. The word Maya means illusion, or veil, or that which spreads. Frawley describes Kosha as "a sheath or encasement". Dr. Ananda Balayogi Bhavanani explains that these five sheaths, layers or bodies are infused or interconnected between each other. According to Feuerstein, Pancha Maya Koshas can be understood as, "five encasements that surround our Atman and or consciousness and prevent the light of our spirit, our transcendental Self, from shining".

The Taittriya Upanishad details the Pancha Koshas: the Upanishads contain a simple commentary to explain complex Vedic teachings in the form of dialogue, questions and answers and stories.

Burke (2013) writes that these five sheaths are vibrational in nature and store our Samskaras, our collected mental, emotional and karmic patterns. In a true healing approach of Yoga, Ayurveda, Siddha and Naturopathy, we need to remove the old negative Samaskars in order to regain our optimal health and well-being.

McCall (2007) describes samskaras as the "habits of action and thought that get deeper all the time". Easwaran (1992) details our present personality as "the sum of our samskaras, the collection of our patterns of thinking". Samaskars are the underlying principles and process behind our behaviour, thoughts, feelings, emotions and choices. These Samaskaras can be positive or negative in nature.

Our Pancha-Koshas resonate with the vibrations of our Samaskars and hence our healing approach of therapeutic yoga has to also reflect on the collection of our desires (Vasanas), delusions (Moha), mental and emotional processes (Chitta-vrittis), and focus on enhancing of our moments of joy, bliss and ecstasy (Sat-Chit-Ananda). To attain this true balance, harmony and health, we must understand the relation between body, mind, energy and soul.

A holistic concept of healing, requires an integration of body, mind, psyche, and spirit. Our Koshas are like the house that we live within and are the instruments of our soul or Atman or Self. The Pancha-Kosha Model helps us to understand the integrated approach of multi-layered-overlapping paths of Yoga like Jnana Yoga, Raja Yoga, Hatha Yoga, Pranayama Yoga, Bhakti Yoga, Karma Yoga, etc. Harmony and integration of the Pancha-Koshas bring unity, equilibrium, homeostasis, polarity, balance and Swasthya. The holistic approach of yoga leads us to a virtuous, brave, graceful, balanced, wholeness of being, from our most physical body to the subtlest layers of Atman or Self. Yoga can help us develop our balance, awareness and full potential, through the healing processes from our skin to our bones, our breathing, heart function, metabolism, hormonal secretions, as well as mental, emotional and spiritual processes.

Yogacharya Dr. Ananda Balayogi Bhavanani explains that our existence in multiple layers is held together by cosmic prana. These are known as five bodies, five sheaths or layers and explained differently in various traditions. We have a physical body, made of food and nourished by food. This is our anatomical existence. This food body becomes the living body with the pranic body. The anatomical structure becomes a living being with pranayama kosha, the life force sheath. Energy sheaths work with the physical body, bringing the physiological process alive. What makes us different to other forms of life is our psychological body known as the Manomaya Kosha, our mental sheath. This is what makes us hu-man. This sheath starts our ability to think. The fourth sheath is Vijnanamaya Kosha, our wisdom sheath, where we start developing higher intellectual concepts of our existence. We start to think how can I become a good human being, how can help others, how can I live in peace?

As we visualise the five koshas, they are not to be thought of as concentric sheaths but as interpenetrating at different levels of subtlety. When our Anandamaya Kosha, the cosmic bliss body is working, we become free from our limited ego, thoughts and emotions. We experience as a total unit within ourselves and our universe. The concept of Vashudhev Kutambakam (we all are a one holistic family) becomes part of our existential attitude. All these Koshas have full potential, every cell in our body is in the Pancha-Kosha. Thinking is not limited to our brain; every cell has the ability to think. What is in me, is what is in universe, and what is in the universe is within me. Micro and macrocosm are one. We can go out from Annamaya Kosha outward to subtler layers or go inward from Ananda Maya Kosha to gross physical body.

Complex Regional Pain Syndrome (CRPS)

Developing an understanding of CPRS can help us. Complex regional pain syndrome (CRPS) can be associated with various organs, muscles, joints and systems in particular areas or functions of the body. It is a form of severe chronic pain, which can develop following injury, surgery, stroke or heart attack. An Individual with CRPS shows neuro-cellular abnormalities. For example, If we have suffered with muscle pain in a particular area for a long period of time which has been treated with pain killers; according to Juris (2014) this painful traumatic memory can adversely affect the functions of the peripheral nerves in that particular area, involving un-myelinated and thinly myelinated nerve fibres. Myelin is the substance that surrounds and insulates some nerve fibres, and these fibres are the ones that carry pain messages and signals to blood vessels. If the protective covering of a nerve fibre is compromised, the nerve may become hyper-aroused and chronically over-stimulated.

The nervous system abnormalities cause abnormal neuro-hormonal functions, which can have negative effects on our breathing, heart, digestion, and metabolism. The National Institute of Neurological Disorders and Stroke (2014) explains that peripheral nerve anomalies cause abnormal neurological function in the spinal cord and brain by predisposing blood vessels to excessive dilation and contraction. When the vessels dilate, fluid leaks into the surrounding tissue. This action starves underlying tissue of oxygen and nutrients. When vasoconstriction occurs, the skin becomes cold and white. The result is damage and increased pain.

Some studies mention that the immune system is also involved in this CRPS. Further studies have also shown grey matter shrinkage in area of the brain's somato-sensory cortex corresponding to the patient's affected limb (Juris, 2014) (Geha, Baliki, Harden, Bauer, Parrish & Apkarian, 2008; Juris, 2014).

We can simply say that under the effect of these traumatic, unhealthy memories, our body system is in a consistently reactive state with the sympathetic nervous system being over active, which affects the limbic system. The limbic system in the cerebral cortex governs emotions of pain and pleasure. Swamiji Dr. Gitananda Giriji in Yoga Step by Step mentions that any form of old trauma stored in our body and mind are constantly coming up to the surface and irritating our health at the cellular level.

These negative memories and traumas can be associated with various health issues, injuries and adverse life experiences. Many times we find a cure, or manage to gradually supress those memories, but the CRPS imprints are still there. It also leaves imprints on our mind or psyche and our pranic energy in the form of anxiety, depression, stress, and lack of energy or drive force.

According to Juris (2014) the imprints of the CRPS never ends and the individual can remain severely disabled. So we may have cured the symptoms or disease on the surface, but deep down at subtle levels, imprints of the disease are still there. Working through the five-body system, enhancing the optimum functioning and integrating of these five bodies can help in releasing these deep rooted painful memories. In my understanding we can apply this model to work with various individual to help them regain their optimal health and well-being.

The Pancha Koshas

We can visualise the Koshas as the sheaths moving outward from gross to subtlest, or from subtlest to gross inward, but in truth these five bodies or layers are inter-connected like Bluetooth connectivity. If we see the sun itself as the physical or gross body, then light can be understood as the subtlest of the layers, the Anandamaya Kosha, which pervades the vast universe. But here the light exists from the centre or core of the sun. Similarly, we think of our physical body as the sun and the bliss body as the light. Each kosha is extending and inter-connecting with all other koshas.

These koshas are known as interdependent of energy. As a yoga therapist, we can bring our healing journey from physical body, Annamaya Kosha. Here our approach can be seen as somato-psychic. Our first sheath or body is known as **Annamaya Kosha**. The word 'anna' means atom, cell or food. Our food body need nurturing and being held upright in the present moment. Understanding the Koshas, makes us appreciate our physical health and existence as well as the realisation of the manifest in the form of the body and the unmanifest in the form of consciousness.

The **Pranamaya Kosha** is our second sheath, layer of the body. This is the vital energy body, which holds the life in our body. As Dr. Ananda Balayogi Bhavanani mentions, the prana brings life to our physical organs and our anatomy transforms to physiology. According to Krafstow (2002) the Pranamaya Kosha is our breath body and our life force, the vital metabolic functions that deliver our health and wellness. This Kosha can be associated with our breath and energy exchange between our breaths and the release of Pranic energy, vital life force from oxygen. According a study by Slovik (2013) moderating the breath allows us to moderate our emotions, our response to stress, our energy levels and the level of pain we are experiencing. Tantra and Kundalini Yoga paths explain that our Chakras and Nadis exist in our Pranamaya Kosha.

The *Manomaya Kosha* is our third body, where our mind, thoughts, samaskaras, becomes connecting force between our physical and energy body. From the anatomical, physiological, mechanical body, we transform into a human being or living being. We attain power to think, feel, and experience. With the help of this body we embrace subtle impressions and their manifestation in our body with the help of pranic energy. Our Manomaya Kosha is the outer manas or awareness and the internal voice in each and every-one of us. According to Kraftstow (1999) it brings our memories into awareness. It includes the knowledge we have gained through experience and education. The Manomaya Kosha is the birth or seed field for our instincts, desires, impulses, perceptions, cognition, choices and actions.

Our *Vijnanamaya Kosha* is our wisdom component of existence. This brings our collective harmony, higher desires and goals to help humanity. When we have access to our Vijnanamaya Kosha we seek for universal peace and prosperity. We also have access to abundance of cosmic wisdom known as Akashik Jnana or readings. This wisdom is like our subtle genetic codes and memories too of nature, evolution and life processes. The easiest way to understand this body is by understanding a seed, the wisdom it carries in it to grow into a plant or tree and make seeds. It knows everything it needs to know, including even when to grow, how much nutrients, water, earth, sun, air it needs take in. According to Frawley (1999) and Miller (2011) with the Vijnanamaya Kosha, our beliefs begin to deconstruct and our ability to discern truth from falsehood is refined. Kraftstow (1999) connects the Vijnamaya Kosha with our intuitive understanding. Burke (2013) mentions that a shift occurs when we connect with Vijnanamaya Kosha because it supports the emergence of spirit and our witnessing consciousness.

This further leads us to the subtlest of our existential un-manifest aspect, this is our innermost as well as all pervading or connected Kosha, Known as the *Anandamaya Kosha* or Bliss body. This naturally brings our heart and mind to the purest of unconditional joy, bliss, love and fulfilment. All true Yoga Sadhakas seek to experience or be connected with this bliss body to free themselves from all the worldly pain and suffering. This is highest state of Swashtya or health, state of SAT-CHIT-ANANDA. Kraftstow mentions that with the Anandamaya Kosha, we focus on union with those things that we most cherish. Here we are living in harmony within ourselves as well as within the rest of the universe. This is a state of non-duality. As Miller (2011) mentions "here we have arrived at the threshold of our non-dualistic nature".

Our Soul or Atman resides in the space between these Pancha-Koshas, interconnecting them all and using them as a vehicle to live our life and go through each and every experience. Our Anandamaya and Vijnanamaya Kosha are unaffected all the changes and sufferings of life. These are beyond the Maya or illusion, or not subject to any change. The issues, or diseases take place in our mind and physical body, which also imbalances our subtle energy body. Yoga Vashistha explains that most of our diseases are rooted in our mind and manifest in our body (adhija-vyadhij). It is further mentioned that our physical problems will cause mental disturbance too (vyadhija-adhija).

To put a program in place for an individual, we need to understand that individual, his or her health problem and our role in this journey to help that individual. In terms of a health protocol, we need to think about a therapeutic plan, causes of the health problem, the nature of the problem, triggering factors and symptoms. We need to consider the suitability of Yogopathy for quick relief and Yoga Chikitsa for healing.

We can make a list of simple questions as a protocol:

- ❖ What is the health issue?
- ❖ What is anatomical course of the health issue?
- ❖ What is physiological course of the health issue?
- ❖ What are the lifestyle causing or worsening factors?
- ❖ What are the family, social, or economic causes?
- ❖ What brings joy to that individual's life?
- ❖ How does that individual's mind work?
- ❖ What sort of treatment has that individual undergone?
- ❖ What is this individual is expecting to gain from yoga therapy?

After knowing some of these basic answers, you may need to think on some basic things:

- ❖ What is your agenda as a therapist?
- ❖ What do you expect to achieve in this journey with this individual?
- ❖ What can you offer to this individual?

❖ Which practices or aspects of yoga is this individual is willing or able to learn and follow?

Here you will be looking into objectivity, receptivity, non-judgement and applications. We can extend these questions a little further to protect ourselves and the individual person we are trying to help.

❖ Do I hold any judgement about this individual that I need to let go?
❖ What is my motivation for working with this individual?
❖ How can a create an authentic and safe environment and practice for me and the individual?
❖ How can I help the individual to release these old painful memories and traumas of various health problems?
❖ How can I help myself and the individual to attain the full potential growth?

This is a general guideline, which we will expand on as we go into more detail of the individual health problems of various individuals. You may have many of your questions and guidelines to put in place too. It is also important to work on our abilities to listen, without judging the individual we are trying to help.

In my understanding to come up with a therapeutic plan, we need to understand the nature, root cause and triggering factors of any health problem. We will also need to understand the trauma points or areas, which can be physical, mental, emotional, pranic, psychic and spiritual. Specially if we are dealing with psychic and pscho-somatic problems, we will also need to understand the environmental, lifestyle, family, social and work factors to understand the underlying causes of a health problem.

Our model is to work with the Pancha-Kosha system to bring a holistic transformation in an individual's life, so you will be looking in to structuring practices for all five koshas:

❖ *Annamakosha* – Yoga Vyayama, Yogic Relaxation, nutritional diet, deep breathing
❖ *Pranayama Kosha* – Pranayama, Yogic Visualisations, Hatha Yoga, Ahara-Vihara
❖ *Manomaya Kosha* – Positive thoughts, associations, relaxation practices, yogic life philosophy, positive sensory information.

- ❖ *Vijnanamaya Kosha* – Meditation, Jnana Yoga, Yogic Life Philosophy, contemplations
- ❖ *Ananadamaya Kosha* – Satsanga, Positive social relations, service and care to needful, meditation, mantras and bhajans

Even though there is a system we can follow, you will need to understand each and every individual before you can design a yoga therapy plan with Hatha Yoga Practices. There are actually no strict prescriptive guidelines, as most of the practices are holistic in their nature and will benefit overall health of the Sadhaka. This means it is more important for us to design a plan that is appropriate, accessible, acceptable and applicable for the individual's body, mind and belief systems. Also, you can have a planned structure of how many sessions and the gaps between them. It can be once a week, an hour session for 6 or 9 sessions, or a regular group classe designed for a particular need group.

With most people who come to you, it may be easy to begin with physical practices and relaxation techniques to bring some symptomatic relief and gradually work on root causes and lifestyle changes for holistic healing.

Kosha	Practices	Adaptations
Annamaya Kosha	Jattis	
Physical Body	Kriyas	Chair Yoga
	Asana	Assisted Yoga
	Mudra	Guided Yogic Relaxations
	Diet	
	Sleep	

Pranayama Kosha Subtle Energy Body	Pranayama Ahara -Vihara Prana drains Prana Boosts Jnana Yoga Kriyas or relaxation techniques	Social activities Time in Nature
Manomaya Kosha Mind Body	Contemplative Sankalpas Short Meditation practices Positive information, associations, readings, and entertainment	Written positive thoughts to remind Pre-recorded guided meditations Recommending books and resources
Vijnanmaya Kosha Wisdom or intellect body	Yogic Wisdom teachings Sharing simple principles of compassion, forgiveness, Cheerfulness, Positive intentions, life virtues	Understanding each and every individual and referencing these virtues according the their belief system
Anandamaya Kosha Bliss Body	Mudras Mantras Naada or Sound Karma Yoga and Service	Introducing these practices to individuals when they are ready

Conclusions

According to Van der Kolk (2014) the imprint of trauma is more than the story. As a therapist we begin with the story and then determine the relationship between the events and the present health situation to come up with a therapeutic protocol. The second part as yoga therapist is to choose the approach and the practices to help that individual to find comfort, meaning and a sense of ease in their life, to live their own optimum life.

Here is a beautiful teaching by Swami Vivekananda from his book How to Know God-

After long searches here and there, in temples and in churches, in earths and in heavens, at last you have come back, completing the circle from where you started, to your own soul and find that He, for whom you have been seeking all over the world, for whom you have been weeping and praying in churches and in temples, on whom you were looking as the mystery of all mysteries shrouded in the clouds, is nearest of the near, is your own Self, the reality of your life, body and soul.

References and resources

1. *Yoga Chikitsa By Dr Ananda Balayogi Bhavanai, www.icyer.com*
2. *Yoga Step By Step By Dr Swamiji Gitananda Giriji, www.icyer.com*
3. *Yoga Therapy research articles by Dr Ananda Balayogi Bhavanani,*
https://www.researchgate.net/profile/Ananda_Bhavanani
https://sbvu.academia.edu/AnandaBhavanani
4. *Exploring Yoga Philosophy by Yogachariya Jnandev*
www.yogasatsanga.org
5. *Burke, M. (2013). The koshas. Retrieved from http://www.healingartscenter.net*
6. *Cloe, A. (2011). How do opiate agonists work. Retrieved from http://www.livestrong.com*
7. *Dubrovsky, A. (2009). Radical healing: Yoga with Gary Kraftsow. Yoga + Joyful Living. Spring, 39-43.*
8. *Easwaran, E. (1992). Dialogue with death: A journey through consciousness.Tomales,*
CA: Nilgiri Press.
9. *Frawley, D. (1999). Yoga and Ayurveda: Self-healing and self-realization. Twin Lakes, WI: Lotus   Press.*
10. *Feuerstein, G. (2003). The deeper dimension of yoga. Boston, MA: Shambhala.*
11. *Geha, P., Baliki, M., Harden, R., Bauer, W., Parrish, T., & Apkarian, A. (2008). The brain in chronic CRPS pain: Abnormal gray-white matter interactions in emotional and autonomic regions. Neuron, 60, 570-582.*
12. *Gregoire, C. (2013). How yoga became a $27 billion industry and reinvented American spirituality. Retrieved from http://www.huffingtonpost.com*
13. *How to know God: The yoga aphorisms of Patanjali (3rded). (2007). (S. Prabhavananda & C. Isherwood, Trans.). Hollywood, CA: Vendata Society of Southern California.*
14. *Juris, E. (2014). Positive options for complex regional pain syndrome (2nd ed). Nashville, TN: Turner Publishing.*
15. *Kraftsow, G. (1999). Yoga for healing. New York, NY: Penguin Compass.*
16. *Kraftsow, G. (2002). Yoga for transformation. New York, NY: Penguin Compass.*
17. *McCall, T. (2007). Yoga as medicine: The yoga prescription for health and healing. New York, NY: Bantam Dell.*
18. *Miller, R. (2011). Awareness and the five koshas: The process of yoga nidra.Retrieved from http://www.healthy.net. National Institute of Neurological Disorders and Stroke. Complex regional pain syndrome. Retrieved from http://www.ninds.nih.gov/disorders/reflex_sympathetic_dystrophy/reflex_sympathetic_dystrophy.htm.*
19. *Northrop, C. (1998). Women's bodies, women's wisdom. New York, NY: Bantam Books. Retrieved from http://www.thebillellisbible.ca/index.php/what-is-healing/.*
20. *Pennsylvania State University. (2004, September 29). Low doses of a common intravenous anesthetic may relieve debilitating pain syndrome. ScienceDaily. Retrieved from www.sciencedaily.com/releases/2004/09/040928111253.htm*
21. *Rae, S. (2007). You are here. Retrieved from http://www.yogajournal.com*
22. *Slovik, R. (2013). The five dimensions of personality. Retrieved from http://www.lunapresenceyoga.com.*

Lesson 37.
Pancha Prana Vayu Model of Diagnosis and Yoga Therapy

One of the key concepts of Yoga Therapy diagnosis is based on the Pancha Prana System, where we try to understand and evaluate our health and well-ness in context with our vital life currents. Ayurveda, Siddha, Yoga, and Naturopathy have all developed sophisticated understandings of the flow of human energy.

Yogic Science has evolved from personal observation, experimentation and experience. The flow of the vital life force energy Prana is of major significance for Yogis, as it is known that through experiencing prana, once can experience the whole universe.

As we have previously examined, according to Yoga we are composed of five bodies (pancha-koshas).

- ❖ Annamaya Kosha (Anatomical body)
- ❖ Pranamaya Kosha (Vital energy body, mechanical being)
- ❖ Manomaya Kosha (mind body, human being)
- ❖ Vijnanamaya Kosha (wisdom body, genetic and epigenetic intelligence)
- ❖ Anandamaya Kosha (bliss body, consciousness)

Yoga explains that there are five major currents in our Pranamaya Kosha, originating from various chakras. These five major vital energy currents are associated with our body and regulate our physiological-psychological-spiritual functions. This is Pancha Prana Model.

If we observe our life, we all follow an organised pattern

- ❖ We intake- food, water, information, experiences
- ❖ We process- or digest them
- ❖ We absorb- the nutrients and knowledge
- ❖ We eliminate- the waste products that we don't need
- ❖ We grow- physically and mentally

This is an example of our pancha prana vayu model in continuous function. By using this model we can understand our physiological and psychological issues we experience.

Here are few typical examples:

- ❖   Diarrhoea – overactive Apana Vayu
- ❖   Constipation – underactive Apana Vayu
- ❖   Cold Hands and feet – underactive Vyana Vayu responsible for circulation
- ❖   Indigestion issue – underactive Samana Vayu
- ❖   Acidity, Gastric Problems – Overactive Samana Vayu

Sometimes it can be as simple as above, while other times it can more complex and several of the Prana Vayus can be involved in health issues.

1. Prana Vayu

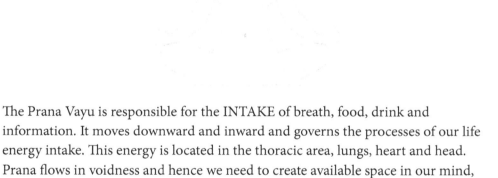

The Prana Vayu is responsible for the INTAKE of breath, food, drink and information. It moves downward and inward and governs the processes of our life energy intake. This energy is located in the thoracic area, lungs, heart and head. Prana flows in voidness and hence we need to create available space in our mind, chest and emotions.

Imbalanced Prana Vayu flow can cause health issues like anxiety, fear, anger (head), breathing disorders, asthma, sleep apnea, and heart problems.

Healing practices include:

- ❖ Lengthening inhalation (Vritti Pranayamas like Savitri (2x1x2x1), Sukha Purvaka (2x2x2x2), Asam Vritti (2x1)
- ❖ Matsyasana, Vyagraha Pranayama, Mukha Bhastrikas
- ❖ Conscious intake of breath, food, drinks, and sensory information.
- ❖ Yoni Mudra and Ujjnayi Pranayama.
- ❖ Positive impressions, Samaskaras and information, contact with nature, color visualisations, sound healing and aromas.

2. Apana Vayus

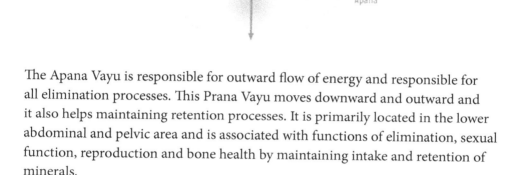

The Apana Vayu is responsible for outward flow of energy and responsible for all elimination processes. This Prana Vayu moves downward and outward and it also helps maintaining retention processes. It is primarily located in the lower abdominal and pelvic area and is associated with functions of elimination, sexual function, reproduction and bone health by maintaining intake and retention of minerals.

Imbalanced Apana can result in constipation, diarrhoea, menstrual and sexual health issues, urinary tract health issues and bone density issues.

Healing practices include:
* ❖ Expansion of Exhalation (Visama Vritti, 2x4)
* ❖ Moola Bandha and Ashwani Mudra
* ❖ Healthy nutritional diet
* ❖ Baddha-Kona Asana and Kriya, Pada Uttana Kriyas, Janu-Siras-asana
* ❖ Prana-Apana :- Polarity

"Mortal beings eat food with Apana, while the immortal beings eat food with the Prana" according to the Vedas. Here the mortals are associated with physical food while the immortals are associated with nourishment we receive directly through our sense organs. The right food helps harmony of Apana while the appropriate sensory information helps harmony of prana. Apana flows in outward life processes while Prana flows in the inward spiritual process.

Apana, which is aligned with the gravitational force of our mother earth and moves downward resulting in disease, aging, death and the shielding of consciousness. Prana, which is aligned with the Vayu (wind) and Akasha (space, voidness) flows upward through the mind and senses. When these two vital forces are out harmony, it leads to loss of mind-body coordination, depolarisation and devitalisation.

Uniting these two primary Vayus results in polarisation and strengthening of our vital energies along with awakening our higher faculties. Our Loma Viloma set of Kriyas and Pranayamas can be useful for balancing and revitalising our depleted energy system. Many Hatha Yogic practices like inversions and Badhas are effective in raising the Apana up and uniting with Prana; while the forward-fold postures and cooling pranayamas draw the prana the down and unite with the Apana Vayu in the middle of the navel region for enhanced polarity and balance of Prana-Apana energy.

A few typical sets of prana-apana balancing postures include-

- ❖ Vajrasana, Dharmika, Sashanga Paripurna, Vajrasana Supta.
- ❖ Dandasana, Paschimottanasana, Dandasana, Pratipahalasana.
- ❖ Padmasana, Yoga Mudra, Padmasana, Matsyasana.

3. Samana Vayu

The Samana Vayu governs the processing of things and moves towards the centre in a spiral motion. It is primarily seated in the navel area. This vital current is responsible for digestion and assimilation of food, information and experiences.

Imbalances of Samana Vayu can lead us to metabolic disorders, poor digestion, gastric issues, bloating, loss of appetite, lack of energy, etc.

Healing practices include:

- ❖ Uddiyana Bandha, Tadagi Kriya and Agnisara Kriya can help enhancing and balancing Samana Vayu
- ❖ Nutritional diet and fasting are also good
- ❖ Navasana, Samatulasana, Veera-Bhadrasana series

Vyana Vayu

The Vyana Vayu governs circulation and the distribution processes. This vital energy current moves outward in a circular and pulsating motion. It is located in the heart but is all pervading and governs cardiac activity, circulation and the voluntary nervous system.

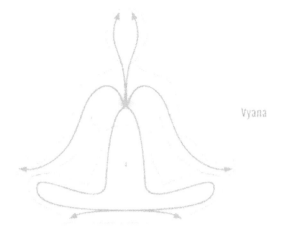

When the Vyana Vayu is out of harmony, it may cause issues like poor circulation, blocked arteries, heart attack, oedema, peripheral neuropathy, MS etc.

Healing practices include:
- ❖ Sukha Pruvaka Pranayama (2x2x2x2 vritti)
- ❖ Madhyama and Adhyama parts of Hathenas, Vibhaga Pranayama and Pranava Aum
- ❖ Slow Surya Namaskars, Hatha Yoga Kriyas especially four-footed set of kriyas, Veerasana Group of postures
- ❖ Surya and Chandra Nadi Pranayama
- ❖ Vyana-Samana Concept

Vyana and Samana Vayus are opposite vital forces of expansion and contraction. Vyana governs the differentiation and distribution of elements and allows help them to reach their separate spheres of activity. Samana brings the integration or union of the elements and helps them staying connected. Samana regulates the Agni (digestive fire), which must ignite and expand evenly for healthy life processes. Vyana governs the movement of Prana through the Nadis, keeping them open and active.

Examples of Hatha Yoga Kriyas for Balancing the Vyana-Samana include moving from closed positions like Dharmika or Shashaka to Chatuspada, Bhujanga, Kokila, Meru Asana, Hastapadasana, Anjali Mudra, Samasthiti and reversing back to Dharmika is a typical balancing set of Kriyas for Vyana-Samana.

Udana Vayu

The Udana Vayu flows upward and helps the vital energy currents for the other four Vayus. It is responsible for growth. This governs our life processes like posture, speech, effort in action, enthusiasm and will power. It is primarily seated in diaphragm and throat area and responsible for certain respiratory functions, speech, communication and mental functions.

Imbalance of Udana Vayu may lead to problems like asthma, emphysema, stuttering, voice hoarseness, depression, poor memory, lack of creativity, direction and drive force.

Healing practices include:
- ❖ Ujjayi Pranayama, Mantra Chanting, Jalandhara and Uddiyana Bandha.
- ❖ Sarvangasana, Halasana, Brahma Mudras
- ❖ And working on all of the Prana Vayus together

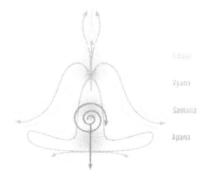

In this lesson we have examined the Pancha Prana Vayu's and the practises, which will support function in each area. They are responsible for the physiology of the entire human system and are a vital tool in the assessment, diagnosis and provision of therapeutic yoga practices for our care-seekers.

Lesson 38.
Yoga for Emotional Release

We may all find ourselves stuck in some negative feelings, emotions and memories, which can play a key role in various mental, emotional and physical health issues. These negative feelings and emotions can really hold us back in our day-to-day life. The founder of our Gitananda Yoga Tradition, Swamiji Dr. Gitananda Giriji explains that many of these chronic negative feelings, emotions and irritating memories can lead to various psycho-somatic health issues. These negative and unexpressed feelings and emotions remain stored in the body in our subconscious and unconscious mind. Over time they create stress, tension, physical tightness, hormonal imbalances, fatigue and even may cause headaches and muscular pains.

Yoga provides us with a wide range of kriyas, prakriyas, concepts and applications, these are the perfect tools for releasing emotional tension stored in the body and activating yogic healing processes, to regain our health and balance known as Swasthya (a state of ease within ourselves and optimum health). Hatha Yoga, Pranayama, Mudras, Bandhas, Jnana Yoga Kriyas and Yoga Nidra practices, along with Jnana Yoga or Yogic lifestyle, can be used to uncover these deep-rooted emotions and feelings, bring them to the surface and then help us to fully let them go.

Feeling Emotional During Your Hatha Yoga or Relaxation
Do you remember how many times you have felt emotional during a hatha yoga sadhana or deep relaxation? Our emotional traumas and tensions are deeply intertwined with physical tensions, digestive health, pelvic health, respiration, heart, endocrine and nervous systems. During a typical hatha yoga session, we begin to release muscular tension and stimulate various anatomical and physiological systems, along with the subtle energies, which activate the releasing process of emotions associated with those parts of body.

A conscious hatha yoga practice with deep breathing improves strength, flexibility, endurance and the health of our physical, mental and emotional bodies and increases our capacity to process and release the difficult and unprocessed feelings and emotions. Subtle and conscious breath and pranayama yoga allows us to relax further and more deeply and develops the awareness of subtle pranic energy currents known as Prana Vayus. As our awareness increases, we become more receptive to the subtle energies which connect us to our true self, leading us to feel more positive, confident and at ease with and within ourselves. Pranayama helps us in clearing the mind, unblocking the nadis or subtle energy channels to enhance our energy flow and ability to release negative emotions and feelings.

A deep relaxation, Jnana Yoga, Shavasana or Yoga Nidra Practice can help us to further develop a deep inner focus and relaxation to free our body, mind and emotions from all forms of unwanted and undesirable stress, memories, feelings and emotions. This process not only makes us aware of these forgotten subconscious feelings, emotions and memories but also liberates our body and mind from them. As our awareness or focus develops, an inner light shines which is enabling for us to see the brighter sides of various life events.

Key Yoga tools for Emotional Release

1. Hatha Yoga or Physical Work

Hatha Yoga practices to open our hip, shoulders, chest and throat areas, can help us with releasing emotional tensions stored in these primary places of emotional storage in the body. You can always begin your hatha yoga with a quick scan through the body to know where the stress and emotions are stored in form of tension, tightness, stiffness or pain.

Conscious Hatha Yoga Kriyas (movement of body with breath and awareness) will help us with removing the physical, mental and emotional toxicity at the surface levels; while holding the asanas will help with releasing the deeper tensions and emotions stored in the body. In which ever postures you feel these uncomfortable tensions, try to hold them for 6 to 9 deep breaths, without causing any harm or injury whilst giving your attention to the points of tension to release those old emotions and traumas.

2. Pranayama or Subtle energy work

There are many Pranayamas, which can help releasing negative emotions including:
- ❖ Sukha Vritti Pranayama (inhale 6 x exhale 6).
- ❖ Savitri Pranayama (inhale 6 x hold in 3 x exhale 6 x hold out x).
- ❖ Nasagra-Mukha Bhastrikas (whooshing the breath out through mouth).
- ❖ Exhaling out through the mouth including gently sighing, whooshing or vigorous hissing, activates the emotional body and is very effective in expressing and releasing the negative and stressful emotions of sadness, grief, pain and discomfort.
- ❖ The 'Haaa' sound of exhalation can help with releasing anger, frustration, anxiety, and tension.

3. Jnana Yoga Kriyas or Relaxation

We all are so caught up in the race of life and tension that we can easily forget to rest and so many of us struggle to have restorative deep sleep. Yogic relaxation and Yoga Nidra techniques are effective, safe and accessible to all to use to not only attain deep relaxation but also release old traumas, tensions and emotions. Relaxation after Hatha yoga, Kaya Kriya or Tada Kriyas can be used as an effective tool for physical, mental and emotional healing.

4. Pratyahara or Inward Flow of Awareness

Pratyahara is the inward flow of our attention and subtle energy currents or prana vayus. We use Hatha yoga, pranayama and relaxation techniques to develop pratyahara, which allows us to become sensitive and aware to various deep-rooted memories and emotions. Whenever you feel there is an emotion, tension or negative memory emerging during your sadhana, try to become aware and let it go fully. Developing the ability to witness these old memories and emotions without being the victim and becoming the knower or the one who knows, further develops dissociation or detachment (vairajna).

5. Nada or Vocalisation

Using the Mantras, Sounds or Nada while holding postures, or with Hatha Yoga Kriyas, opens various chakras, nadis and especially the throat chakra or vishuddha chakra to release mental and emotional traumas. Practices which are very effective in releasing these negative emotions and painful memories include:

❖ The Brahma Mudras
❖ Bhramari Pranayama
❖ Pranava Pranayama
❖ Hakara Kriyas
❖ Nada Kriyas

6. Yoga Darshan or Yogic viewpoints of Healthy Attitude

Having Yoga Darshan or the yogic life style and attitude teaches us to stay positive and live in equanimity, to enjoy peace, bliss and tranquillity. Here few of the many yogic tools for mental and emotional release and health:

❖ Ahimsa- Non-violence or inner peace
❖ Samtosha- Contentment, self-satisfaction
❖ Kshama- Forgiveness
❖ Vairajna- Detachment or dissociation
❖ Niskama Karma- Do your best and leave the rest

- ❖ Maitri- Friendliness
- ❖ Karuna- Compassion or kindness
- ❖ Mudita- Cheerfulness or joyfulness

Things to be Mindful of

1. A Safe Space - For emotional release, as a yoga teacher or sadhaka or therapist we need to make sure that we are providing a safe space, environment and time for the emotional release.

2. Acceptance, Seeking and Letting Go - A sadhaka or seeker needs to be accepting and prepared for any emotional release. Accepting the issue, seeking for the solution and letting go are key to achieving success in mental and emotional release and healing.

3. An Appropriate Practice – There is no prescriptive hatha yoga for emotional release that is going to work for every individual and also not everyone can do every hatha yoga sequence or asana and mudra. Hence as a yoga teacher or therapist it is important to understand and plan an appropriate hatha yoga, relaxation, mantra or sankalpa practice for each individual.

Key Yoga Asana or Poses for Emotional Release

- ❖ Raja Kapota Asana (King Pigeon Pose)
- ❖ Nikunja or Balasana (Childs Pose)
- ❖ Meru Asana (Mountain Pose)
- ❖ Uthita Janu Sirasasana (Head to knee pose)
- ❖ Matsyasana (Fish Pose)
- ❖ Chakrasana (Wheel Pose)
- ❖ Veera Asana (Warrior Pose)
- ❖ Trikonasana (Triangle Pose)
- ❖ Dhanurasana (Bow Pose)
- ❖ Navasana (Boat Pose)

This lesson has examined the benefits that Yoga can offer for releasing emotional tension stored in the body and activating yogic healing processes, to regain our health and balance known as Swasthya, the state of ease within ourselves and optimum health.

Lesson 39.
Muscle Tension Caused By Trapped Emotions and Yogic Remedial Healing

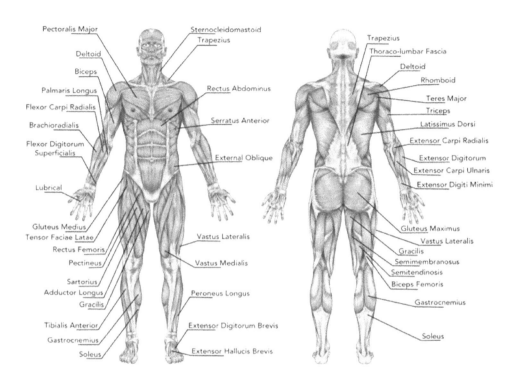

Many studies show us that more than 10% people suffer with some sort of chronic muscular pain in day-to-day life. One study in America showed that 17.6% of people were suffering from severe levels of pain. Many of us suffer with muscle tension and pain on a daily basis.

During my younger years I struggled with neck pain and injuries, thanks to some the yogic practices like Brahma Mudra Kriyas, this has totally healed now. I used to also suffer with stiff muscles and ligaments in the legs and groin areas due to some of the sports activities I used to take part in. Many of the surya namaskars, kriyas and asanas can help in healing and enhancing flexibility, mobility and endurance of muscles across the body.

It is easy to understand the connection between physical muscular injuries and pain, but there is also an intimate link between old memories and emotions and muscular pain. If you can reflect in your own life, you will see that whenever you are going through mental and emotional tensions, the weakest part of your body tends to suffer with health issues.

You can easily feel how your muscles are relaxed when you are feeling happy and joyful. As we relax our muscles, our thoughts and emotions are also released. Mentally and emotionally we may be living in a form of deprivation, an isolation tank of old negative memories and emotions, causing muscular and organic strain, tension and pain, which in long term leads to many serious health issues. We tend to feel them most in deep relaxation or at the moment of letting go. I have seen so many people during yogic relaxation, who cannot relax or let go due to mental and emotional fears. I have also observed many regular yoga students experience some physical and mental spasms during deep relaxation.

We all are different as individuals and there are not any exactly known places of the affected areas in our body where these emotions are stored; however we can easily associate various emotions more specifically with certain areas in the body.

Emotions, Traumas and Health Issues

The word emotion comes from the Middle French word émotion, which means 'a (social) moving, stirring, agitation'. We experience a variety of emotions every day. These emotions only cause a problem for us when we get stuck in a particular emotional pattern or are unable to process them. Our Body is a map and manifestation of every experience we have had and are going through. When we connect the mind body and spirit (adhi-vyadhi, psycho-somatic), we can better understand the connection between trapped emotions and physical ailments causing pain, tension and suffering. Many people can go years and even decades without realising that they have trapped unprocessed emotions, feelings, traumas and experiences. We wind up our body, mind and spirit by holding on to blocked energies, which can manifest into tension, pain and suffering.

Our Social, mental, emotional and postural conditioning begins in our early years and is reinforced throughout the rest of our lives by our parents, friends, teachers, family members and society. Some of the muscle tension that we carry can be the result of many unspoken and unprocessed social beliefs that we are taught to adopt as way of being 'acceptable, or 'likable'. This can make us run on auto-pilot or in our fight-flight responses.

A trauma can be caused by an overwhelmingly negative event or experience that causes a lasting impact on our mental and emotional stability. Traumas can be caused by physical, mental and emotional violence.

When these negative traumas, emotions and feelings are not being consciously dealt or processed, they can cause chronic fear, stress and anxiety. This chronic tension, anger, anxiety, guilt and grief tends to get stored in our body causing muscle tension and various physical, mental and emotional illness like digestive disorders, mental illness, pelvic health problems, skin disorders, muscular pain and even cancer.

Psychological tension is any form of anxiety, frustration, sadness or anger that we develop as a result of our perceptions. The negative, fearful or fault-finding perspective results in storing tension in our muscles as we tend to be always tensed for one thing or other.

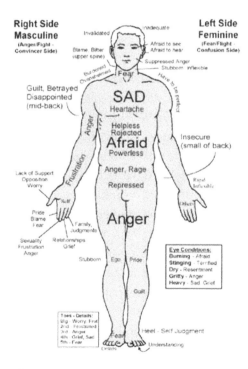

General Mapping of Our Emotions

Our Front Side reveals our social and public self, this is what the world sees in us. It reflects day-to-day active postural, mental and emotional living factors. It includes communication, desires, caring, loving, happiness and sadness. This can be seen on our face, posture and in our body language.

Our Back Side reflects our private and unconscious elements of life. This becomes storehouse of everything we can't or we don't want to deal with or process. Our hidden and unexpressed feelings gradually freeze into our body structure. This shows that lots of negative emotions can be stored in our spine, back, buttocks and back of legs. Most negative and harmful emotions like anger and fear are stored in our back.

Neck Tension: Communication Issues and discomfort

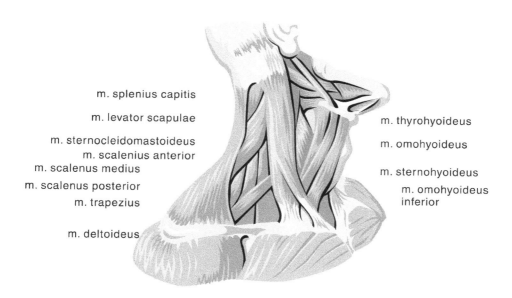

Our neck is associated with the throat chakra responsible for purity and communication. Our inability to communicate and express our feelings, thoughts and ideas around others causes muscular tension in the neck area. Fear and anxiety also causes tension in this area as it is associated with our subconscious and unconscious mind. Our neck is venerable to our physical response to danger, uncertainty and uncomfortable situations. Neck muscles are also associated with trust issues.

Shoulder Tension: Individual, Family, Social Burdens and Responsibility

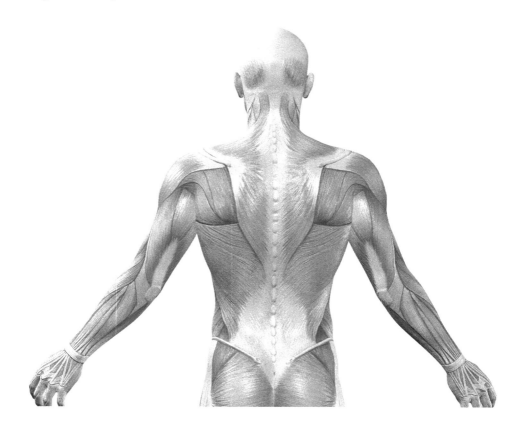

When we struggle with the weight or stress of life, approval and validity within ourselves, family and society, we tend to accumulate these feelings and emotions in our shoulder areas. Our famous expression of 'carrying the weight of the world on our shoulders', can be explained from this idea. Our shoulder tension is intimately connected with our social, economical and emotional responsibilities; including unconsciously carrying the burden of other people's pain. Many healers, people with empathy and care-takes can struggle with chronic shoulder tension.

Upper Back, and Upper Chest Region: Grief, Sorrow, Sadness and Lack of Self- Belief

Any sort of unprocessed and unreleased sadness and grief tend to adversely affect our upper back and chest region. This area is also the storage area of feelings and emotions associated with heartbreak, loss and lack of love and intimacy in life.

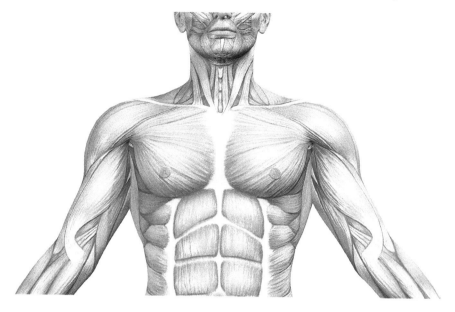

Middle Back: Insecurity and Lack of Power and Intent

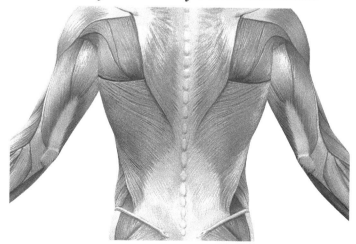

Many healing paths like reflexology and tantra link our middle back pain with feelings and emotions of helplessness and insecurity. Also negative feelings due to lack of support by people we live with or associated in our life also causes tension in this part of our body.

Lower Back: Guilt, Lack of Self-worth and Shame

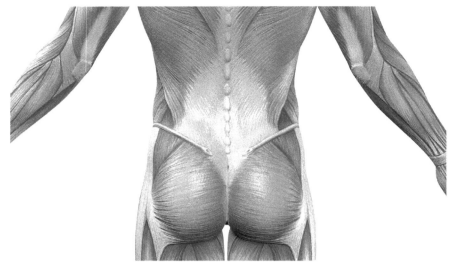

Any of the negative feelings and emotions associated with guilt, shame, lack of self-worth and lack of self-acceptance affects our lower back adversely. Even feelings of sexual inadequacy, traumas, and guilt may be stored in the muscles associated with the lower back.

Diaphragm and Stomach Area: Anxiety, Worry and Inability to Process Emotions

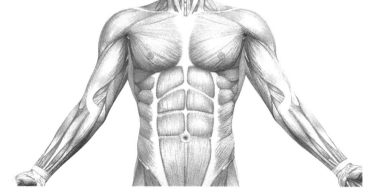

When we are struggling with mental and emotional instability and inability to process them, we can feel the tension in stomach area and even may feel nausea, indigestion and upset stomach. We use the saying, 'I cannot digest it', which describes this sensation of stomach tension. We feel soreness and stiffness in the stomach and diaphragm areas when we struggle with negative or positive unprocessed feelings and emotions.

Buttocks : Anger, Rage, Obsession of accumulating wealth

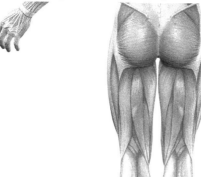

There is another of well known saying we hear so often referring to other people as a 'pain in bum'. Our suppressed anger, rage and sexual tensions are stored in our buttocks. You can easily notice when your head is caught in turmoil of emotions, how your buttocks are also tensed. People who stress about accumulating wealth and money and are very tight in spending in the day-to-day, also tend to struggle with tension in buttocks.

Inner Thighs: Fear of Vulnerability and Sexual Abuse

When we are nervous and struggle to trust people around us, we tend to struggle with tension in inner thighs. Even people with social anxiety disorders tend to struggle with pain in inner thigh muscles. This is caused because of fight-flight response, to run when we spot signs of danger or fear.

Outer Thighs : Frustration and Impatience

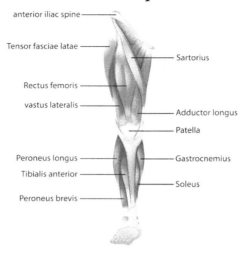

When we live our life mindlessly and impatiently, we easily get frustrated and this energy is stored in our outer thigh muscles. Our hectic jobs and personal lives also contribute to tension and pain in this area.

Pelvic Floor – Incontinence and Sexual Health

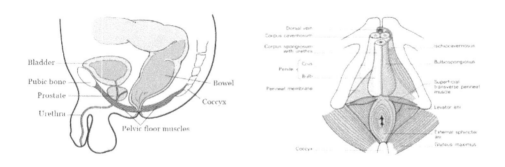

Both men and women experience urinary incontinence. Stress incontinence can happen with a cough, sneeze, running or jumping as well as several mental and emotional disturbances. Urge incontinence is an involuntary loss of urine due to an inappropriate contraction of the bladder. Both kind of incontinence cause further emotional and mental reactions in men and women, and feelings of embarrassment, fear and anxiety are common.

Dyspareunia is pain with intercourse; if intimacy is painful, it is not pleasurable. The body tenses with painful experiences. When dyspareunia continues over an extended period, the body naturally will become tense in preparing for intercourse. Many women, even if they desire to be intimate with their partner, they find themselves avoiding intimacy. This leads to relationship problems, and separation.

Many men also experience pain with intercourse. It can happen with an erection or ejaculation. This can cause erectile dysfunction or premature ejaculation. This leads to feelings of anxiety, fear, failure and inadequacy. Erectile dysfunction is a common pelvic health problem in men. The problem could be transitory, but once experienced, it takes on a life of it's own and occupies the thought patterns of the male and diminishes natural arousal or the ability to sustain arousal.

Victims of sexual abuse often have deep rooted emotional scars, which can affect their ability to have healthy relationships as well as affecting the health of the pelvic organs and muscles.

How to Release Muscular Stress and Trapped Emotions and Traumas?

1. *Gentle Therapeutic Hatha Yoga*- A holistic therapeutic hatha yoga sadhana with jattis, kriyas, asanas, mudras and pranayama can help releasing these deep-rooted emotions and traumas as well as enhance muscle strength, flexibility and endurance.
2. *Kaya Kriya* – Kaya Kriyas are a beautiful set of movement with conscious breathing of legs, arms, head and all three together to release deep rooted tensions and traumas from thighs, hips, pelvic, shoulders, chest, neck and head. With Kaya Kriyas we can also add Pranava Pranayama to release physical, mental, emotional and social tensions and traumas.
3. *Moksha Kriya* – A lovely set of step-by-step reflective Jnana Yoga or Yogic relaxation practice to release old memories and traumas stored in body, mind and memories.
4. *Tala Kriyas* – Tala Kriyas are great cellular emotional letting go kriyas for our back, hips, shoulders and sides.
5. *Nagapuchi Kriyas* – These are little snake movements to release many of trapped old emotions and feelings from our spine, back, hips, and shoulders.
6. *Gardhabha Kriyas* – Gardhabha is donkey and this kriya helps releasing old abdominal, spinal and chest traumas, negative memories, anger, frustration and guilt.

7. *Pawan Mukta Kriyas* – These Kriyas help us releasing wind and negative energy accumulated in abdominal and pelvic areas and hence can help releasing old memories and traumas trapped in pelvic and abdominal areas.

8. *Spanda Nispanda Kriya* – This is another lovely set of simple therapeutic yogic vyayama to release old tensions and emotions from our body from feet to head. We create tension in each part of the body and let go and release with exhalation. We repeat it three times from feet to head in each part.

9. *Tada Kriyas* – Palm tree stretching movement with spanda -nispanda can be done on floor in shavasana, on chair as well as in standing to stretch and relax our whole body.

10. *Shavasana* – Yogic relaxation, and Jnana Yoga Kriyas are proved to be helpful in releasing physical, mental, emotional and karmic tensions.

11. *Yoga Nidra* – Yoga Nidra is a powerful conscious sleep sadhana to awaken the inner consciousness and release all sorts of old tensions, traumas and blocked negative energies.

12. *Brahma Mudra Kriyas* – Great kriyas for releasing tension from neck, shoulder and head region as well as subconscious and unconscious unprocessed emotions and memories.

13. *Body Massage*- Any of the therapeutic body massages are helpful in releasing tension and traumas accumulated in muscles and organs.

14. *Steam and Sauna* – Hot Bath, steam and Sauna are also proved to help releasing physical, mental and emotional stress and strains.

15. *Healthy Diet* – A healthy and nutritional diet helps improving our immunity and stress-coping abilities.

16. *Yogic Lifestyle* – Yogic Lifestyle and attitude like non-violence, compassion, letting go, do your best and leave the rest, skill in action, forgiveness are few of the examples which can help us releasing mental and emotional tensions and traumas.

Symptoms list: by Louise Hay

(https://alchemyofhealing.com/causes-of-symptoms-according-to-louise-hay/)

A

Abdominal Cramps: Fear. Stopping the process.

Abscess: Fermenting thoughts over hurts, slights and revenge.

Accidents: Inability to speak up for the self. Rebellion against authority. Belief in violence.

Aches: Longing for love. Longing to be held.

Acne: Not accepting the self. Dislike of the self.

Addictions: Running from the self. Fear. Not knowing how to love self.

Adrenal Problems: Defeatism. No longer caring for the self. Anxiety.

Alcoholism: Feeling of futility, guilt, inadequacy. Self-rejection.

Allergies: Denying your own power.

Alzheimer's Disease: Refusal to deal with the world as it is. Hopelessness and helplessness. Anger.

Amenorrhea: Not wanting to be a woman. Dislike of the self.

Anemia: "Yes-but" attitude. Lack of joy. Fear of life. Not feeling good enough.

Ankle: Inflexibility and guilt. Ankles represent the ability to receive pleasure.

Anorexia: Denying the self life. Extreme fear, self-hatred and rejection.

Anxiety: Not trusting the flow and the process of life.

Apathy: Resistance to feeling. Deadening of the self. Fear.

Appetite, Excessive: Fear. Needing protection. Judging the emotions.

Arm: Represents the capacity and ability to hold the experiences of life.

Arteries: Carry the joy of life.

Arthritic Fingers: A desire to punish. Blame. Feeling victimized.

Arthritis: Feeling unloved. Criticism, resentment. – Rheumatoid Arthritis: Feeling victimized. Lack of love. Chronic bitterness. Resentment. Deep criticism of authority. Feeling very put upon.

Asthma: Smother love. Inability to breathe for one's self. Feeling stifled. Suppressed crying.

Athlete's Foot: Frustration at not being accepted. Inability to move forward with ease.

B

Back Issues: Represents the support of life. Back Problems: – Rounded shoulders: Carrying the burdens of life. Helpless and hopeless. – Lower Back Pain: Fear of money or lack of financial support. – Mid-Back Pain: Guilt. Stuck in all that stuff back there. "Get off my back!" – Upper Back Pain: Lack of emotional support. Feeling unloved. Holding back love. – Back Curvature: The inability to flow with the support of life. Fear and trying to hold on to old ideas. Not trusting life. Lack of integrity. No courage of convictions.

Bad Breath: Anger and revenge thoughts. Experiences backing up.

Balance, Loss of: Scattered thinking. Not centered.

Baldness: Fear. Tension. Trying to control everything.

Bedwetting: Fear of parent, usually the father.

Belching: Fear. Gulping life too quickly.

Bell's Palsy: Extreme control over anger. Unwillingness to express feelings.

Bladder Problems: Anxiety. Holding on to old ideas. Fear of letting go. Being "pissed off".

Bleeding: Joy running out. Anger.

Blisters: Resistance. Lack of emotional protection.

Blood Pressure: – High: Longstanding emotional problem not solved. – Low: Lack of love as a child. Defeatism.

Body Odor: Fear. Dislike of the self. Fear of others.

Bones: Represent the structure of the universe. – Bone marrow: Represents deepest beliefs about the self. How you support and care for yourself. – Breaks: Rebelling against authority.

Brain: Represents the computer, the switchboard. – Tumor: Incorrect computerized beliefs. Stubborn. Refusing to change old patterns.

Breast: Represents mothering and nurturing and nourishment. – Cysts, Lumps: A refusal to nourish the self. Putting everyone else first. Over mothering. Overprotection. Overbearing attitudes.

Breath: Represents the ability to take in life. – Breathing Problems: Fear. Not trusting the process of life. Getting stuck in childhood. Fear of taking in life fully. – Bronchitis: Inflamed family environment. Arguments and yelling.

Bruises: The little bumps in life. Self-punishment.

Bulimia: Hopeless terror. A frantic stuffing and purging of self-hatred.

Burns: Anger. Burning up. Incensed.

Bursitis: Repressed anger. Wanting to hit someone.

C

Calluses: Hardened concepts and ideas. Fear solidified.

Cancer: Deep hurt. Longstanding resentment. Deep secret or grief eating away at the self. Carrying hatreds.

Candida: Feeling very scattered. Lots of frustration and anger. Demanding and untrusting in relationships. Great takers.

Canker Sores: Festering words held back by the lips. Blame.

Carpal Tunnel Syndrome: Anger and frustration at life's seeming injustices.

Cataracts: Inability to see ahead with joy. Dark future.

Cellulite: Stored anger and self-punishment.

Cerebral Palsy: A need to unite the family in an action of love.

Chills: Mental contraction, pulling away and in. Desire to retreat.

Cholesterol: Clogging the channels of joy. Fear of accepting joy.

Circulation: Represents the ability to feel and express the emotions in positive ways.

Colds: Too much going on at once. Mental confusion, disorder. Small hurts.

Colic: Mental irritation, impatience, annoyance in the surroundings.

Colitis: Insecurity. Represents the ease of letting go of that which is over.

Coma: Fear. Escaping something or someone.

Conjunctivitis: Anger and frustration at what you are looking at in life.

Constipation: Incomplete releasing. Holding on to garbage of the past. Guilt over the past. Sometimes stinginess.

Corns: Hardened areas of thought – stubborn holding on to the pain of the past.

Coughs: A desire to bark at the world. "Listen to me!"

Cramps: Tension. Fear. Gripping, holding on.

Crohn's Disease: Fear. Worry. Not feeling good enough.

Crying: Tears are the river of life, shed in joy as well as in sadness and fear.

Cuts: Punishment for not following your own rules.

Cysts: Running the old painful movie. Nursing hurts. A false growth.

Cystic Fibrosis: A thick belief that life won't work for you. "Poor me."

D

Deafness: Rejection, stubbornness, isolation. What don't you want to hear? "Don't bother me."

Depression: Anger you feel you do not have a right to have. Hopelessness.

Diabetes: Longing for what might have been. A great need to control. Deep sorrow. No sweetness left.

Diarrhea: Fear. Rejection. Running off.

Dizziness: Flighty, scattered thinking. A refusal to look.

Dry eyes: Angry eyes. Refusing to see with love. Would rather die than forgive. Being spiteful.

Dysmenorrhea: Anger at the self. Hatred of the body or of women.

E

Ear: Represents the capacity to hear. – Ache: Anger. Not wanting to hear. Too much turmoil. Household arguing.

Eczema: Breath-taking antagonism. Mental eruptions.

Edema: What or who won't you let go of?

Elbow: Represents changing directions and accepting new experiences.

Emphysema: Fear of taking in life. Not worthy of living.

Endometriosis: Insecurity, disappointment and frustration. Replacing self-love with sugar. Blamers.

Epilepsy: Sense of persecution. Rejection of life. A feeling of great struggle. Self-violence.

Epstein-Barr Virus: Pushing beyond one's limits. Fear of not being good enough. Draining all inner support. Stress.

Eye: Represents the capacity to see clearly past, present, future. – Astigmatism: "I" trouble. Fear of really seeing the self. – Hyperopia: Fear of the present. – Myopia: Fear of the future.

F

Face: Represents what we show the world.

Fainting: Fear. Can't cope. Blacking out.

Fat or Weight issues: Oversensitivity. Often represents fear and shows a need for protection. Fear may be a cover for hidden anger and a resistance to forgive. Running away from feelings. Insecurity, self-rejection and seeking fulfillment. – Arms: Anger at being denied love. – Belly: Anger at being denied nourishment. – Hips: Lumps of stubborn anger at the parents. – Thighs: Packed childhood anger. Often rage at the father.

Fatigue: Resistance, boredom. Lack of love for what one does.

Feet: Represent our understanding – of ourselves, of life, of others. – Foot Problems: Fear of the future and of not stepping forward in life.

Fever: Anger. Burning up.

Fibroid Tumors: Nursing a hurt from a partner. A blow to the feminine ego.

Fingers: Represent the details of life. – Thumb: Represents intellect and worry. – Index: Represents ego and fear. – Middle: Represents anger and sexuality. – Ring: Represents unions and grief. – Little: Represents the family and pretending.

Food Poisoning: Allowing others to take control. Feeling defenseless.

Frigidity: Fear. Denial of pleasure. A belief that sex is bad. Insensitive partners. Fear of father.

Fungus: Stagnating beliefs. Refusing to release the past. Letting the past rule today.

G

Gallstones: Bitterness. Hard thoughts. Condemning. Pride.

Gas: Gripping. Fear. Undigested ideas.

Gastritis: Prolonged uncertainty. A feeling of doom.

Genitals: Represent the masculine and feminine principles. Worry about not being good enough.

Gland Problems: Represent holding stations. Self-staring activity. Holding yourself back.

Gout: The need to dominate. Impatience, anger.

Glaucoma: Stony unforgiveness. Pressure from longstanding hurts. Overwhelmed by it all.

Gray Hair: Stress. A belief in pressure and strain.

Growths: Nursing those old hurts. Building resentments.

Gum Problems: Inability to back up decisions. Indecisive about life.

H

Hands: Hold and handle. Clutch and grip. Grasping and letting go. Caressing. Pinching. All ways of dealing with experiences.

Hay Fever: Emotional congestion. Fear of the calendar. A belief in persecution. Guilt.

Headaches: Invalidating the self. Self-criticism. Fear.

Heart: Represents the center of love and security. – Heart Attack: Squeezing all the joy out of the heart in favor of money or position. Feeling alone and scared. "I'm not good enough. I don't do enough. I'll never make it." – Heart Problems: Longstanding emotional problems. Lack of joy. Hardening of the heart. Belief in strain and stress.

Heartburn: Fear. Fear. Fear. Clutching Fear.

Hemorrhoids: Fear of deadlines. Anger of the past. Afraid to let go. Feeling burdened.

Hepatitis: Resistance to change. Fear, anger, hatred. Liver is the seat of anger and rage.

Hernia: Ruptured relationships. Strain, burdens, incorrect creative expression.

Herpes Genitalis: Mass belief in sexual guilt and the need for punishment. Public shame. Belief in a punishing God. Rejection of the genitals.

Herpes Simplex: Bitter words left unspoken.

Hip: Carries the body in perfect balance. Major thrust in moving forward. Fear of going forward in major decisions. Nothing to move forward to.

Hives: Small, hidden fears. Mountains out of molehills.

Hodgkin's Disease: Blame and a tremendous fear of not being good enough. A frantic race to prove one's self until the blood has no substance left to support itself. The joy of life is forgotten in the race of acceptance.

Hyperactivity: Fear. Feeling pressured and frantic.

Hyperventilation: Fear. Resisting change. Not trusting the process.

Hypoglycemia: Overwhelmed by the burdens in life.

I

Impotence: Sexual pressure, tension, guilt. Social beliefs. Spite against a previous mate. Fear of mother.

Incontinence: Emotional overflow. Years of controlling emotions.

Indigestion: Gut-level fear, dread, anxiety. Griping and grunting.

Infection: Irritation, anger, annoyance.

Inflammation: Fear. Seeing red. Inflamed thinking. Anger and frustration about conditions you are looking at in your life.

Influenza: Response to mass negativity and beliefs. Fear. Belief in statistics.

Ingrown Toenail: Worry and guilt about your right to move forward.

Injuries: Anger at the self. Feeling guilty.

Insanity: Fleeing from the family. Escapism, withdrawal. Violent separation from life.

Insomnia: Fear. Not trusting the process of life. Guilt.

Intestines: Represent assimilation and absorption.

Itching: Desires that go against the grain. Unsatisfied. Remorse. Itching to get out or get away.

J

Jaundice: Internal and external prejudice. Unbalanced reason.

Jaw Problems: Anger. Resentment. Desire for revenge.

K

Kidney Problems: Criticism, disappointment, failure. Shame. Reacting like a child.

Kidney Stones: Lumps of undissolved anger.

Knee: Represents pride and ego. Stubborn ego and pride. Inability to bend. Fear. Inflexibility. Won't give in.

L

Laryngitis: So mad you can't speak. Fear of speaking up. Resentment of authority.

Left Side of Body: Represents receptivity, taking in, feminine energy, women, the mother.

Leg: Carry us forward in life.

Liver: Seat of anger and primitive emotions. Chronic complaining. Justifying fault-finding to deceive yourself. Feeling bad.

Lockjaw: Anger. A desire to control. A refusal to express feelings.

Lump in the Throat: Fear. Not trusting the process of life.

Lung: The ability to take in life. Depression. Grief. Not feeling worthy of living life fully.

Lupus: A giving up. Better to die than stand up for one's self. Anger and punishment.

Lymph Problems: A warning that the mind needs to be recentered on the essentials of life. Love and joy.

M

Malaria: Out of balance with nature and with life.

Menopause Problems: Fear of no longer being wanted. Fear of aging. Self-rejection. Not feeling good enough.

Menstrual Problems: Rejection of one's femininity. Guilt, fear. Belief that the genitals are sinful or dirty.

Migraine Headaches: Dislike of being driven. Resisting the flow of life. Sexual fears.

Miscarriage: Fear of the future. Inappropriate timing.

Mononucleosis: Anger at not receiving love and appreciation. No longer caring for the self.

Motion Sickness: Fear. Bondage. Feeling of being trapped.

Mouth: Represents taking in of new ideas and nourishment. Set opinions. Closed mind. Incapacity to take in new ideas.

Multiple Sclerosis: Mental hardness, hard-heartedness, iron will, inflexibility.

Muscles: Resistance to new experiences. Muscles represent our ability to move in life.

Muscular Dystrophy: "It's not worth growing up."

N

Nails: Represent protection. – Nail Biting: Frustration. Eating away at the self. Spite of a parent.

Narcolepsy: Can't cope. Extreme fear. Wanting to get away from it all. Not wanting to be here.

Nausea: Fear. Rejecting an idea or experience.

Neck: Represents flexibility. The ability to see what's back there. Refusing to see other sides of a question. Stubbornness, inflexibility. Unbending stubbornness.

Nephritis: Overreaction to disappointment and failure.

Nerves: Represent communication. Receptive reporters.

Nervous Breakdown: Self-centeredness. Jamming the channels of communication.

Nervousness: Fear, anxiety, struggle, rushing. Not trusting the process of life.

Neuralgia: Punishment for guilt. Anguish over communication.

Nodules: Resentment and frustration and hurt ego over career.

Nose: Represents self-recognition. – Nose Bleeds:A need for recobnition. Feeling unnoticed. Crying for love. – Runny Nose: Asking for help. Inner crying. – Stuffy Nose: Not recognizing the self-worth.

Numbness: Withholding love and consideration. Going dead mentally.

O

Osteomyelitis: Anger and frustration at the very structure of life. Feeling unsupported.

Osteoporosis: Feeling there is no support left in life. Mental pressures and tightness. Muscles can't stretch. Loss of mental mobility.

Ovaries: Represent points of creation. Creativity.

PQ

Pain: Guilt. Guilt always seeks punishment.

Paralysis: Paralysing thoughts. Getting stuck. Terror leading to escape from a situation or person.

Pancreas: Represents the sweetness of life.

Pancreatitis: Rejection. Anger and frustration because life seems to have lost its sweetness.

Parasites: Giving power to others, letting them take over and life off of you.

Parkinson's Disease: Fear and an intense desire to control everything and everyone.

Peptic Ulcer: Fear. A belief that you are not good enough. Anxious to please.

Phlebitis: Anger and frustration. Blaming others for the limitation and lack of joy in life.

Pimples: Small outbursts of anger.

Pituitary Gland: Represents the control center.

Pneumonia: Desperate. Tired of life. Emotional wounds that are not allowed to heal.

Poison Ivy: Allergy Feeling defenseless and open to attack.

Polio: Paralysing jealousy. A desire to stop someone.

Premenstrual Syndrome: Allowing confusion to reign. Giving power to outside influences. Rejection of the feminine processes.

Prostate: Represents the masculine principle. Mental fears weaken the masculinity. Giving up. Sexual pressure and guilt. Belief in aging.

Psoriasis: Fear of being hurt. Deadening the senses of the self. Refusing to accept responsibility for our own feelings.

R

Rash: Irritation over delays. Immature way to get attention.

Right Side of Body: Giving out, letting go, masculine energy, men, the father.

Ringworm: Allowing others to get under your skin. Not feeling good enough or clean enough.

S

Scabies: Infected thinking. Allowing others to get under your skin.

Sciatica: Being hypocritical. Fear of money and of the future.

Scleroderma: Protecting the self from life. Not trusting yourself to be there and to take care of yourself.

Scratches: Feeling life tears at you, that life is a rip off.

Senility: Returning to the so-called safety of childhood. Demanding care and attention. A form of control of those around you. Escapism.

Shin: Represents the standards of life. Breaking down ideals.

Shingles: Waiting for the other shoe to drop. Fear and tension. Too sensitive.

Sinus Problems: Irritation to one person, someone close.

Skin: Protects our individuality. Anxiety, fear. Old, buried things. I am being threatened.

Slipped Disc: Feeling totally unsupported by life. Indecisive.

Snoring: Stubborn refusal to let go of old patterns.

Solar Plexus: Gut reactions. Center of our intuitive power.

Sores: Unexpressed anger that settles in.

Spleen: Obsessions. Being obsessed about things.

Sprains: Anger and resistance. Not wanting to move in a certain direction in life.

Sterility: Fear and resistance to the process of life or not needing to go through the parenting experience.

Stiffness: Rigid, stiff thinking.

Stomach: Holds nourishment. Digests ideas. Dread. Fear of the new. Inability to assimilate the new.

Stroke: Giving up. Resistance. Rather die than change. Rejection of life.

Stuttering: Insecurity. Lack of self-expression. Not being allowed to cry.

Sty: Looking at life through angry eyes. Angry at someone.

Suicidal thoughts: See life only in black and white. Refusal to see another way out.

T

Teeth: Represent decisions. – Teeth Problems: Longstanding indecisiveness. Inability to break down ideas for analysis and decisions. – Root Canal: Can't bite into anything anymore. Root beliefs being destroyed. – Impacted Wisdom Teeth: Not giving yourself mental space to create a firm foundation.

Throat: Avenue of expression. Channel of creativity. – Throat Problems: The inability to speak up for one's self. Swallowed anger. Stifled creativity. Refusal to change. – Sore throat: Holding in angry words.

Feeling unable to express the self.

Thrush: Anger over making the wrong decisions.

Thymus Gland: Feeling attacked by life. They are out to get me.

Thyroid Gland: Humiliation. I never get to do what I want to do. When is it going to be my turn. – Hyperthyroid: Rage at being left out.

Tics, Twitches: Fear. A feeling of being watched by others.

Tinnitus or Ringing in the Ears: Refusal to listen. Not hearing the inner voice. Stubbornness.

Toes: Represent the minor details of the future.

Tongue: Represents the ability to taste the pleasures of life with joy.

Tonsillitis: Fear. Repressed emotions. Stifled creativity.

Tuberculosis: Wasting away from selfishness. Possessive. Cruel thoughts. Revenge.

U

Urinary infections: Pissed off, usually at the opposite sex or a lover. Blaming others.

Uterus: Represents the home of creativity.

V

Vaginitis: Anger at a mate. Sexual guilt. Punishing the self.

Varicose Veins: Standing in a situation you hate. Discouragement. Feeling over-worked and overburdened.

Vitiligo: Feeling completely outside of things. Not belonging. Not one of the group.

Vomiting: Violent rejection of ideas. Fear of the new.

WXYZ

Warts: Little expressions of hate. Belief in ugliness. – Plantar Warts: Anger at the very basis of your understanding. Spreading frustration about the future.

Wrist: Represents movement and ease.

References and Resources

1. https://www.vocabulary.com/dictionary/emotion]
2. https://thejoyfulapproach.com/mapping-how-emotions-get-stored-in-the-body/
3. https://www.handson-austin.com/pelvic-floor-muscle-dysfunction-and-the-emotional-component/?doing_wp_cron=1608058280.9377009868621826171875
4. Yoga Step By Step by Swamiji Dr Gitananda Giriji, www.icyer.com
5. Yoga Chikitsa by Dr Ananda Balayogi Bhavanani, www.icyer.com
6. Yogic Approach of Stress Management by Dr Ananda Balayogi Bhavanani, www.icyer.com

Lesson 40.
Healing Powers of Yoga Nidra

Stress, Psycho-Somatics and Yoga Nidra

Our modern health professionals and neurophysiologists have established a scientific relation between the body and the brain, our stress and health issues known as psycho-somatics. The great Ancient Yogis have known this for thousands of years as Adhi-Vyadhi. Various parts of body are regulated from different parts of brain. Neuro-surgeons have been able to demonstrate that each part of the body is precisely mapped out along the surface of the central sensory-motor cortex of the brain.

Our brain is the physical instrument of consciousness, which links body, mind, emotions and awareness into one unit. In Hatha Yoga we stimulate the brain by stimulating, stretching and consciously moving a part of the body. In yoga nidra we begin with stimulating the nerve pathways or reflexes for heightened awareness of the body and then stimulating the brain for recharging and rejuvenation. This enhanced awareness of our body, pranic energy currents and channelling them to their highest potential, naturally induces a deep relaxation of the body and mind. Yoga nidra enables us to rejuvenate our nadi and pranic energy system, which deeply relaxes our brain and mind.

In Yogic terms our stress-related problems originate in our mind due to our ignorance (avidya); the excessive association of our consciousness with our psyche, mind and desires, with the physical body through sensory information. This leads to nervous depletion and exhaustion. When this goes on and on, as a chronic issues, it does not allow our brain and nervous system to repair, causing neural, physical and mental health problems.

In Yoga Nidra this deteriorating effect of stress and psycho-somatic effect is alleviated by reversing the route of relaxing the body, enhancing the subtle energy currents, to relax, purify and heal our mind and nervous system. Yoga Nidra practices discharge abundance or Pranic energy in our central nervous system, which can help the sadhaka to prevent, overcome, rehabilitate or better manage many pscho-somatic and somato-psychic health problems. In Yoga Nidra, the energy flowing in sensory channels is withdrawn and redirected for the healing and rejuvenation of over exhausted tissues, muscles, glands, organs and nerves.

Yoga Nidra : Somato-Psychic Relaxation

The practice of yoga nidra awakens awareness of the subtle energy flows at the subtlest level. Once we relax the sensory-motor reflexes in the brain, It is like being well established in the core centre of the cortex of the brain, but fully connected to each and every cell in our body.

In our body tissues we have numerous amount of especially adapted sensory nerve endings, which respond to specific types of stimuli like touch. These sensory nerves, the proprioceptors of the joints, the Pacinian corpuscles beneath the skin and the pain and temperature receptors, continuously gather information from all the parts of the body and transfer it back to the brain for processing and the taking of any action that is needed to maintain homeostasis.

Neuroscientists have located the important centres in our brain. The important centres are associated with food and water intake, temperature regulation and experiences of pain and pleasure. Due to chronic exposure to stress, physical exertion and other problems, gradually our brain shuts down these centres and the nerves associated with receiving the information may not function properly; this disturbs our body's ability to restore balance and homeostasis. In Yoga Nidra we awaken these sensory centres in our brain and this can help us restore our balance and the natural healing processes of body and mind.

Spanda – Nispanda

Hatha Yoga practices are based on concept of Spanda (action, stretch, motion) and Nispanda (relaxation, inaction, stillness). Yoga Nidra brings both these beautiful elements for empowering our health and well-being together. There is an element of active awareness, while we are in a deep resting state of body and mind.

Many Yoga Nidra techniques begin with some tension and feeling of heaviness, which leads our body to create the feeling or need for rest and relaxation. This is first step towards deep musculo-skeletal-nervous relaxation. There are deeply rooted tensions, injuries and traumas in the complex network of postural muscles and nerves. The intention or suggestion of feeling heavy in our body, stimulates the relaxation response in our brain to encourage our postural muscles to relax and let go. We all experience this heaviness and tiredness to prepare our body and brain to fall asleep.

This is followed with the feeling or intensions of feeling light, relaxed and awake. Consciously we aim to awake the sensations of lightness and ease in the body. This is a process of electro-physiological principles of the brain, sending message to our body in the form of electro-magnetic impulses. Once we come into a deep relaxation, these nerve electric currents start firing back to brain, leading to a heightened awareness and awakening.

In any adverse situations or stimuli, a neuron fires and transmits an impulse for the brain to know what is going on and make any required changes. When the same cell continues to fire frequently for prolonged periods of time, its message is no longer acknowledged as it becomes habituated as constant electrical background feature; just like playing music in background while you are reading, eating or doing other things. This is an in-built quality in our brains to help us cope with unnecessary nerve impulses and information, to keep us calm and focussed.

In Yoga Nidra we begin with heightened awareness and sensations through the body. When this lasts for a few minutes continuously, our brain starts to ignore these impulses, which allows us to disconnect our awareness from the body, this fires all the nerve impulse energy back to the brain and help us transcend our awareness from the body, into subtle energy currents and mind fields, bringing on a natural and spontaneous relaxation. Lightness and awareness drifts away from mundane experience to transcendental experience. In this phase we can transmit yoga wisdom ideas and practices to go deep inward to enhance the pranic energy flows; clearing our minds, activating and balancing the Nadis and Chakras for the subtlest healing of body, mind and spirit.

Yoga Nidra and Emotional Healing

There are specific parts of the hypothalamus, limbic system and amygdala regions of the brain, which deal with the emotional responses like rage, aggression and fear. For many of us controlling these negative emotions is harder compared to the positive emotions like love, joy, pleasure, compassion and security. Yoga Nidra empowers a deep relaxation response and enhances the areas that create positive emotional responses in the brain.

This deep relaxation response of the whole body develops simultaneously operating nerve circuits in the opposite hemispheres of the brain, transforming the neuro-plasticity of the brain. This brings a harmonious neural connection between the right and left brain, enabling the balancing of opposite emotions of love and hatred, pain and pleasure, joy and sorrow; enhancing witnessing awareness and dissolving of conflicting emotions. Patanjali mentions in the Yoga Sutras that to deal with negative emotions, we need to replace them with positive emotions (Pratipaksha Bhavanam – think opposite), Yoga Nidra empowers this idea from the inside out.

By the repetitive Sadhana of Yoga Nidra, these nerve connections become well established, enabling our human consciousness to go beyond the sufferings arising due to attachment and aversion (raga-dwesha) and the duality of life events.

At the psycho-physio-pranic level Yoga Nidra helps in developing the attitude and outlook of detachment, maturity and control of emotional reactions and autonomic sympathetic responses. Yoga advocates this idea of Vairajna or detachment and letting go off physical, mental and emotionally disturbing stresses and strains. This develops our abilities to be able to better manage stressful situations, through enhanced perception and awareness and better emotional control.

Through deep relaxation and Yoga Nidra, we can attain awareness of the subtlest elements of our body and develop some insight into our health problems: our body immunity can then find its way to alleviate those issues, even before they manifest as actual symptoms. Yoga is very well known for the prevention of diseases. Patanjali mentions that by being aware and maintaining equanimity, we can avoid many of the problems yet to come. We carry the solutions to all our problems at the deeper levels of our mind and consciousness. We can allow them to manifest by detaching from the material world and connecting with the inner healing powers of our mind and prana through yoga nidra.

There is research available now from Yoga, Psychology and Medical researchers, which is showing that Yoga Nidra can be prescribed as a preventive and curative therapy for many psycho-somatic health problems associated with stress and sleep. People suffering with tension, frustration, anger, guilt, traumas and low self-confidence can greatly enhance their well-being and outlook by practising yoga nidra.

Yoga Nidra and The Relaxation Response

Researchers have shown that Yoga Nidra is able to integrate the response of the hypothalamus, by decreasing excitatory sympathetic responses and increasing relaxing parasympathetic responses. This relaxation response is reversing the process of the 'fight-flight' response and in this way, Yoga Nidra helps to reduce the harmful effects of stress induced fight-flight responses.

In modern terms we can use the phrases like 'hypnagogic state' the state of being immediately before we fall asleep, or the 'conscious relaxation response', which is the opposite of the stress response and a state of profound rest. With regular practice, this state of deep relaxation in Yoga Nidra creates a well of calm which can be dipped into when the need arises, enabling an individual to evoke the relaxation response to reduce stress. In the state of psycho-physio-pranic rest in Yoga Nidra our metabolism slows down to where the autonomic nervous system can go through controlled balancing processes.

During Yoga Nidra this can be measured by:

❖ Frequencies and electric waves of the brain
❖ Decreased heart rate
❖ Decreased blood pressure
❖ Altered levels of stress hormones (adrenaline and cortisol) in blood circulation
❖ Deep, relaxed and rhythmic breathing
❖ Increased galvanic skin resistance (GSR) indicating lowered autonomic arousal

Many psychological studies have shown a reduced neuroticism index, enhanced concentration abilities and higher levels of mental and physical well-being as a result of yoga nidra practice. During Yoga nidra, we release healing energies inherently latent in the mind and pranic energy fields, known as Manomaya Kosha and Pranamaya Kosha.

Yoga Nidra and the Neuro-Hormonal Transformation

Yoga Nidra opposes or counters our neuro-hormonal reactivity to stress. It changes the somatic or physical response to stressful situations and enables us to respond instead of reacting. It is able to counterbalance the over active sympathetic nervous system and stress hormones released in our blood stream. The relaxation response of yoga nidra helps the organs and systems in our body to attain a deep, psycho-physiological rest and empowers our bodies powerful healing and inherent regenerative mechanism of homeostasis. This prepares our body tissues and organs to deal with stress stimuli and become less susceptible to the harmful effects of negative situations and toxicity. Yoga Nidra helps balancing our vital energies and nadis and allows the free flow of vital energies for optimum physical and mental health.

References and resources

1. Swami Satyananda Saraswati :- Talk at the First International Yoga Convention, Bihar School of Yoga, November 5, 1964, originally printed in YOGA, Vol. 3, No. 2, 1965.
2. Yoga Step By Step, by Swamiji Dr Gitananda Giriji. Ananda Ashram, Puducherry, India
3. Yoga Nidra by Swami Satyananda Saraswati, Bihara School of Yoga, India.
4. Bahrke, M.S., (1979). Exercise, meditation and anxiety reduction: a review.
5. Amer. Corr. Ther. J. Bhushan, Siddhartha & Sinha, Pammi, (2000). Yoga Nidra and Management of Anxiety and Hostility. Journal of Indian Psychology (under publication).
6. Carrington, P., Collings, G., Benson, H., (1980). The use of meditation-relaxation techniques for the management of stress in a working population.
7. J. Occup. Med., 22(4): 221-231. Cooper, M.J. & Aygen, M.M., (1979). A relaxation technique in the management of hypercholesterolemia.
8. J. Hum. Stress, pp. 24-27. Datey, K.K & Bhagat, S.J., (1977). Stress and heart disease and how to control it with biofeedback and shavasana.
9. Quart. J. Surg. Sci. (Banaras Hindu University), 13(3-4). Erskine-Milliss, J. & Schonell, M., (1981). Relaxation therapy in asthma: a critical review. Psychosom. Med., 43(4).
10. Gersten, D.J., (1978). Meditation as an adjunct to medical and psychiatric treatment.
11. Scand. J. Behav. Ther., 8(4): 119-204. Lekh Raj Bali, (1979). Long term effect of relaxation on blood pressure and anxiety levels of essential hypertensive males: a controlled study. Psychosom. Med., 41(8).
12. Mangalteertham, Sannyasi (Dr A.K. Gosh), (1998). Yoga Nidra - Altered State of Consciousness. In Swami Satyananda's Yoga Nidra. Bihar School of Yoga, Munger, 6th edition.
13. The conscious Brain by Stephen Rose; 1973, Littlehampton Book Services Ltd.

Lesson 41.
Neuroscience of Breathing and Pranayama

Our Vritti, which includes our pattern of breathing and our sectional breathing, is regulated by the medulla and the pons areas of brain. Our breathing has two parts: Involuntary and Voluntary. Involuntary respiration is the part of our breathing which is possible without the control of the voluntary nervous system, such as during sleep. Our cellular breathing and metabolic functions are also involuntary. We also have a voluntary part of our breathing which is regulated by the cortex part of brain.

According to Gallego, Nsegbe and Durand (2001) the differentiation between voluntary and automatic metabolic breathing is that automatic breathing requires no attention to maintain, whereas voluntary breathing involves a person directing a given amount of focus. Ritz and Roth (2003) found that breathing techniques and patterns that are regularly advocated for relaxation, stress management and control of psycho-physiological states to improve organ function.

Yogis and Pranayama masters have realised the connection of our breathing with our mind and brain thousands of years ago. Many yoga scriptures explain that to calm, quieten and refine our minds and thoughts (chitta-vrittis), we need to change our breath into a deep, rhythmic pattern. In order to maintain equanimity or balance of mind and emotions, which is associated with our sympathetic and parasympathetic responses, we need to maintain and follow rhythmic breathing patterns. The Hatha Yoga Pradipika mentions that to activate the relaxation response and stimulate the parasympathetic nervous system, the practice of the gentle retention of breath known as khumkhaka should be practiced: a typical example of this kind of Pranayama is the Savitri Pranayama.

Involuntary Respiratory Centres in the Brain
The respiratory centre is located in the medulla oblongata, which connects the brain stem and the spinal cord; medullary respiratory rhythm generators are modulated from various sites in the lower brain stem and are output as motor activities through the brain stem and spinal cord. Involuntary respiration is controlled by these respiratory centres of the upper brainstem, which is part of our lower brain along with the cerebellum which has a role in the co-ordination of autonomic respiratory actions particularly under situations of respiratory challenge. This part

of brain also regulates other involuntary functions like cardiovascular activities and movements of involuntary muscles.

According to Willmore and Costil (2004) the respiratory centre knows how to control the breathing rate and depth from the amount or percentage of carbon dioxide, oxygen and acidosis in the arterial blood. The respiratory centres in the brain contain chemoreceptors that can detect the pH levels in the blood and return signals to adjust the rate, rhythm, depth and ventilation rates of breathing: this changes the acidity in the blood by increasing or decreasing carbon dioxide in the blood. Carbon dioxide is linked to levels of hydrogen ions in blood.

The amount of carbon dioxide increases and decreases depending on our metabolic rate and the physical activities that we are performing. For example if you are performing Surya Namaskars or a vigorous Hatha Yoga Vinyasa, the metabolic rates increases to fulfil the energy needs of muscles, which increases carbon dioxide levels in blood. This alerts the chemoreceptors to notify the respiratory centres in the brain to increase the rate and depth of breathing. At the end of your practice, when you return back to relaxed state, your breathing rate and depth return back to normal as the carbon dioxide levels drop and the breathing rate will be restored back to normal levels and the respiratory centre is relaxed.

According to Gallego, Nsegbe and Duranda (2001) this arterial pressure regulation feedback system that the carbon dioxide, oxygen and blood acid levels provide, is referred to as the metabolic control of breathing. Yogis refers to Shunyaka, the natural cessation of breath where a Sadhaka attains state of absolute body-mind relaxation within a trance or meditation. It is said that in this state a Yogis body remains unchangeable, which can be seen as cessation of metabolic activities at a cellular level, where there is no more need for breathing. There are also peripheral chemoreceptors in some of the blood vessels that perform this function as well, which include the aortic and carotid bodies.

The Medulla

The medulla oblongata is the primary respiratory control centre. Its main function is to send signals to the muscles that control respiration to cause inspiration and expiration to happen.

The medulla has two different parts regulating respiration:
- ❖ The ventral respiratory group stimulating exhalation
- ❖ The dorsal respiratory group stimulating inhalation

The medulla also regulates our reflex actions and other non-respiratory air movements, like coughing, sneezing, swallowing, vomiting, etc.

The Pons

The other respiratory regulating centre is located underneath the medulla, known as the Pons. The main function of the pons is to regulate the rate or speed of involuntary respiration.

The pons has two main regions to play this role:
- ❖ The apneustic center, which sends signals for long and deep inspirations. It controls the intensity of breathing and is inhibited by the stretch receptors of the pulmonary muscles at the maximum depth of inspiration, or by signals from the pnuemotaxic center. It increases tidal volume.
- ❖ The pnuemotaxic center sends signals to inhibit inspiration that allows it to finely control the respiratory rate. Its signals limit the activity of the phrenic nerve and inhibit the signals of the apneustic center. It decreases tidal volume.

The apneustic and pnuemotaxic centers work against each other and together control the respiratory rate.

Voluntary Respiration or Neural Mechanisms (Cortex)

The cerebral cortex area of the brain regulates our voluntary respiration. This part of respiration is under the conscious control of our brain. This is important for functions requiring control of breathing like voice, singing, chanting, blowing etc. According to Guz, (1997) speaking, singing and playing some instruments (e.g. clarinet, flute, saxophone, trumpet, etc.) are good examples of the voluntary control of breathing and are short-lived breath interventions.

The Motor Cortex

The primary motor cortex regulates our voluntary respiration. This neural centre is responsible for initiating any voluntary muscle movement. The nerve signals are sent to the spinal cord, which further sends the signals to the muscles it controls supporting the respiration, for example the diaphragm. This neural pathway is known as the ascending respiratory pathway.

However the different parts of voluntary respiration like diaphragmatic and intercostal breathing are controlled by different parts of the cerebral cortex. The internal and external intercostal muscles (mid chest breathing), is governed by the superior portion of the primary motor cortex and within the superior part of the primary motor cortex is the governing parts for diaphragmatic breathing which is located to the posterior of the thoracic control point. The inferior part of the primary cortex is involved in regulating exhalation.

The responses or signals of voluntary respiration can be easily overridden by chemoreceptor signals from involuntary respiration. During periods of danger and emotional stress, the hypothalamus takes over respiratory function and increases the respiratory rate to support the fight or flight response.

Our breathing patterns can also be easily disrupted by fatigue or prolonged sympathetic nervous system arousal, under conditions of stress, fear, anxiety and negative emotions. One therapeutic goal of yogic breathing is to reduce or alleviate some of the chronic negative effects of stress. This is one of the reasons the breath and pranayama has been chosen as the one of the main tools by Yogis to attain stillness of body, mind and energy.

Pranayama, Breathing and Energy

Pranayama has four parts:
* ❖ Puraka (inhalation)
* ❖ Antar Kumbhaka (inner retention of breath)
* ❖ Rechaka (exhalation)
* ❖ Bahira Kumbhaka (external retention of breath)

Swamiji Dr. Gitananda Giriji in *Yoga Step By Step* explains that we can perform pranayama's of various rhythms or patterns to stimulate various parts of the brain:

we are able also to perform various Prana Mudras to stimulate these particular areas of brain and stimulate the voluntary respiration in the lower, mid and upper lobes of the lungs. These Mudras are: Chin Mudra; Chinmaya Mudra; Adi Mudra; and Mahata Yoga Mudra. Swamiji also taught us Hathenas to stimulate the voluntary muscles associated with our sectional breathing.

Dr. Ananda Balayogi Bhavanani in his extensive Yoga research as part of his medical team in JIPMAR, Puducherry, India, has found how deep rhythmic breathing through Pranayamas brings positive results for our physical, mental, emotional and spiritual health. Prana in Yoga refers to the subtle vital life energy: this energy is related to all our life functions and we receive it from the external environment. Our breathing is one of the continuous pathways to inhale this cosmic life energy and exhale stagnant energy we need to get rid of.

Dr. Ananda explains that when we inhale this cosmic potential energy in inhalation, it transforms to the kinetic vital energy governing all of our life functions. When we exhale, we exhale the individual by products of this energy out into the universe. This is a perfectly balanced interchange of energies between the macro and microcosms.

Yogic scriptures explain that the Prana or vital energy is released from the air as it enters into our bodies, this can be associated with our cellular metabolism. When we receive oxygen, it helps a healthy metabolism producing an abundance of energy required for our body and mind functions.

According to Jerath et al., (2006) although the purpose of yoga breath training is not to over-ride the body's autonomic systems, there is clear evidence that pranayama breathing techniques can positively effect oxygen consumption and metabolism. In some ways in the therapeutic approach, we can understand the aim of the Pranayamas as to balance the autonomic nervous system and inhibit the over active sympathetic excitatory dominance. The study by Jerath et al., (2006) shows that Pranayama can have positive effects on immune function, hypertension, asthma, autonomic nervous system imbalances and psychological and stress-related disorders.

Studies by Dr. Ananda Balayogi Bhavanani have also found a significant positive therapeutic role for rhythmic Pranayama practices in psychosomatic disorders. Pranayama practices positively alter the brain's information processing, experience, perception and response: in this way Pranayama helps us to transform our psychological inner profile.

The spiritual purpose of Pranayama is to increase our ability to focus our mind at a single point by refining our mind and energy. This further helps us to improve our awareness and understanding of the cognitive functions, physical functions and breathing styles described in Swara Yoga. Our Pranayama Sadhana includes the ability to focus our mind in a very relaxed manner on the flow of the breath to refine and control our respiratory movements and stimulate the respiratory centres in the brain, as in the Sadhana of Hathenas and Vubhaga Pranayama. Through enhancing the breath in deep rhythmic patterns, we can attain a calm and peaceful mind just as Lord Krishna explains in the Bhagavat Gita.

This conscious, voluntary, slow, deep, rhythmic breathing can help us in resetting the autonomic nervous system through the stretch-induced inhibitory signals and hyper-polarisation, the slowing of the electrical action potentials though the nerves currents. This can help us with synchronising the neural governing bio-chemicals regulating the heart, lungs, limbic system and cortex for their optimum functioning health.

Nerves Involved in Respiration
There are several nerves responsible for the governing of the muscular functions involved in respiration.

There are three types of important respiratory nerves:

❖   The phrenic nerves- These nerves stimulate the activity of the diaphragm. They are composed of two nerves, the right and left phrenic nerve, which pass through the right and left side of the heart respectively. They are autonomic nerves.

❖   The vagus nerve- This nerve supplies the diaphragm as well as the movements of the larynx and pharynx. It also provides parasympathetic stimulation for the heart and the digestive system. It is a major autonomic nerve.

❖   The posterior thoracic nerves- These nerves stimulate the intercostal muscles located around the pleura. They are considered to be part of a larger group of intercostal nerves that stimulate a the thoracic and abdominal regions. These are somatic nerves.

These three types of nerves continue the signal of the ascending respiratory pathway from the spinal cord to stimulate the muscles that perform the movements needed for respiration. This explains the association of Prana and breath and why Yogis chose breath as a tool for Pranayama.

Understanding Classical Pranayama and their Applications

Pranayama yoga is **the science of breath**, the control of the vital force (prana) that is present in the air that we breathe. The Sanskrit term pranayama is made from two words: 'Prana' the divine universal creative energy or power; and 'Yama' meaning control or the science of control.

The word 'prana' can be broken further as 'pra' meaning to exist independently, or to have had prior existence; and 'Ana', which is a short form of 'anna' meaning a cell, or collectively 'ana'. Thus 'prana' means 'that which existed before any atomic or cellular life came into being'. Such life is termed as the manifestation of the divine.

Behind all the manifestation of creation and life, there is this divine energy prana. Most of the prana we receive is from the air that we inhale, but we also receive it in some extant from the food that we eat and the air that surrounds us, as some part is also absorbed directly in through the skin from the atmosphere.

Remember that the prana is not the oxygen or the other gases that we inhale and also it is not the nutrients that we take from the food that we eat. The truth is that behind these things, using all these nutrients and the gases for breathing, this divine energy prana plays the role as the catalyst. Prana is absorbed through the exposed nerve endings of the body and especially in the nostrils, mouth and the back of the throat. Thus, eat slowly and masticate properly to allow the releasing and absorbing of the prana. Water should be sipped slowly to allow the absorption of prana in throat and mouth.

We must learn pranayama from the beginning to do Dirgha Pranayama, deep slow and controlled breath. Most of us nowadays are shallow breathers and lack the prana or the oxygen for the normal functioning of our body, mind and emotions. Most of the present diseases are caused because of improper breathing: all the illnesses can be elevated by practicing pranayama properly and through getting perfection in them. For a yogi breathing should be under our total awareness: this conscious breathing brings the autonomic functions under the control of the nervous system or the will.

Improper breathing, dyspnea or labored breathing is not a recent problem; but it has become more prominent now, because people are living a stressful life and in addition adverse environmental conditions are making it worse. The Yogi Gorakshanatha travelled the whole of India giving this message- "Oh men and women of India! You have defaulted from good health by being shallow breathers". He stated that people were breathing only one-eight of their capacity and he cured many diseases just by teaching the asanas and pranayama.

When we shallow breath, the nerve receptors sited deep in the lungs are unaffected. Only when we breath in and out deeply can these inspiratory and expiratory receptors get stimulated and call for their desired activity, sending reflexo-genic feed-back to the brain which governs control of the in and out breath, along with the holding in and holding out breath.

Breath is also related to our life and spirit or the soul. It is said that there is life in the body, if there is breath in the body. In Sanskrit the word Brahman is used for the breath. The taking in of the breath is termed as inspiration in Greek, which comes from 'in-spiro' meaning being in tune with the spirit or the god. While expiration originates from the 'ex-piro' meaning to be out of the spirit. In India if someone dies, it is said that prana has left the body.

The yogis performed the pranayama and found that they can fulfil their need of prana by only getting it through the air. They don't need to eat food and they are known as the 'breatharian'. Even today there are yogis in various parts of the world who are alive without food and even some are without water. So it is important that we understand the concept of prana as our vital life force, a manifestation of the energy of the entire universe.

Lesson 42.
Pranayama- is not just a breathing exercise

The yogic practice called pranayama starts by first taking firm and pleasant asana (sthirama-sukham-asanam), then turning the attention upon the inhalation and exhalation of the breath, in order to extend and refine the prana (ayama). According to Patanjali, Pranayama is an awareness/observation practice, not a mechanical wilful practice.

Firstly we need to understand that the most common mistranslation is that "pranayama is the control or regulation of the inhalation, exhalation and retention of the breath". This is what we would call 'swashayama'.

The first misinterpretation of the word, prana as breath, makes the definition redundant as well as misleading. Prana is 'life energy' and 'ayama' is expansion, thinning, rarefaction or extension: so Pranayama is the extension, spreading, thinning, refinement or expansion of energy. You can also break the word 'Yama' down differently as in 'ya' meaning to bring forth and 'ma' meaning to nurture. The definition of 'Yama' as control or regulation, reflects concepts from Hatha yoga, which believe that liberation can be attained through forcefulness and control of the body, breath and mind. The word 'control' thus reflects another assumption, similarly there are other mistranslations: 'nirodha' as control, 'tapas' as self-abnegation, 'swadhyaya' as scriptural study, or 'brahmacarya' as sexual restraint. We need to be cautious of over-simplification and misrepresentation of essential concepts.

We must learn to expand and refine the prana by observing and breaking apart the movements of the breath as it occurs in inspiration and expiration, so that it is no longer controlled by the unconscious winds of karma, thoughts, emotions, and unconscious habit, but rather it comes into the light of awareness. In this way our energy and mind changes as well as our karma.

Pranayama can be started first as the process (gati) of becoming aware of our vital energy, by breaking it down into its gross external components as manifest in the profound linkages between mind and energy, which are inherent in the breathing process. Try to inculcate and instil awareness of how energy enters our body and mind; how it leaves it; and how it becomes discontinuous or inhibited. Then we can obtain awareness of how energy is extended, refined and made more subtle, so that we can open up the nadis (the flows of the prana) and activate the body's higher potential.

Prana with a capital 'P' permeates all of the Universe, without it nothing moves, but prana with a small 'p' denotes the vital energy (prana) as it permeates the physical body. It is strongly associated with the breath as the animating principle and as the sustainer, which links creation with Infinite Source.

Indeed, breathing is the most primal activity of human life. Breath performs a bridge between the unconscious (autonomic) and conscious (central) nervous systems. In Hatha, Kundalini and Tantra yoga, pranayama is not just a powerful awareness tool, but a focused practice capable of balancing and synchronizing the autonomic and central nervous systems, also the afferent and efferent nervous systems; the sympathetic and parasympathetic nervous systems: as all polarities can be accessed through the breath. Similarly, Hatha yoga tells us that by becoming aware of and accessing the breath consciously, we can also directly access our psycho-neurological, bio-psychic pathways, nadis, matrices, energy cysts and cellular and energetic imprints, which hold the samskaras in place, thus breaking them up, breaking up past karma, kleshas and vrtti.

The various pranayama exercises of exploring the energetic processes of inhalation, exhalation and stoppage of breathing, especially in Rishiculture are given to us to achieve this awareness, observe this process and thus eventually achieve purity of body, mind and emotions, followed by karmic purification to attain liberation (from karma and vrtti). The goal is not the control of the breath; our goal is to inculcate the awareness of the subtle and eternal operations of prana shakti or kundalini shakti.

In many of the practices of Hatha yoga, Laya yoga and Prana vidya, practices to control the normal flow of the breath are given to both develop awareness and oneness. A secondary aim is to disrupt old mental patterns (vrtti) and karma, fructifying the previously dormant or energy towards spiritual evolution. There are innumerable pranayama practices through which one could investigate the affects of many types of breathing patterns upon on our energy field and thus become more aware of the breath processes (vicchedah) and also becoming more aware of and integrated with Vital Prana.

Our 'normal' subconscious habitual breathing is called karmic breathing; pranayama practice not only breaks up old karma, but burns it up to make the practitioner free from karmic bondage. Various pranayama practices using the breath, can be used for healing and propelling the practitioner beyond their past conditioning and karma altogether. Just simple breath awareness helps us to be free from the dissipations of monkey mind (Vakala) and concentrates the cit-prana. In Rishi-culture tradition pranayama practices go deeper and work faster combining, pranayama, pratyahara, dharana, mudra and asana as one integrated practice.

In simple pranayama's like the sukha-pranayama or the vibhhaga pranayama, we can simply notice the changing qualities of the breath according to how the mind becomes distracted or focused. We bring our awareness to the breath and refine and extend it, if it has become coarse or restricted. After practice this relationship between the empty and quiet mind and the breath becomes harmonious and a doorway opens into the operations of the cit-prana and the operations of the mind. Then eventually the origin of mind, the Infinite Mind, or simply the Natural Unconditioned Mind is revealed through at first the very simple method learning how to observe the breath and how it changes. Then one learns how to balance and direct the cit-prana, the mind, and the breath all at once.

Pranayama brings us into awareness of the opposites, the expansion, and the contraction of the divine pulsation of Shiva/Shakti (spanda), the movement of spirit as it inspires and the eternal dance of love through the expiratory medium of the living temple.

Bandhas

There are three Bandhas. The elaboration of the Bandhas is available in the Yogatatvopanishad and the Shandilyopanishad. Air runs towards an empty space, the detention of air from the incoming and outgoing breath on a physical level is called Bandha. But for a spiritual yoga Sadhaka, bandhas are understood to refine, control and redirect the flow of the pancha-pranas upwards into the higher chakras.

❖ *Moola-bandha*: Sit in Siddhasana, place the left heel against the perineum, the middle point in-between the anus and the genitals. Gradually place the right heel against the left, on top of the genitals. Now shrink the anal muscles and lift the Apanvayu (intestinal gas) up. This is Moola-bandha.

❖ **Jalandhara-bandha:** Sit in Sidhasana. After completing a deep Poorak (inhalation), place your chin down to your collar-bone or chest and focus at ajna-chakra, in the middle of the eye brows. This is Jalandhara-bandh. Unlock the Bandha with the Rechaka (exhalation). Perform the same Jalandhara-bandha in the Bahira-kumbhaka (breath retention).

❖ **Uddiyana-bandha:** Sit in Sidhasana. After a complete exhale or Rechaka try to squeeze your abdominal muscles towards the backbone as much as you can. This is called Uddiyana-bandha.

❖ **Mahabandha:** Performing all the three Bandhas together is known as Mahabandha. Sit in siddha-asana and exhale you breath. Now squeeze and lift the anal muscles, press the abdominal muscles towards the backbone and touch your chin down to chest firmly. Hold three bandhas together if you can hold the breath out. When you need to breathe in release all the bandhas and follow with a few deep breaths and repeat the same again.

Is Pranayama a Breathing exercise?

The answer to this is no; even though we use the breath or breathing exercises as the primary tool, Pranayama is enhancement of the quality, quantity and vibration of Prana. We use the breath as a tool in various rhythms, nostrils, lengths and sounds to tune into various biorhythms, energy flows and chakras to purify our body, mind and naris; which allows the prana to flow freely to bring lightness, health and happiness.

Why do we practice Pranayama?

Pranayama can be taken as practice for its benefits to improve breathing, enhance mental clarity, balance our energy flows, purify body-mind system, recharge the pranic body, activate or recharge chakras and bio-energy flows etc., etc. Classically Pranayama is understood as the Forth limb of Raja Yoga and is practiced to purify the body, mind and naris, to prepare for higher or internal limbs of yoga like concentration, meditation and samadhi.

Pranayama according to Ammaji Meenakshi Devi Bhavanani

Ancient Sanskrit sources proclaim that Pranayama is a 'holy science' leading to inner spiritual development. "Prana is the fundamental basis of whatever is, was, and will be" (Atharvaveda XI, IV, 10:XI, IV, 15). "Pranayama is a technique bringing under control all that relates to Prana (Vital Force)" (Vishnu Puranam, VI, VII, 40). Whatever our source, the ancient Rishis all agree that there is a vital energy called 'Prana' and that it can be controlled, 'Ayama'; the science of this control is 'Pranayama'.

Lesson 43.
The Classical Eight Pranayama

Pranayama has four parts where universal and individual prana find their connection, flow and union between each other.

These are as follows-

Sanskrit	English	Type
Puraka	Inhalation	Prana
Antar Kumbhaka	Hold in	Vidharana
Rechaka	Exhalation	Prachardana
Bahira Kumbhaka	Hold out	Apana

For advanced Sadhaka there is also fifth part known as Sunyaka where breath naturally ceases, or prana completely absorbs in its source or point of origin.

What is classical Pranayama's according to Hatha Yoga Pradipika?
The Hatha Yoga Pradipika, Chapter two details the following eight pranayama-

❖ *Sitkari*- Make a hissing sound with the mouth (while inhaling air) and exhaling only through the nostrils. Through this repeated Yoga practice one becomes a second god of beauty (Kamadeva)(v, 54). Verse 55 describes how a yogi who does this practice, becomes an object of high regard amongst the circles of Yogins; "he is able to create and destroy; neither hunger, nor thirst, somnolence or indolence arise [in him]." Verse 56 continues "By this practice, strength of body is gained and the Lord of Yogins, becomes surely free of afflictions of every kind on this earthly sphere".

❖ **Sitali Pranayama**- Protruding the tongue a little outside the lips, inhale with the tongue (curled up to resemble a bird's beak) and perform Kumbhaka as before. "Then the intelligent [practitioner] should slowly exhale the air through the nostrils" (v,57). Verse 58 explains that this Kumbhaka named Sitali destroys diseases of the abdomen and spleen and fever, biliousness, hunger, thirst, and (the bad effects of) poisons.

❖ **Bhramari Pranayama**- Breathing in rapidly with a resonance resembling the sound of a bee, exhale slowly, making the humming sound of a female bee. "By the Yoga, which consists in practicing thus, there arises an indescribable bliss in the hearts of the best amongst the Yogins" (v,68).

❖ **Bhastrika Pranayama**- "Having assumed Padmāsana properly, with the neck and abdomen in line, the intelligent [practitioner] should close the mouth and breathe out the air through the nostrils with effort, till it is felt to resound in the heart, throat and up to the skull. Then air should be inhaled rapidly till it touches the lotus of the heart (v,60-61). When the two feet are placed upon (opposite) thighs, that is the Padmāsana which destroys all ill effects (v,59). Again, he should exhale in the same manner and inhale thus again and again. Even as the blacksmith works his bellows with speed, he should with his mind, keep the Prana in his body (constantly) by moving. When tiredness is felt in the body, he should breathe in by right nostril (v,62-63). After the interior of the body is quickly filled with air, the nose should be closed tightly with the thumb, the ring finger, and the little finger (v,64). Having performed as prescribed, the breath should be exhaled through the left nostril. This removes (disorders rising from) excess of wind, bile and phlegm and increases the (digestive) fire in the body (v,65)".

❖ **Murcha Pranayama**- At the end of inhalation, very firmly assuming Jalandhara Bandha, exhale breath slowly. This is called 'Murccha' as it reduces the mind to a state of inactivity and confers happiness (v,69). "Having performed Kumbhaka with comfort, let him withdraw the mind from all objects and fix it in the space between the eyebrows. This causes fainting of mind and gives happiness. For, by this joining the Manas with the Ātma, the bliss of Yoga is certainly obtained" (Ch5, v2).

❖ **Suriya Bhedana**- Assuming an Asana on a comfortable seat, the Yogi should slowly draw the air outside through the right Nadi (Pingala) (v,48).

Then he should practice Kumbhaka, restraining the breath to the utmost till it is felt from the hair (on the head) to the ends of the nails (in the toes, that is, pervading the whole body). Then, he should slowly exhale through the left Nadi (Ida)(v.49). This excellent Surya Bhedana should again and again be practiced as it purifies the brain, destroys diseases rising from excess of wind, and cures maladies caused by worms (bacteria) (v,50). Prior to this Swatmarama Suri says generally about Pranayama in Verse. 45 that at the end of inhalation (Puraka), the Jalandhara Bandha should be practiced. At the end of Kumbhaka and at the beginning of exhalation (Rechaka), Uddiyana Bandha should be practiced.) Contracting the throat (in the Jalandhara Bandha) and the anus (in Mula Bandha) at the same time, and by drawing back the abdomen (in Uddyana Bandha) the Prana flows through Sushumna Nadi (Brahma Nadi) (v,46).

❖ *Ujjayi Pranayama*- Closing the mouth, draw in air slowly through both nostrils till the breath is felt to be sonorous from the throat to the heart (v,51). Perform Kumbhaka as before and exhale through Ida. This removes disorders in the throat caused by phlegm and stimulates digestive fire (v,52). It puts an end to the diseases of the Nadis and the Dhatus as also dropsy. Walking or standing this Ujjayi should be practiced (v,53).

❖ *Plavini*- Owing to the air, which has been abundantly drawn in, completely filing the interior, the Yogi floats easily, even in deep waters, like a lotus leaf(v,70).

Lesson 44.
Dr. Swami Gitananda Giri Ji on Pranayama

"God is breath" is the oldest Sanskrit writing. Etymologists have stated that our Sanskrit word 'Brahman' is a synonym for 'breath'. "Breath is life, life is breath." The Hebrew mystic states, "God breathed into Man the Breath of Life and he became a living Breath (Soul)". To be 'in breath' is to be 'in God'. The Greek word for the taking-up of the breath, 'in spiro' means to be 'in Spirit'. 'Ex spiro', the expelled breath, is 'to be parted from God'. The taking of breath is a holy, divine function and those who aspire to Divinity must master the Kriyas and Prakriyas of Pranayama, the Yoga of Controlled Breathing.

How in depth is Hatha Yoga Science in Gitananda Tradition according to Ammaji Meenakshi Devi?

The Eight Classical Pranayama's detailed here are considered by the Rishi Culture Ashtanga Yoga Tradition of Dr. Swami Gitananda to be relatively advanced practices, which should be taught only after basic training in proper breathing is given, especially the Hathenas, or Forcing Techniques which condition the body to deep, controlled, conscious breathing. Yoga maharishi Dr. Swami Gitananda Giri was the lineage holder of the Yoga Bengali Tantric tradition of Yoga maharishi Kanakananda Bhrigu. This tradition is part of the Dakshina Marga Tantra, which aims at the control of Shakti through an elaborately structured lifestyle, and cultivation of hundreds of Yoga techniques. In this tradition more than 375 Asanas, Kriyas, Mudras, Bandhas and cleansing practices are taught along with more than 120 Pranayamas, designed to cleanse, purify, strengthen and sensitize the body, emotions and mind; making the human-being, a fit vehicle of the Divine Spirit.

As Swamiji often said, "God breathed the Breath of Life into man, and he became a living soul". Now, it is our duty as evolving beings to guard and cherish that 'Breath of Life' as our spiritual treasure. We must deepen it, lengthen it, control it, expand it and become conscious of it and its potentiality to link us with our Highest Nature. That is the real Pranayama, the ancient spiritual Science of Vital Control."

Is there connection between mind and prana?

Yes. In the Geeta Lord Krishna states that the mind is the vehicle of prana. Thus, your awareness goes where your thoughts go. Your mind goes where your awareness goes and there goes the prana. Thus, the mind or the thoughts and emotions need the prana, or consciousness to travel in and out. Those who do mental work, at the end of the day can feel more tired in comparison of the person doing only physical work, why? Because our mental and emotional processes consume more prana than the physical process. So be careful and aware of what you think and what you feel. You need to be aware of the mental and emotional process to check and remove them.

What is success in Pranayama?

Success in pranayama is entirely dependent upon the direct experiential sensitivity to and conscious relationship with the prana and its source. After practice, one realizes that the wavelike operations of the mind (cit-vrtti) are dependent upon the operations of the prana. The vibrations of the prana are available through the vibrations in the air. By refining the air and prana and by making them highly subtle, eventually the mind opens to its vast potential. This requires a requisite amount of direct experiential sensitivity of inner wisdom. As the mind empties, as the breath empties, as the prana becomes most subtle (empty), as the mental objects dissolve, then the total purity of mind is attained and samadhi dawns as we are filled with Divine vibration (spanda).

Basic Requirements for Good Pranayama

Firstly if you have any of the breathing problems related to shallow breathing, they should be corrected. Then the environmental conditions should be also considered, for example, to be free from damp atmospheres. Proper sectional breathing should be practiced. Your yoga mat should be clean and dust free.

Your yoga room should be regularly cleaned. Never allow the dirt to be accumulated on the walls, corners and the cloths you are using. Bed covers and other clothes should be ideally of cotton.

Use of powders, fumes, scents, essences, body lotions etc. should be avoided and especially in the case you have any allergy problems. Even you may be allergic to soap, some toothpastes, or facial creams, be aware and avoid the harmful things.

These preparations should be done properly before starting your pranayama or hatha yoga practice as directed by Swamiji Gitananda below:

❖ Comb and tie up your hair properly. Loose hair may create problems in complete breathing.

❖ Clean your body before the practice with a light warm bath. Please never take too hot and to cool a bath before the hatha yoga practice.

❖ Clean, loose comfortable clothes should be preferred if possible. Tight clothes, undergarments, jewelry, belts, etc. should be avoided.

❖ After the yoga practice a cool shower should be taken. This will strengthen the body's tolerance power to cold air and water.

❖ Keep your mat properly folded and covered with cotton cloths to avoid the damp and dust (more so in India).

❖ Your area of practicing yoga should be a well ventilated, open a window, air ventilation should be maintained.

❖ Do all the practices at least three hours after eating food. All practices should be done with an empty stomach. A light tea, or limewater can be taken. Avoid all the mucus producing foods. If there is any desire to empty the bowel or urine, do so, at the priority.

This lesson by Dr. Swami Gitananda Giri Ji on Pranayama, takes us back to fundamental and practical considerations. We are reminded that the mind is the vehicle of prana; our awareness goes where our thoughts go and this requires the development of our awareness.

Lesson 45.
Classical Pranayama Abhyasa or Sadhana and Applications

In this lesson we will explore important pranayama, which can be used with our chikitsaks. We are reminded that these practices benefit us through: improving our breathing; enhancing mental clarity; balancing our energy flows; purifying our body-mind systems; recharging the pranic body; and activating or recharging chakras and bio-energy flows.

Pranayama Mudra

These are the mudra we use in our Classical Pranayama Abhyasa or Sadhana and Applications-

- ❖ *Vishnu mudra*- For this mudra, place your right palm in front of the nose. Now place the middle finger in the middle of the eyebrows, ajna chakra. Keep the index finger at the right nostril and ring finger at the left nostril. Thumb and the small finger should be straight and free.
- ❖ *Jnana mudra*- Touch the tips of the thumb and the index finger and make a good circle. Remaining three fingers should be straight. Place your hands on the knees. This is known as the jnana mudra.
- ❖ *Nasagra mudra*- Place the first and the second fingers of the right hand are bent down at the knuckles. The knuckles are placed against the root nerve where the nose joins the face. The thumb is then used to close the right nostril and the third and forth fingers are used to close the left nostril.

Anu-nasika pranayama (Gitananda Tradition)

This is the cleansing pranayama for the whole nasal cavity, ear, eye, face and head. All of the mucus and cough trapped in the respiratory system is thrown out by the practice of the anu-nasika pranayama. In this pranayama the breath is thrown out very vigorously through the nose. This cleans out all the toxins accumulated in the facial muscles. This is extremely good for sinus problems, asthma, nasal blockages, respiratory allergies, eye and ear problems etc. It should be practiced for six days continuously for the desired results. In one breath cycle you could practice three, six, or the nine strokes of throwing the breath out through the nose. Starting with the one cycle on the day first you have to increase the one cycle each day. You may practice once, twice or thrice in day, for example morning, afternoon and evening.

- ❖ *Sit straight in vajrasana*. Place right hand in Vishnu mudra and left in Jnana mudra below the navel.

- ❖ **Step-I**. Inhale deeply through both the nostrils. Exhale rapidly through both the nostrils while exerting the inner nostrils and throat with stroking the diaphragm. Do three, or six strokes in one breath. Repeat this for three times.
- ❖ **Step-II**. Close your left nostril and inhale deeply through the right nostril. Do the same number of strokes of rapid exhalation through the right nostril. Repeat this for three times.
- ❖ **Step-III**. Close your right nostril and inhale deeply through the left nostril. Do the same number of strokes of rapid exhalation through the left nostril. Repeat this for three times.

This is a complete cycle of the anu-nasika pranayama. Starting with one cycle on the first day, you have to increase by one cycle each day and on the sixth and final day you have to do six cycles of the anu-nasika pranayama. Swamiji suggested six strokes in one breath, but I would like to suggest you to do three strokes per breath. Six strokes may become too strenuous for you on the sixth day especially when we are using these pranayamas as yoga therapy tools.

Note: If you are suffering with blocked nostrils, or sinus, wait until your nostrils are clear.

Advisory: Jala and Sutra Neti are advisory practices before Anunasika Pranayama.

The benefits of this practice include-
- ❖ Clearing nostrils
- ❖ Benefits in mitigating sinus problems, migraine, hay fever and nasal allergies
- ❖ Balancing nadis and removes Vata Dosha
- ❖ Purifies respiration and blood
- ❖ Energy enhancer and nervous system rejuvenation

Anuloma Viloma Pranayama
'Anu' means atom or subtle. In our Gitananda Tradition, all living beings are explained as having polarity. Our right side is associated with Loma, Sun, Solar or positive energy and the left side is associated with Viloma, Lunar, Moon, or negative energy.

Our right nostril is associated with the Pingala Nadi, the left brain and the right side of the body or Loma- Solar energy. Our left nostril is associated with the Ida

Nadi and the right brain, the left side of the body and Lunar energy. Our breath and energy cycles change every few hours according to our bio-rhythms, as well as our physical, mental and emotional states. Our right nostril or Loma breathing activates fire, active energy and sympathetic response, while the left nostril or Viloma breathing activates cooling, relaxing energy and parasympathetic response. Due to Dosha imbalances, toxicity, health issues, stress and unhealthy lifestyles; our nadis and subtle energy flow is disharmonised.

The Anuloma-Viloma Pranayama can help balance our Doshas, balance our Nadis, and energy flow, enhancing our polarity and general health and well-being-
   ❖ Sit comfortably and straight in one of the meditation posture with your spine erect
   ❖ Use your right hand in one of the Pranayama Mudra to control your breathing pattern in Nasagra or Vishnu Mudra
   ❖ Exhale through both your nostrils
   ❖ Close your left nostril and inhale through the right nostril
   ❖ Close your right nostril and exhale through the left nostril
   ❖ Close your right nostril and inhale through the left nostril
   ❖ Close your left nostril and exhale through the right nostril
   ❖ This makes one round of Anuloma-Viloma Pranayama
   ❖ Follow nine rounds of this pranayama with Sama-Vritti like 4x4, or 6x6
The health benefits of this practice include:
   ❖ It helps in balancing the three doshas in our body
   ❖ Brain cells are revived, and neuroplasticity is enhanced
   ❖ Relaxes and rejuvenates facial muscles
   ❖ Balances and strengthens the autonomic nervous system
   ❖ Removes drowsiness
   ❖ Removes toxic air from lungs and improves breathing.
   ❖ Purifies the blood and strengthens the heart
   ❖ Tones digestive system
   ❖ Prepares mind for meditation.

Nadi Sodhana Pranayama
The Nadi Sodhana Pranayama is practiced to purify our blocked Nadis, the subtle energy channels. Nadi Sodhana Pranayama is a highly recommended pranayama for people suffering with energy depletion, nervous exhaustion, imbalanced doshas and for removing old accumulated traumas and negative memories. People with

heart and breathing disorders or epilepsy should begin with Sukha Pranayama and Anuloma Viloma Pranayama for few months before trying the Nadi Sodhana Pranayama.

- ❖ Sit comfortably and straight in one of the meditation postures with your spine erect
- ❖ Use your right hand in one of the Pranayama Mudra to control your breathing pattern in Nasagra or Vishnu Mudra
- ❖ Exhale through both your nostrils
- ❖ Close your left nostril and inhale through the right nostril and hold your breath in (atar-kumbhaka)
- ❖ Close your right nostril and exhale through the left nostril and hold your breath out (bahir kumbhaka)
- ❖ Close your right nostril and inhale through the left nostril and practice antar kumbhaka
- ❖ Close your left nostril and exhale through the right nostril and practice bahira kumbhaka
- ❖ This makes one round of Anuloma-Viloma Pranayama.
- ❖ Follow nine rounds of this pranayama with Savitri (2x1x2x1) or Visama Vritt. (2x4x2x4) ratio.
- ❖ Use of Bandhas is advisable for full benefits of Nadi Suddhi Pranayama.

Note- In the Gitananda Tradition, Swamiji guides us through more advance Nadi Suddha and Nadi Suddhi Pranayama.

Seetkari Pranayama

The word "seetkari" means 'cooling'; in this Pranayama sadhana we produce the sound 'seeee'.

- ❖ Sit comfortably and straight in one of the meditation posture with erect spine
- ❖ Follow few rounds of Savitri Pranayama
- ❖ Join your upper and lower teeth together, keep the tongue gently touching behind the teeth with keepings your lips apart
- ❖ Inhale slowly through the gap between your teeth as if you sipping your breath in with hiss sound
- ❖ At the end of inhalation, hold your breath in with holding Jalandhara and Moolabandha as long as it is comfortable
- ❖ Release your Bandhas and exhale through both nostrils gently with producing the hang sound. Hold your breath out with retaining Mahabandha
- ❖ You can follow Sama-Vritti rhythm of 4x4x4x4, 6x6x6x6 or higher rhythms.
- ❖ Follow 9 rounds of this Pranayama

Sheetali Pranayama

The word Sheetali means 'the cooling one'. The technique is very similar to the Seetkari pranayama.

- ❖ Sit comfortably and straight in one of the meditation posture with an erect spine
- ❖ Follow a few rounds of Savitri Pranayama
- ❖ Bring your tongue out and make a tube shape or peak of your tongue
- ❖ Inhale slowly through the tube of your tongue as if you are sipping the breath in
- ❖ At the end of inhalation, hold your breath in with holding Jalandhara and Moolabandha as long as it is comfortable
- ❖ Release your Bandhas and exhale through both nostrils gently. Hold your breath out with retaining Mahabandha
- ❖ You can follow Sama-Vritti rhythm of 4x4x4x4, 6x6x6x6 or higher rhythms
- ❖ Follow 9 rounds of this Pranayama

The health benefits of these pranayama include-

- ❖ Both Sheetali and Seetkari are effective in cooling the system down and hence great for people suffering with excess of Pitta Dosha
- ❖ Help healing ulcers and acidity problems
- ❖ These two Pranayama can help calm the nerves down and also help calm the mind
- ❖ Helps deal with stress more effectively
- ❖ Lowers blood pressure
- ❖ Lower body temperature
- ❖ Improves sleep and help dealing with insomnia.
- ❖ Develops Mental calmness and enables us to deal better with anger and anxiety.

Note- These two pranayamas are cooling practices and hence should be avoided in the cold winter months.

In this lesson we have been given detailed instructions for the practices of the classical Pranayama Abhyasa or Sadhana and their applications for yoga chikitsaks. These practices are important ones for us as Yoga Therapists as they are able to help with the balance of our doshas and energy systems.

Lesson 46.
Vasanas – Past Impressions and Deep-Rooted Desires

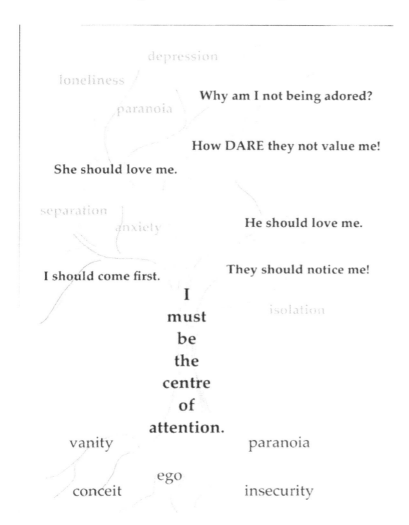

Vasana is a Sanskrit term that refers to a past impression in the mind that influences behaviour. Vasanas can be good or bad. A vasana is our habitual or automatic response to situations. Vasana can be understood as ingrained patterns of behaviour and deep-rooted seeds of desires, thoughts and individual viewpoints or Drishti. Vasana can also mean a desire for or expectation of something or knowledge derived from memory.

Vasanas are of four kinds:

- ❖ **Pure** (Suddha)- desires towards health, happiness, peace, harmony with holistic means
- ❖ **Impure** (Malina)- desires for mundane pleasures by wrong means
- ❖ **Mixed** (Madhya)- mix of above two
- ❖ **Good** (Sat)- desires towards higher or pure bliss

The Jnanis are also of four kinds:

- ❖ **The Supreme** (varishtha)
- ❖ **The Best** (variya)
- ❖ **Better** (vara)
- ❖ **Good** (vit)

Their fruits are reaped in three ways: of our own will (swechha); by others' will (parechha); involuntarily (anichha).

According to the Vivek-Chudamani (composed by Adi Sankaracharya), the endless vasanas remain strong even after a person has acquired wisdom or Jnana from the scriptures and by reasoning (Viveka). The true wisdom and experience is that he is not the five sheaths (pancha-koshas) and is identical or ONE with Brahman. These Vasanas make us the victim and enjoyer and are the cause of all unhealthy changes and movements.

These have to be removed by Sadhana of Pratyahara (withdrawing the senses and mind away from the external objects and subjects of sensory experiences) and focussing the mind on Brahman or Supreme Consciousness.

Many Sages have mentioned that elimination of the vasanas is Kaivalya or liberation. A Jnani or wise person should develop dissociation with the notions of: 'I' and 'Mine'; the body; the senses; and mundane desires, by keeping the mind focussed on the 'Real Self' or 'Atman' which not subject to any change. Becoming one with the innermost, subtlest eternal or Real Self (Purusha), which is the witnessing awareness of the intellect (buddhi) in the form of 'I am Brahman' and remaining free of associations with 'I-ness' (Asmita) in the worldly self. We are to be free from all the material desires and only study, watch, listen and take part in activities useful in attaining liberation.

Viveka-Chudamani in the Upanishad mentions about liberation from 'loka-anuvartanam, deha-anuvartanam and sastra-anuvartanam'. These three are reffered as Loka-Vasanas, Deha-Vasana and Sastra-Vasana.

Impure Vasana are of three kinds:

- ❖ Desires for the worldly pleasures (loka vasana)
- ❖ Desires for our body and senses (deha vasana)
- ❖ Obsession with learning (sastra vasana)

The meaning of Loka Vasana is around getting praised, approved of and noticed by others; which can build a huge pressure and is not always easy to attain. We have peer pressure, family pressure, work pressure and social pressure, which are one of the major causes of stress in our life. As we all are social beings it is not easy to escape these Loka Vasanas. Even the greatest of warriors like Arjuna had his delusion around what people will think of him if he either takes part in the war or if he doesn't take part in the war. Speaking ill off others or taking part in such gossip adds fuel to our worldly vasanas.

We all judge each other based on our life choices, work, food, religious beliefs etc. I have heard of people being caught in their extreme beliefs of one way or another in life. We can become caught up in proving something as part of these worldly vasanas, in order to get approval, or in the effort to prove our point, or through forcing our ideas on others: this becomes painful for our individual life as well as for the people living around us.

The pressure people put upon others, or that we let others do to us, can be seen as bullying. These worldly desires and mind sets cause division in our inner self, in our families and in society. We all need to live in harmony and acceptance within ourselves and within society. Learning to praise others and not force our ideas and beliefs on others as well mastering to 'do our best and leave the rest' can be a key practice. Also the practice of Maitri (friendliness), Karuna (compassion), Mudita (cheerfulness) and Apeksha (equanimity) are relevant here.

Sastra Vasana or the obsession to learn is of three kinds: obsession to study, study of scriptural texts and the performance of rituals can lead us away from actually living our life. It is quite an obsession in modern times of studying and learning course after course and not actually allowing the time to practice any of them. The pressure of academic grades is another one of the major causes of stress especially in our younger generation. It is recognised in yoga that sadhana or practice is more important than studying and trying to memorise things. I have known people who try to learn things word for word.

We can also be obsessed with accumulating scriptures and books and we can carry them around like a burden. Once a sage Durvasa went to see Lord Shiva with a cart-load of scriptures pulled by bulls; Sage Narada ridiculed him by comparing him to a donkey carrying a huge load on his back. Durvasa got very angry and threw all the books into the ocean. Lord Shiva then blessed him with the highest teachings on Atma Jnana (self-realisation) and Brahma Jnana (divine realisation).

People can also be obsessed with religious ceremonies and rituals. People can be obsessed with various beliefs and practices that they never find anyone good enough or any place pure enough to live in. It is also our expectations from others, situations and places, to behave in certain ways. All the vasanas, viewpoints, desires and expectation around the scriptures, knowledge, ideas, belief systems, will fall in this category. These are placed in a negative category as they cause vanity, negative judgement, anger, frustration, and guilt towards ourselves and others.

The Deha Vasanas are of three kinds: seeing the body as the Self or Atman; obsession about making the body attractive; and making it free from defects and marks. These lead us into being overly obsessive with the body, our appearance and extremes of make-up, exercise, surgical modifications and pleasure seeking activities. These are all obstacles in living our natural life and growing spiritually. There is so much pressure felt in our society about our looks, appearance and attractiveness and whether we are liked or not by other people.

These three types of Vasanas can be different for different people at different points of their lives. They can cause an immense amount of tension and pain in an individual's life. The Upanishads explains that as long as vasanas are there, knowledge and experience of the Self (Atma Jnana) cannot manifest.

The true essence, beauty and blissful illuminating light of the spirit is hidden beneath these Vasanas and Samaskaras, like the fragrance in a sandalwood-stick which remains hidden inside it. When it is burned or rubbed or the external odours are removed and its natural fragrance emerges in its full potential.

At a deeper level we all also possess the Atma-Vasana (desire to attain self-realisation). But this is buried deep beneath the worldly, knowledge and bodily mundane desires. The Loka, Sastra and Deha Vasanas are also known as Anatma-Vasanas, seeking to join in the unreal or things which are subject to change. By seeing ourselves as bundles of ever-changing processes, we can undermine anxiety and live more peaceful lives.

In Chapter 5 of the Bhagavad Gita Lord Krishna mentions that knowledge is covered by ignorance (avidya) and so all living beings are deluded under the Maya or Illusion. The Jiva or Individual soul, is identical with the Brahman or Supreme Consciousness and so this Jnana is very nature of our being. However this is obscured by our ignorance.

The Kathopanishad explains that the divine has given us the sense to go outward to live in harmony with the external environment, but we cannot experience the Real Self (Jiva or Purusha) by means of the sense organs. We need to withdraw our mind from our senses, the objects and subjects of senses and sensory information and then focus the mind on the Self (Atman) and let it become one with the Higher Self (Brahman). The more we focus our mind on positive intentions and desires, the negative vasanas and desires causing health issues, tension and pain in our life will be removed. When all the negative vasanas are removed, we attain the state of 'Sat-Chita-Ananda'.

When we are well established in our higher self, our mind also remains still, calm and peaceful. We become free from our mundane likes and dislikes. Our Vasanas are the propensity of the mind to react to the situations, by the rising of anger, frustration, guilt, jealousy and other similar emotions without any consideration of the consequences.

Vasanas can also be categorised as Tamasic, Rajasic and Sattvic. When our mind is calm and peaceful, rajasic and tamasic vasanas are taken over by sattvic vasanas.

According to Lord Krishna in the Bhagavad Gita-
"*The tamasic qualities such as drowsiness and laziness are removed by rajasic qualities such as activity, transformation. The rajasic qualities are eliminated by the cultivation of sattvic vasanas or desires to attain oneness with the divine, helping others through service, etc. Ultimately one should go beyond sattva-guna by focussing the mind on Nirguna Bhraman (Formless Supreme Divine Consciousness)*".

The Three Gunas

SATTVA	RAJAS	TAMAS
Balance	Movement	Inertia
Harmony	Activity	Inactivity
Positive	Energy	Negative
Peace	Excitement	Apathy
Clarity	Passion	Dullness
Light	Desire	Dark
Creativity	Agitation	Delusion
Openness	Anxiety	Depression
Intelligence	Egotism	Ignorance

As a Yoga Therapist we can help people with finding positive, healthier and higher Vasana. As in many mind-healing practices imagery is quite an important tool. Here we like to imagine what it will be like to become 'a healthy being', or 'a happy being'. Helping people to create a positive mind-set, outlook, desires, thought process and feelings, can be a great tool for healing.

This Sadhana begins with removing the idea body being the self and distinguishing the body-mind complex from the real self. Some beautiful contemplations can help us develop this attitude:

❖ Tat tvam asi – Brahman and Atman are One
❖ Soham – I am the divine spirit
❖ Sat-Chita-Ananda – Absolute bliss is the only reality
❖ Atma-Nityam – The soul is eternal

It is like when the space or voidness inside a pot merges in the universal space or voidness as soon as we remove the lid from the pot, we also become one with the divine or higher self as soon as remove these mundane and negative vasanas. Allow your true self to dissolve in the divine self.

Like an actor discards the role after the play is over, we all need to discard these painful vasanas, experiences and memories just like the actor, to return back to our state of ease or Swasthya. We all need to dissociate from these gross experiences and desires and focus them on higher and eternal aspects of our life. What we identify with the 'I' is the experience of the ego or ahamkara. While what we experience free from asmita or I-ness arises from our witnessing awareness, which is eternal.

According to the Sruti, identification with 'I', one's own family, clan, name, place, birth and all that is related to the physical body; brings pain and suffering and is the cause of our birth and death cycle. To attain liberation, one must give up these associations.

Similarly, to become healthy, happy or free from any suffering we must let go of our associations and identification with any form of physical, mental, emotional, and spiritual issues and conflicts.

References and Resources

1. *Yoga Step By Step Course by Swamiji Dr Gitananda Giriji*
2. *Pranayama Book by Swamiji Dr Gitananda Giriji, Pranayama*
3. *Research Work by Dr Ananda Balayogi Bhavanani and his teachings as my direct Guru.*
4. *Yoga Chikitsa Book by Dr Ananda Balayogi Bhavanani*
5. *Collins, C. (1998). Yoga: Intuition, preventive medicine, and treatment. Journal of Obstetric, Gynecologic, and Neonatal Nursing, 27 (5) 563-568.*
6. *Gallego, J., Nsegbe, E. and Durand, E. (2001). Learning in respiratory control. Behavior Modification, 25 (4) 495-512.*
7. *Guz, A. (1997). Brain, breathing and breathlessness. Respiration Physiology. 109, 197-204.*
8. *Jerath, R., Edry J.W, Barnes, V.A., and Jerath, V. (2006). Physiology of long pranayamic breathing: Neural respiratory elements may provide a mechanism that explains how slow deep breathing shifts the autonomic nervous system. Medical Hypothesis, 67, 566-571.*
9. *National Center for Health Statistics. (2002). U.S. Department of Health and Human Services. Centers for Disease Control and Prevention.*
10. *http://www.cdc.gov/nchs/products/pubs/pubd/hestats/asthma/asthma.htm*
11. *Pal, G.K. Velkumary, S. and Madanmohan. (2004). Effect of short-term practice of breathing exercises on autonomic functions in normal human volunteers. Indian Journal of Medical Research, 120, 115-121.*
12. *Repich, D. (2002). Overcoming concerns about breathing. National Institute of Anxiety and Stress, Inc.*
13. *Ritz, T. and Roth, W.T. (2003). Behavioral intervention in asthma. Behavior Modification. 27 (5), 710-730.*
14. *Sovik, R. (2000). The science of breathing – The yogic view. Progress in Brain Research, 122 (Chapter 34), 491-505.*
15. *Willmore, J. and Costill, D. (2004). Physiology of Sport and Exercise (3rd Edition). Champaign: Human Kinetics.*

DESIRE

HEALTHY   **UNHEALTHY**

HEALTHY DESIRE IS FOR the BELOVED

UNHEALTHY DESIRE IS FOR ME

FOR WHO? (AND FOR WHOSE BENEFIT?)

Healthy desire sees, with great clarity, appreciation — even reverence and devotion — what (or who) it desires. It upholds, uplifts, and benefits the beloved in many ways. It steals nothing from the beloved, but passionately works to give to the beloved. This is the heart's way.

Desire is unhealthy when we desire from a selfish, separate point of view — focusing on our own interests and pleasures to the exclusion of others. "I'll pursue what I want. And if my gain means their loss, that's okay." That ignores the heart's desire to help, heal, uplift, to create closeness & harmony.

DESIRE FOR A FRIEND OR A LOVER

It's healthy to want a person for who they are in their wholeness. That alone feeds and strengthens them, and makes them feel truly desirable. When you see someone for who they are, you naturally want them. And you're moved to love and support them *in their entirety*. That's healthy desire; it's for *them*, not you.

From a separate, selfish point of view, you think of your friends or lovers as "for me, to fill my needs." You may appreciate their beautiful qualities, but only insomuch as you can *have* them. Just wanting what you want, you don't honor the tree that produces fruits for you. ("You don't want me, Harold, you just want my _____!")

TO ADD TO ONESELF OR BECOME SOMETHING

The heart of humanity is driven to create happiness for others. That moves us to develop skills and create things that bring joy, delight, pleasure, relief, comfort, healing. That's the healthy form of desire for self-improvement.

Unhealthy desire pursues skills and objects in a selfish spirit: "This will add to me. This will impress me. It will make me somebody. It will help me get what I want." It's not to serve others, just to serve oneself.

Strong, healthy desire is our natural response to seeing and loving the beauty of those around us. Moved by love, we want each other, and give freely of ourselves. God made us that way.

Unhealthy desire fades when we feel guilty for desiring too selfishly. Desire is weak when the object of desire is of relatively little value to the spirit. Desire is crippled if we are conflicted because we don't WANT to desire as much as we do.

HEALTHY DESIRE FILLS the ONE WHO DESIRES

UNHEALTHY DESIRE EXTENDS LACK

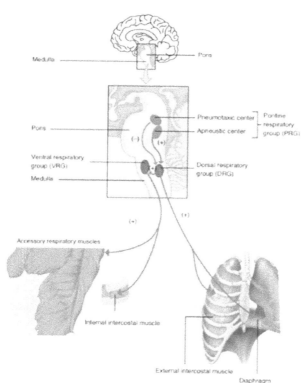

Medulla — Pons

Pons

Pneumotaxic center — Pontine respiratory group (PRG)
Apneustic center

(–) (+)

Ventral respiratory group (VRG)
Medulla

Dorsal respiratory group (DRG)

(+) (+)

Accessory respiratory muscles

Internal intercostal muscle

External intercostal muscle
Diaphragm

Lesson 47.
Understanding Health and Evolutionary Concept of Karma, Samaskaras and Epigenetics

Yoga is a path, an end goal, a set of Kriyas and Prakriyas, a concept and application based on Abhyasa and Vairajna for attaining out true or highest potential, our Swasthya or state of self-realisation, of being at ease with the self. When we understand the concept of Karma and how Samaskaras (can be associated with epigenetics); we can learn how to evolve from lower or negative karma and samaskaras to the higher or conscious karma and gradually transcend the Karma and Sanaskaras to attain Kaivalya or Absolute Liberation. This is one of the fundamental principles and goals of Yoga. In this Satsanga, Yogachariya Jnandev will try to discuss some of these living yoga principles.

When we consider Epigenetics, we need to firstly understand the genes:

❖ Cells are fundamental working units of every human being. All the instructions required to direct their activities are contained within the chemical deoxyribonucleic acid, also known as DNA.

❖ DNA from humans is made up of approximately 3 billion nucleotide bases. There are four fundamental types of bases that comprise DNA: adenine; cytosine; guanine; and thymine.

❖ The sequence or order of the bases is what determines our life instructions. Interestingly enough our DNA sequence is mostly similar to that of a chimpanzee. Only a fraction of distinctively different sequences makes us human.

❖ Within the 3 billion bases, there are about 20,000 genes. Genes are specific sequences of bases that provide instructions on how to make important proteins – complex molecules that trigger various biological actions to carry out life functions.

❖ DNA gives the instructions for various functional proteins to be produced inside the cells, this process is the central dogma of molecular biology known as genetics.

Epigenetics

❖ Epigenetics affects how our genes are read by cells and subsequently whether the cells should produce relevant proteins.

❖ Epigenetics Controls Genes. This is achieved through- (a) nature: epigenetics is what determines a cell's specialization (e.g., skin cell, blood cell, hair cell, liver cells, etc.) as a foetus develops into a baby through gene expression (active) or silencing (dormant) and (b) nurture: environmental stimuli can also cause genes to be turned off or turned on.

❖ Epigenetics is everywhere and in everything. What we eat, where we live, who we interact with, when we sleep, how we exercise and all of this eventually causes chemical modifications around the genes and turn those genes on and off. Various illness will switch the genes opposite to healthy state.

❖ Epigenetics makes us unique. Even though we are all human, we all are individuals in colour, body, build, hair, speech, etc. Some of us are more social than others, or more talkative than others. The various combinations of genes that are turned on and off makes us all unique.

❖ Epigenetics is reversible. We all are unique with various combinations of genes being turned on or off. By knowing the possible arrangements and making all necessary changes, we can reverse the epigenetics and cure many health issues and transform our life.

Tri-Gunas, Creation, Nature and Human Life

According to Yoga and other Vedic teachings, the entire universe is composed of the three Gunas: Sattwa; Rajas; and Tamas. These three Gunas are all pervading and permeating in varying degrees. Each and every individual is seeking for health, happiness and self-satisfaction in their own ways, means and goals depending on their individual Guna ratios and Doshas or their constitution.

The three gunas are Sattwa (purity), Rajas (action) and Tamas (inertia). Each life has four-purusharthas or human goals

❖ Dharma: righteous living
❖ Artha: Material fulfilment
❖ Kama: Sensual desires and procreation
❖ Moksha: Spiritual realisation.

A Sattwic person is primarily inclined towards Dharma, while a Rajasic and Tamasic persons are inclined towards Artha (the pursuit of wealth or material advantage) and Kama (desire, longing and pleasure). However as Yogis, we desire to transcend the Gunas and follow the path to liberation or Moksha. A Sattwic person follows the path of Dharma and seeks for happiness in service, compassion and harmony in life. They follow the social law and order and are in harmony with nature. They accumulate good Karma and enjoy health and peace in life.

Rajasic people are highly energetic and pursue down to earth policies and follow the goals of Artha and Kama. Wealth and power brings happiness to them and goals are more important compared to the means. They carry fear of losing their possessions, wealth and power.

Tamasic people are short sighted as the Tamas or inertia veils the intellect. Their happiness lies in sensual gratification. Food, drinks, tactile stimulus, attractive visual objects and sensory fulfilment brings gratification to them. They can easily fall prey to depression, dullness, laziness, sloth and loneliness.

In the fourteenth chapter of the Bhagavad Gita, Lord Krishna explains that:

❖ **Sattwa** is pure, without impurities, illuminating and free from sickness. It binds the soul through attachment with happiness (Ananda) and knowledge (Jnana) (14.6).

❖ **Rajas** is full of passion (ragatmakam) and is born out of "thrishna" (thirst or intense desire) and "sanga" (attachment). It binds the soul through attachment with action (14.7).

❖ **Tamas** is the darkness and the coarseness in man. It is "ajnanajam" (born of ignorance) and "mohanam" (the cause of delusion). It binds the soul through recklessness, indolence and sleep (14.8).

Yogis seek to follow the path of conscious evolutionary living to attain self-realisation and transcend the tri-gunas altogether to attain liberation from the life cycle of birth and death. The Gunas are the primary qualities and the root cause of our ever changing or evolving universe and life. Our Atma or Soul is eternally permanent and is non-changing in nature. Yoga explains that our Samaskaras and Karma determines the ratio of the Gunas in each individual and these can be changed or transcended at any point in life. At a deep state of meditation and Samadhi, these three Gunas reach a state of equilibrium. This is state known as 'Niroddha' and lord Krishna in the Bhagavat Gita refers this state as 'Gunateeta' (free from Gunas). This is the absolute state of health (swasthya), love and bliss (Sat-chita-ananda).

This concept of Tri-Gunas and its various combinations, explains how each and everyone of us, as well as all forms of living beings and non-living materials, carry individual qualities similar to epigenetics in modern medical language. It is stated in the Vedanta that as our state of mind changes, our reality, experience and biology changes too. Our combination of Gunas, genetic codes and epigenetics may be determined by our Karma and Samaskaras, as it is explained in Yoga, the Upanishads and Vedas.

The Meaning & Significance of Karma

Karma is a Sanskrit word originated from the root 'Kri', which means 'to do' or 'to make' or more simply 'action'. In generally we mostly refer Karma as the infinite chain of actions, reactions and fruits, which are performed and experienced by each of one of us. The Vedas, Upanishads and Yoga Texts explain that all our life events are derived from our past actions and choices keeping us in the cycle of birth and death.

Our Karma further refers to the actions as the seeds we have sown or performed in the past (including our past lives) and also those actions we are continuously performing, which are the cause of the fruits we are reaping in current situations. These Karmas can be seen as our Karmic Burden or Karmic Baggage or Karmic Blessings, depending on their nature and intention as positive or negative actions.

Lord Krishna in the Bhagavat Gita explains that all our actions and choices, either physical, emotional or mental and every movement that we are taking part in or not taking part in, at the gross plane (Sthoolam) or on the astral planes (Sookshma) including our eating or not eating, sleeping or not sleeping, walking or not walking, talking or not talking, working or not working, thinking or not thinking, etc., are all classified as Karma producing energy changes or a Seed (Bija).

Lord Krishna further explains that all these Karmic Bija (seeds) that we are sowing out of desire, aversion, love, hatred, happiness or sadness, will undoubtedly go on to produce fruits or consequences at an appropriate time. The Vedas explain that, our 'I' ness' consists of desires, our 'will' consists of desires and deeds and our karma consists of both our desires and our will. Whatever deed that 'I' performs, that 'I' will reap. Just to be clear here, our Karma is not our fate or destiny. Unlike our fate and destiny, Karma can be changed and we have full control on our Karma and Choices.

The Four Types of Karma

* *Sanchita Karma*- The sum total Karma or accumulated actions, Sanchita Karma is the accumulation of Karma as 'seeds' from present and previous lifetimes, which is waiting yet to fruit. This is our total cosmic Karmic debt or credit depending on the nature of the Karma that we have taken part in. These Karmic seeds are waiting for the perfect opportunity to fructify. This Sanchita Karma is the root cause of our endless life cycles.
* *Praarabdha Karma*- The Fructifying Karma or Karmic Seeds set in motion. This is part of the accumulated (Sanchita) Karma fruiting in our present life, which has full influence on our present incarnation. We visualise this part of Karma as a template of our present life path and experiences we need to work through. Our birth, place, family, culture, time, situation, health, etc. are determined by our Praarabdha Karma. This explains how we chose to be born with certain genetic and epigenetic codes, Gunas and Doshas in our present life.
* *Kriyamana Karma*- The Instant, Current Karma or Being Done Here and Now, Kriyamana Karma includes all our on-going actions and choices with their instant fruit. Think of all your actions and choices where you experience the fruits of your actions and you are able to recognise, when you planted the seed or have taken the action. Some of these also contribute to our future Karma and later on may change into Sanchita Karma. You can think of getting caught in breaking a law, getting a parking ticket or a speeding ticket, feeling full of energy after a healthy meal or a good sleep, gaining flexibility and health as you follow a regular Hatha Yoga practice. Kriyaman Karma is sub-categorised in two types: firstly Arabdha Karma, the Karma that has literally

began, is being undertaken and is 'sprouting' in present times, for example when you have completed a task and are being rewarded for what you have done. Secondly Anarabdha Karma, Karma that is not commenced and it is in dormant or seed form also known as Sabija Karma, for example if you have completed your task in a work situation, but your manager has neglected to notice you and has not credited you for some reason.

❖ *Aagami Karma*- Our Future Karma, Aagami Karma is the future Karmic Map that we are going face due to the outcomes of present and previous Karmas. These are the accumulation of our present Karma projected into our Sanchita Karma. If we fail to work these Karmas out, they change into Sabija or Seed Karma and wait for the opportunity to come in motion or fruition.

Samaskaras

The word Samaskara comes from two Sanskrita roots: Sam (complete or joined together) and Kara (action, cause, doing). Literally Samaskaras can be understood as the habitual patterns and mental and emotional impressions that we all play over and over again without even knowing it. These deep-imprinted mental impressions are the accumulation of our experiences, traumas, emotions and perceptions. The Samaskaras can be positive or negative, based on their nature and experience.

Each action we perform, deposits a subtle impression in our mind-field. Each time we repeat the same physical, mental or emotional action of process, the impression becomes stronger and becomes a habit. The stronger the habits are, the less mastery we have over our mind and our choices. Our thoughts, speech, and actions can be ruled by habits and they affect our biology. When these habits become so strong that they affect our thought processes and perceptions, they are known as Samaskaras. These Samaskaras govern our physical, mental, emotional and spiritual life patterns. At this point we don't even know when or how we make so many of the life choices; we make them unknowingly. These Samaskaras now become the determining factors of our health, perceptions and personality.

The Samaskaras also influence our experiences and perceptions of external life events and are the root cause of all our karmic choices and actions. Yoga advocates wiping out these old Samaskaras and developing mindfulness and total awareness. Samkhya explains that our sense organs (Indriyas) are sending sensory information to our brain, where it is analysed by our Chitta or mind; based on our Samaskaras and ego this leads us all to have our individual perception. This is one of the causes of our Chitta-Vrittis (whirlpools of the mind).

Our Samaskaras can be positive or negative depending on their nature. To understand the role of Samaskaras in our birth, health, colour, cast, family, etc., we can classify Samaskaras in following categories:

- ❖ *Vyaktigat Samaskara* – Individual mental impressions
- ❖ *Vansha Samaskaras* – Collective family mental impressions
- ❖ *Samajik Samaskaras* – Collective social mental impressions
- ❖ *Desha Samaskaras* – Collective country or place of birth mental Impressions
- ❖ *Adhyatmic Samaskaras* – Collective mental impressions seeking for self-realisation

How to Transform and Evolve Karma, Samaskaras and Epigenetics?

The Yogic Journey of health and well-being begins with living mindfully and developing awareness of our Samaskaras and replacing the negative one's with positive ones. This practice is known as 'Swadhyaya' or introspection. In brief the ultimate goal of yoga is to liberate the self from ever binding Samaskaras and Karmas. This is a process of learning to avoid the miseries of sufferings yet to come (Heyam duhkham anagatam). Here are the steps we can follow to regain our health and wellness at subtlest of our karma, samaskaras and gunas at the genetic and epigenetic levels.

- ❖ **Sankapa:** This literally means 'intention'. As a sadhana, sankalpa is a thought, a prayer, a determination of our mind and heart, by the individual for itself. It is the desire and determination to transform our own health and wellness.
- ❖ **Tapas:** This is the intensity and dedication in which we follow the path and practices to bring transformation. Swawiji Dr. Gitananda Giriji explains this as "regularity, repetition and rhythm". Tapas may include regular Hatha Yoga: pranayama; meditation; healthy diet; and discipline of the body, mind and life energies.
- ❖ **Sakshi Bhava or Swadhyaya:** Our Samaskaras are subconscious processes and most of our choices and actions are done unconsciously under the influence of habits or Samaskaras. Developing Sakshi Bhava (witnessing awareness) through Swadhyaya will help to slow down this unconscious process of making choices and doing things. This will help in developing intuition and attentiveness in our actions (Karma)and thoughts (Vichara).
- ❖ **Vidya or Jnana:** This is right knowledge, which illuminates our body, mind, emotions and soul. Vidya or Jnana helps us to differentiate what is right and wrong or good and bad for us. It will help us in replacing negative Samaskaras

and behavioural patterns with positive or healthy Samaskaras. It gives us the ability to reason, question and seek for solutions.

❖ *Abhaya:* Abhaya means fearless. It is explained in Upanishads that fear is one of the root causes of suffering. Fear holds us captive and does not allow necessary changes to be made. Having fearlessness enables us to face the unknown and develops the ability to tolerate unpleasant situations in life like grief, anger, criticism, guilt or embarrassment. Swamiji Dr. Gitananda Giriji mentions in *Yoga Step by Step* that "fear causes constant irritation to respective cells and may lead to various health problems at cellular levels".

❖ *Darshana:* Darshana means Vision or view-points. Developing a healthy spiritual and humanistic mindset and yogic life vision is a powerful tool to remove all old Samaskaras and behavioural patterns. In mind healing techniques, the concept of imagery is one of the most powerful healing tools, which can be used to make changes at genetic and epigenetic levels. Replacing all the negative ideas, concepts and images with positive and healthy ideas and images will free us from negative energy patterns and help developing healing powers. Our healthy life philosophy and attitude is also very important.

❖ *Ahara-Vihara:* Our food and life-style is determining our body, mind and energy. Also the food we eat carries its own genetic and epigenetic codes with it and will directly influence our body, mind, Samaskaras and epigenetics. A healthy, vegetarian diet prepared with love and nurture will become healing food. Our lifestyle including our sleeping, eating, waking up, social interactions, entertainment, exercise, etc. are also major factors in the process to remove negative Samaskaras and replace them with positive or healthy ones.

❖ *Abhyasa Vairajna:* Abhyasa is the regular dedicated practice to develop healthy life patterns and our Samaskaras. So many of us actually know what we need to do to become healthy or happy, but not many of us actually follow them. Abhaysa is doing what need to be done to develop a positive mindset and healthy Samaskaras. Along with Abhyasa, Vairajna or detachment and letting go of all the unhealthy life patterns, Samaskaras and associations with pain and suffering, is equally important.

❖ *Sadhana:* Sadhana means daily Adhyatmic (spiritual) practice to attain Atma-Jnana or self-realisation. This can include Hatha Yoga, contemplation, mantra chanting, meditation and Satsanga.

Once we can understand our Gunas, Samaskaras, Karmas and Epigenetics, through Jnana, Abhyasa, Vairajna and sadhana we can unfold and live our true potential.

References and resources

Yoga Step by Step Course by Swamiji Dr Gitananda Giriji, www.icyer.com
Yoga Chikitsa by Dr Ananda Balayogi Bhavanani, www.icyer.com
What Are Samskaras and How Do They Affect Us?, Pandit Rajamani, https://yogainternational.com/article/view/what-are-samskaras-and-how-do-they-affect-us
The Yoga Sutras of Maharishi Patanjali: Simple contemplative translation of Yoga Sutras by Yogachariya Jnandev, www.yogasatsanga.org
Exploring Yoga Philosophy: 121 Authentic Yoga Lessons, by Yogachariya Jnandev, www.yogasatsanga.org
The Tripple Gunas, Sattwa, Rajas and Tamas, https://www.hinduwebsite.com/gunas.asp
Srimad Bhagavad Gita by Gita Press Gorakhapura, https://www.gitapress.org
https://www.whatisepigenetics.com/what-is-epigenetics/
https://www.nature.com/scitable/topicpage/epigenetic-influences-and-disease-895/
https://medlineplus.gov/genetics/understanding/howgeneswork/epigenome/

Lesson 48.
Chakras and Yoga Therapy

Pancha Kosha or Five Energy Bodies

Yoga and Tantra Science explains a five-body concept; 'pancha' means five and Kosha means sheath or layer. It is very important to understand this concept to understand the concepts of Chakras and Kundalini.

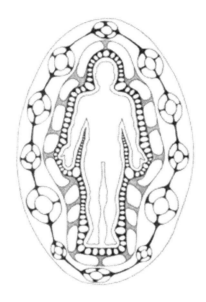

Anamaya Kosha

The Physical or Food Body: This is the first layer, made up of food and the five elements. 'Anna' means atom or food. This body is a tool or instrument for all the other bodies. It is nourished through fulfilling our biological needs of hunger, thirst and sex. This body has a vital role in our life and death processes, as well as in our evolution. We cannot experience anything in this world without this body. In the Upanishads it is stated that even the Gods have to come in human forms and have this body to experience and fulfil the duties they need to carry out. There are so many examples of incarnations of divine beings like Krishna, Buddha, Jesus, Mahavira, etc.

Hatha Yoga provides a wide range of asana, mudra, pranayama and cleansing practices to keep this body healthy, strong and full of vitality.

Pranamaya Kosha

The Subtle Energy Body: This is the second layer, composed of subtlest cosmic vital forces. 'Prana' means vital, psychic and cosmic energy. Prana literally means the energy which exists before the beginning of universe. This body has 72,000 naris or subtle energy channels. The Prana or life force governs all of our physical and psychological functions.

In yoga, Prana is described as the eternal life force, which governs all the physical, psychic and spiritual functions of the whole universe. It also carries all the knowledge, wisdom, processes and formulas of manifestation, existence and evolution of all living and non-living activities. It is like the DNA in our body, which carries all the genetic codes of our life processes.

Manomaya Kosha

The Mind Body: This is the third energy body or layer. 'Manas' means mind; this is our mind or mental body and it is comprised of all our thoughts, feelings, emotions, memories and life experiences from all the previous lives. This body is interlinked with and has a direct influence on both our physical and pranic bodies and at the same time, it is influenced by them too.

Vijnanamaya Kosha

The Intellect or Wisdom Body: This is the fourth body. 'Vijnana' means wisdom or knowledge of life and universal processes. This is the conscious body, which governs our insights, intuition, reasoning and conscience. Only through meditation and spiritual practices can we access this body; which is known as transcendental awareness or realization.

Anandamaya Kosha

The Blissful Body: 'Ananda' means joy or bliss, this is the purest of the energy bodies in the form of pure love, joyfulness and bliss. This body is in the realm of super-consciousness or the higher-self. In this body one achieves self-realization or Samadhi.

Chakras

All our Chakras exist in the subtle energy body, the Pranamaya Koska and not in our physical body. You can say that the Chakras or the energy wheels are the junctions or meeting points between our pranic body and our physical body. Our Chakras act like little dynamos or transformers to transform the cosmic or subtle prana, in to sub-pranas and pancha-vayus to govern all our psycho-physiological functions. The Pranamaya or the Subtle body is in many ways beyond scientific explanation for now. You will also need to go beyond your physical body through yoga and meditation to experience this energy body.

The Chakras are a very well known concept in the Yoga world and it fascinates most of us. There are many theories, ideas and myths and mysticism around the idea of chakras and kundalini energy. Here we are going to try to understand the basics of chakras and kundalini and their role in our personality.

To make it easier to understand if you are going on a journey, it is quite good and helpful to know the plans, routes and what to expect on that journey. The journey of meditation is the inner journey. We are going to go on an inner journey in the unknown. It is most the complex as well as the most beautiful and liberating experience. We have to go through our physical body, subtle body and chakras to reach to the goal of Samadhi or Union of Self with the Higher Self.

The first body our physical body (sthula sarira) we all know very well as we can see it, we can touch it and we can feel it. The second group of bodies known as Sukshma Sarira or subtle body is made of vital life forces (prana), our thoughts, ideas, emotions and experiences (manas or mind), our karma or deeds and soul or spirit (purusha or atman). The Pranic body is the most important to understand. All our chakras are based in this Pranic Body and they work by connecting or linking points between the pranic and the physical body.

In very simple terms, we can think of chakras like those electromagnetic dynamos, which can produce electricity if they are spun in a magnetic field. Our Chakras spin at various speeds in order to transform the subtlest prana into various forms of energy and to sustain our psycho-physio-spiritual functions.

Prana is the subtlest, vital, eternal energy. The sanskrita term prana is derived from 'pra' which means 'which existed before' and 'anu which means 'atom'. Hence, it is the subtlest electro-magnetic energy at the sub-atomic and quantum level. Great Yogis and Rishis have known about this energy for thousands of years. To protect this energy, they always recommended that a thick layer of insulation in the form of a straw bed, lion or deer skin, thick wool or jute blanket should be used for yoga and meditation sadhana. Otherwise, during your meditation practice or yoga sadhana, the energy can be drawn and lost down into the earth.

This Pranic body, just like the electric or magnetic force has positive and negative 'ions'. Yogic, Vedantic and Tantric traditions described men as dominated with positive prana and women as dominated with negative prana. Positive and Negative energies are naturally attracted to each other to complete the energy cycle. Hence men and women naturally feel attracted to each other. These positive and negative energies determine the way we behave, act, react and think. A yogi seeks to balance these energies to live in equanimity or harmony.

Swami Gitananda Giriji mentions the concept of 'Nara', which means an imbalance of Pranic bodies. In a way our physical bodies are merely a tool and even though we might be living in a male or female body, our true self will be defined by the pranic energy and its type in us. If the positive prana becomes dominant in a woman, she will behave more like a man and will naturally feel attracted to woman.

The Pranic body holds our body, mind, karma and soul together. As the soul departs or leaves the body, so does the prana. Most ancient cultures that have become aware of this pranic body, prefer to do the funerals as soon as possible after death, otherwise the prana will still feel attracted to the physical body and this will prevent the soul from moving on to next life.

The energy from the pranic body gets transformed into various life forces by the Chakras and flows outward into various physical parts of our body as well as the mental, emotional and spiritual aspects of our being. Once we start meditating, this pranic energy will start flowing back into our pranic body or its source.

In other words, these Pranic energies are transformed by our Chakras in various sub-pranas and flow in various directions from the Pranamaya Kosha into our Annamaya Kosha and Manomaya Kosha. These energies are always controlled by our senses, thoughts, feelings, life events, situations and desires. There is always one or another Chakra or sub-prana dominating the others, which causes us to think, feel, act or react in a certain way.

In our pranic body we have seven chakras. These are junction points where our major naris the Ida, Pingala and Sushumna are meeting or criss-crossing each other. If you imagine a figure of eight on top of each other, that is how it will look with a straight line through the middle of them.

When you walk around in your garden and see so many plants, flowers and vegetables, these all are growing in the same soil and environment. They get the same air, water and sun, but they are all so are different. It is so fascinating that each seed takes what it needs be able to grow. It's also so interesting to notice that each of them have their own shaped leaves, flowers or seeds. This is all written in their genetic code and so it is also the way they receive or absorb various ingredients, light, air and water.

The same applies to us human beings, even though we all have similar physical structures with bones, flesh, muscles and organs; our physical, mental, emotional and spiritual behaviours are completely different. Even the response or reaction to the same stimulus is very different between all of us. Furthermore, if you look into it further, our own behaviours, reactions, responses or action can be different when exposed to the same stimulus but in different situations, events or phases of our life. Our Chakras have a main role to play in all our psycho-physio-spiritual activities.

The first chakra is located at the base of the spine and is known as the Mooladhara, the root or foundation Chakra. This is the chakra where our kundalini rests coiled up in the form of a serpent. Our seventh chakra is known as the Sahashrara or thousand petals chakra and it is based at the top of our head or crown. All the Yogis aim to open these two chakras to attain self-realisation or Samadhi.

The other five chakras define our personality and who we truly are. They also govern various psych-physiological functions in our body and hence blockages or imbalance of any of these chakras result into physical or mental health problems associated to those chakras, hence the balance of these chakras is key to a balanced health and well-being.

Our second chakra is known as the Swadhisthana or self-dwelling place chakra. This is based around our pelvic area and it is associated with the reproductive organs and kidneys. This chakra is naturally active or awakened in most human beings as part of the natural process to reproduce life and to sustain the life processes. The energy from this chakra flows and expresses itself through sensual or sexual pleasures in a gross form. While in subtle form it expresses or fulfils life through arts and creativity.

Our third chakra is known as the Manipura or jewel city Chakra. This chakra is associated with the solar plexus, stomach, liver, pancreas and upper digestive system. This is the centre of the fire element and provides us with the necessary life forces to fulfil our karma and dharma. When this chakra is fully open we feel strong, brave and fearless while, if it is blocked, we are fearful, anxious and worried.

Our fourth chakra is the Anahata or unstruck chakra. It is associated with heart and lungs. This chakra gives us force to give and receive unconditional joy, love and happiness. When this chakra, is blocked, we feel a lack of faith or trust in ourselves or others and tend to be more self-centred. While, when it is open fully, we feel positive, confident, caring and nurturing towards ourselves as well as others.

The fifth chakra is known as the Vishuddha or purity Chakra. This chakra is associated with our throat and thyroid. This governs our general well-being and outward personality. If it is open freely we always feel positive and confident in expressing ourselves to others.

The sixth Chakra is known as the Ajna or command chakra. This chakra is associated with our pineal gland and brain. We have to train ourselves to fully activate this chakra. This chakra governs our will power and self-worth, it helps us to follow our thoughts, ideas and practices wilfully.

Activating And Balancing Chakras

Once we understand the basics of these seven chakras and the pranic body, the next step in order to begin our journey is to find out where we are now, which chakra is more active and which chakra is less active. We need to know this, as this will be the starting point of our inner journey of meditation.

The simplest food or tool to recharge or activate your chakras is our mind or awareness. If we can focus our mind on each chakra even for a few minutes every day, it will help us re-align our chakras and regain our general health and well-being. Balancing our pranic energy and chakras can truly transform our life into a more meaningful existence and benefit our true self as well as others.

All our seven chakras have their existence in our pranic body and not in our physical body, that's why a surgeon will never find them even if he operates and cuts apart the whole body. Our spine or backbone can be seen as the axis for the spinning of the chakras. We can see the chakras as the lotuses around our body from the centre of the spine, as if we are sitting in middle of each lotus.

You can choose any of the comfortable sitting postures, keeping your back straight with ease and letting your head rest in the centre. Follow at least 9 rounds of 6x3 6x3 savitri pranayama to balance your pranic energies and to relax your body and mind.

Now focus your mind in each chakra one by one, beginning from the base or root chakra. Try to visualise as if warm sun is rising in each chakra. Follow it through up to the seventh chakra.

Chakras and Healing

1. Mooladhara Chakra

This chakra is associated with all the elements in the consciousness that are concerned with security, survival and trust. This is the closest to earth and represents the earth's elements and grounding. For most of us, security is connected to our life's events, jobs, relationships, money and basic desires.

Imbalances in this chakra could cause problems in the legs, and allergies to any of the products from earth or the mothering element, i.e., allergies for dairy products, wheat and pollens as in hay fever.

When imbalanced we feel fear, we feel unstable and lack trust or faith in others and ourselves; we struggle with our own life events and find it hard to deal with day-to-day hassles.

Meditating on the chakra by visualizing the red colour helps to restore the balance. This will help us become fearless, strong and stable. You will feel that your life forces are with you and supporting you in your life events. You will start to live your life with happiness and joy without worrying about what will happen in the future.

2. Swadhisthana chakra

This chakra is associated with pleasure in general and primarily with the desires concerned with our principal biological needs. These are hunger, thirst and sex. It represents our potential forces that manifest into our day-to-day life activities. These forces in their physical form represent sensuality, reproduction, family and social values or responsibility.

Imbalances in this chakra could cause excessive cravings, indulgence or deprivation of food, and / or drink and/or sex. This also causes lack of self-esteem, self-awareness or love. It disturbs functions of kidneys, adrenal glands and gonads.

Meditating on this chakra by visualising the orange colour, restores the balance and health. When this chakra is balanced or spinning freely, we enjoy being ourselves, life becomes meaningful and our hormones are balanced.

3. Manipura Chakra

This chakra is associated with the power, control, freedom and ease with which we can be ourselves. It represents our stomach or digestive areas. When fully active or balanced, the individual is full of energy, enthusiasm and feels positive. Imbalances in this chakra could cause problems related to the digestive system, eyesight and diabetes. It causes anxieties, worries and mental instability, lethargy or inertia. Over-activeness represents ego, might cause us to be controlling, domineering and /or overpowering over other people.

Meditating on this chakra by visualizing the yellow colour restores balance and health. When this chakra is open or spinning freely, we feel free, we live in the moment and we are active and responsible.

4. Anahata Chakra

The Heart or Anahata Chakra represents our feelings, emotions and love. When it's open we feel unconditional love for others and ourselves. We live in peace and harmony.

From this chakra onwards, they key word is 'relating'. All the remaining chakras from the heart chakra upwards relate to our relationship with the world and environment. This chakra signifies us receiving, perceiving, giving and experiencing, love and affection.

Imbalances in this chakra could cause cancer and heart problems. On a mental and emotional level, when this chakra is blocked, it causes us to become dependent on others. We always feel the need of appreciation or praise by others. We become vulnerable physically, mentally and emotionally.

Meditating on this chakra through visualisations of the green colour restores its balance and health. When this chakra is open you feel love and harmony within you and with the outside world.

5. Vishuddha Chakra

This chakra is associated with the expression and reception and the manifestation of our goals. It is also associated with our voice and our ability to communicate: this expression is inner and outer. It affects how we talk, think and behave towards others and ourselves in the outer world.

Imbalances of this chakra could cause problems in the arms, thyroid, lack of confidence, inability to express or speak out when needed and issues with throat's related organs.

Meditating on the chakra by visualising the blue colour restores its balance and health. When this chakra is open we feel free to express ourselves whilst respecting others. We appreciate others and ourselves naturally without judging, comparing and manipulating.

6. Ajna Chakra

This chakra is associated with the deep inner being, the atman or the spirit. This chakra represents our intuition, instinct and wisdom.

Imbalances in this chakra could cause problems in the physical growth and in the nervous system. Imbalance and blockage of this chakra results in ignorance, dullness or bluntness in behaviour, thoughts and expressions. Lack of memory, reasoning and inability in decision making are few of the signs of a blockage in this chakra.

Meditating on the chakra by visualizing the indigo colour restores its balance and health. When this chakra is open, our intuition and instinct always guide us in our life. We find easy to make the right choice, and reasoning becomes the root of our behaviour and expression.

7. Sahasrara chakra

This chakra is associated with the part of us that is concerned with unity or separation. It represents our relationship with our Divine, Guru or teacher, parents and or authority in general.

Imbalances in this chakra could cause problems in the nervous system, self-indulgence, self-centredness or selfishness. If this chakra is blocked, we might experience muddled thoughts and emotions and lack of clarity of goals in life. We could also get carried away easily in life's situations. Morals, ethics and harmony become the last choice when it comes to following our biological desires and sensual pleasures.

Meditating on this chakra by visualizing the violet colour restores its balance and health. We feel harmony within ourselves and with the outside world. We establish our connection with the cosmic energy or wisdom. When this chakra is fully open, we have access to the cosmic wisdom and understanding of life.

Lesson 49.
The Neurophysiology of Chakras

So far we are trying to understand the concept of chakras from a yogic and tantra perspective. Now we need to explore if there is any connection between this and our modern anatomy and physiology. In this chapter we will explore the chakras and nerve plexus and the many interesting anatomical, life process and energetic associations.

Our human body and many of its functions are governed by our nervous system. Our nervous system has many nerves conveying messages to and from the brain via the spinal cord and nerve plexus. These nerve plexus or nerve bodies or ganglia, regulate major physiological functions like breathing, heart rate, digestion, elimination and sex.

We have three major types of nerves –

3 main types of nerve cells

sensory
neurone

relay
neurone

motor
neurone

- ❖ *Autonomic nerves:* These nerves control the involuntary or partially voluntary activities of our body, including heart rate, blood pressure, digestion, and temperature regulation.
- ❖ *Motor nerves:* These nerves control our movements and actions by passing information from our brain and spinal cord to our muscles.
- ❖ *Sensory nerves:* These nerves relay information from our skin and muscles back to our spinal cord and brain.

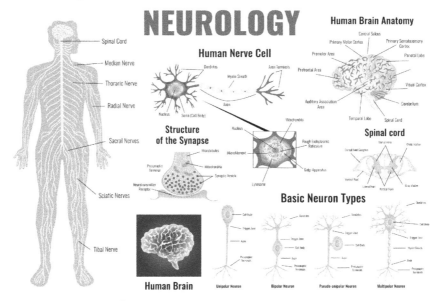

Our nervous system has two parts:

- ❖ *Central nervous system-* The central nervous system (CNS) regulates most functions of the body and mind. It consists of two parts: the brain and the spinal cord. The brain is the center of our thoughts, the processor of our sensory cognitive functions and it has control over the body's movements which are under our will.
- ❖ *The Peripheral Nervous System-* The PNS is composed of the cranial and spinal nerves and works like the wiring network of nerves. The peripheral system allows the brain and spinal cord to receive and send information to other areas of the body, which allows us to react to stimuli in our environment. This is composed of Somatic Nervous system and Autonomic nervous system.
- ❖ *The somatic nervous system-* (SNS or voluntary nervous system) is the part of the peripheral nervous system associated with the voluntary control of body movements via our skeletal muscles. The somatic nervous system consists of afferent nerves or sensory nerves and efferent nerves or motor nerves.

❖ *Autonomic nervous system*- The autonomic nervous system is a control system that governs all the functions which are not under the control of our will. This system regulates major life functions like the heart rate, digestion, respiratory rate, pupillary response, urination, and sexual arousal. This system is comprised of the sympathetic and parasympathetic nervous system and primarily controls the fight-or-flight response.

The Peripheral and the Central Nervous Systems

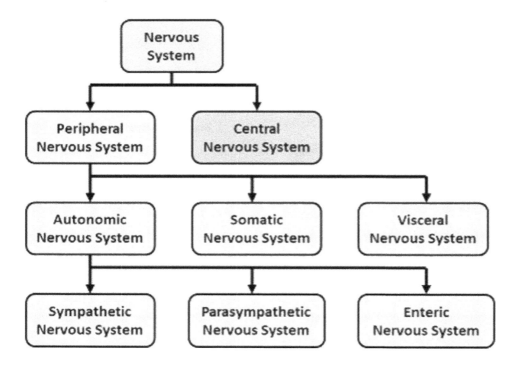

Even though all our involuntary functions are governed by autonomic nervous system, but we can train our body and mind to conscious control them like we learn controlling our bowel and urination at very early stage in our life. Yogis find the way to master our breath, heart, digestion and subtle nervous system functions including thoughts and emotions.

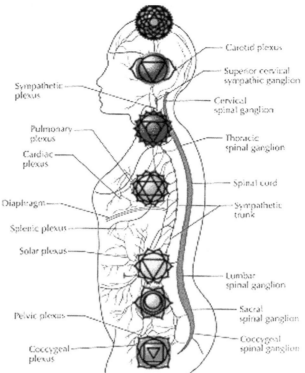

Carotid plexus

Superior cervical sympathic ganglion

Cervical spinal ganglion

Thoracic spinal ganglion

Spinal cord

Sympathetic trunk

Lumbar spinal ganglion

Sacral spinal ganglion

Coccygeal spinal ganglion

Sympathetic plexus

Pulmonary plexus

Cardiac plexus

Diaphragm

Splenic plexus

Solar plexus

Pelvic plexus

Coccygeal plexus

The Mooladhara Chakra and Lumbar Plexus

Our Mooladhara or root chakra is located at the base of spine near the tailbone. This chakra can be associated with the lumbar plexus. This is a complex plexus consisting of the lumbar plexus and the sacral plexus: it controls the lower extremities and the activities of the pelvic floor via the pudendal nerve and has anterior and posterior parts. The function of the rectum, anus and sensations from these areas are governed by this posterior sacral cluster of nerves.

The smooth muscles of the intestines are controlled through stretch receptors and peristaltic reflexes. At the anal opening area, the immense amount of nerve receptors expands to include receptors for hot and cold, light touch, vibration and both sharp and dull pain.

When these nerve receptors are stimulated by touch, attention or activity, the sensory nerves of the posterior pelvic floor send an immense amount of impulses to the sacral plexus with nervous energy facilitating the motor nerves in the plexus itself which control autonomic reflexes like urination, ejaculation and moving the bowels. This is how we can experience this immense energy flow or awakening with Moola-bandha, Ashwani mudra and or by paying focus to our Mooladhara Chakra.

The Swadhisthana Chakra and the Sacral Plexus

The Swadhisthana or sacral chakra is located at the pelvic area between our genitals and navel. This chakra and its functions are associated with the anterior part of the sacral plexus. Our sacral plexus generally gets a more attention compared to the others, due to its associations with sex, arousal, erection, ejaculation and orgasm, which are all regulated or mediated through the nerves from this plexus.

The shared space of our limbo-sacral plexus governs functions of our body parts and organs below our waist. Focusing attention on the sacral area activates or stimulates all the motor nerves connected with the sacral area, which awakens the nerves associated with self-pleasure and feeling good, for example an orgasmic experience.

The Manipura Chakra and the Solar Plexus

The Manipura, also known as Nabhi Chakra or navel chakra is located behind navel and corresponds with celiac plexus that governs the upper digestive system, from the stomach to the first two thirds of the colon and other associated organs like the liver, pancreas and spleen. This plexus is also known as the solar plexus, which radiates the sun-like energy in the nerve fibres spreading in every direction.

The celiac plexus is associated with our mind and conveys the feelings of nausea and colic or feelings of inner calmness, satisfaction and gratification. The manipura is known to be the chakra of our will and personal mind power. We use the word 'guts' for courage, which refers to the association of our mind power with the abdominal area. We also have 'gut feelings', referring to our inner intuition in various situations. This represents our deepest selves even more than the heart or breathing.

Hidden in the walls of the digestive system is the enteric nervous system (ENS), sometimes called the second brain. The ENS is two thin layers of more than 100 million nerve cells lining the gastrointestinal tract from oesophagus to rectum. The ENS may trigger big emotional shifts and the feelings originating from solar plexus mostly are some kind of warning or precautionary signals.

Research suggests that the gut micro-organisms influence the function of the brain by releasing chemicals: cytokines, neurotransmitters, neuropeptides, chemokines, endocrine messengers and microbial metabolites such as short chain fatty acids and peptidoglycans. The intestinal microbiome can divert these products to the brain through the blood which then impact different metabolic processes. Studies have found communication between the hippocampus, the prefrontal cortex and the amygdala which act in the gut brain behavioural axis influencing emotions and motivation.

Our solar plexus generally is calm, patient and contemplative unless it is under attack from negative whirlpools in our mind and in fight-flight situations.

The Anahata Chakra and the Cardiac Plexus

The anahata or heart chakra is located in our heart area, where our cardiac plexus is also found. This is the centre for governing our spiritual balance and also the processing of all contradictory or opposing ideas, emotions and feelings.

According to neuroscience, the cardiac plexus is composed from the sympathetic nervous system cardiac nerves and the parasympathetic components, originating from the vagus nerve descending from the brainstem.

The cardiac plexus governs our warm feelings of love and compassion as well as our emotional pain and feelings, like a broken heart, anger, resentment, guilt etc.

The Vishuddha Chakra and the Cervical Plexus

The Vishuddha or throat chakra is located around our throat area and is known to be associated with the cervical plexus of nerves. This chakra is associated with sound and communication. Our vocal cords are regulated by the vagus nerves from our brain and not the cervical plexus. Our diaphragm is governed by the phrenic nerves which arises from the cervical plexus, which is under voluntary control and reflex actions including coughing and hiccups.

The Cranial nerve nuclei are based above the cervical plexus in the brainstem; they control speech through the vocal cords, tongue and month. The lower cranial nerves can be easily associated with the functions of Vishuddha Chakra. The cervical plexus is also associated with the thyroid gland, which governs metabolic function. The thyroid directly responds to the pituitary gland via the thyroid stimulating hormone known as TSH. Thyroxin governs metabolism, body temperature and mental awareness. Hypothyroidism leads to symptoms of cold intolerance, coarse features and a low, husky voice. So our Vishuddha Chakra governs communication, voice, mental clarity or focus and energy levels, bone health, breathing and metabolism, which are all significantly under the influence of the cervical plexus.

The Ajna Chakra

The Ajna or third eye centre translated as the 'command centre', is also known as Guru Chakra. This is located between the eyebrows deep within. As described in this chakra, the Ida and Pingala Nadi terminates and merges in the Sushumna Nadi. Our Ida and Pingala Nadi can be associated with the parasympathetic and the sympathetic nervous systems. This union is the representation of the end of duality. In this area, similarly our brain takes over the central control.

Some of the cranial nerves are interconnecting in the midbrain and brainstem regulating the muscles of facial expression and sensation with sight, hearing, balance and the movements of the eyes. Our central brain processes the complex information and governs higher skills and activities. This phenomenon relates our third eye chakra with the midbrain.

The Sahasrara Chakra

The Sahasrara or crown chakra is related with spirituality and cosmic consciousness leading us to experience divinity, oneness and self-realisation.

The cerebral cortex is composed of tens of billions of nerve cells in groups interconnected by trillions of synapses. All the information that we learn and inherit is stored in this part of our brain. This shows a significant visual metaphorical association with the thousands of petals of the crown lotus.

Our thalamus area also known as the core of the brain, controls the rest of the brain by sending waves of excitation through the brain at a rate of ten per second. This enables the nerves that are active and in use to act in synchronicity, which enables the development of complex and coherent ideas.

The nerves fire in bursts lasting up to two seconds, hence our experiences or perceptions overlap and allow us to be aware, as well as be aware of awareness itself. Our brain creates the perception of the external world from all the raw information provided by our sensory information and past memories, creating consciousness. So our brain creates a sense of self and the external world. We experience our own witnessing awareness and all other painful and pleasant sensations through this complex system of our brain.

The brain enables us to communicate and find harmony within ourselves, as well as with the external environment. Cortical centres govern learning processes of grammar and vocabulary, as well as the ability to recognise faces and facial expressions, posture and gestures. This gives us a step forward to understand how Yogis used mudras or gestures to activates various energy fields, chakras or organs. Many of these mudras stimulate particular nerve plexus or parts of brain to enhance the functions of associated body parts.

The hippocampus part of the brain can hold more than one idea and does the comparison to make decisions based on judgement. It learns from experiences and can also imagine and fantasise while awake and dream when we are sleep.

All the functions of conscious awareness are constructed and experienced by the cortex part of our brain. The electricity and magnetic fields of our brain and nerves can be recorded in the brain and on the surface by highly sensitive machines. This resembles the shining energy or magnetic field of our crown chakra and also our physical body. Our alpha, beta and gamma waves produced from the brain in various states of our mind or thoughts, can be recorded in respect to the colours and energy patterns around our crown chakra.

The Endocrine system

Many physical reactions in our body that result from the activity of the autonomic nervous system are produced by the actions of the endocrine glands. The endocrine glands are ductless glands that secrete the secretions known as hormones directly into the blood. Hormones are chemical messengers that are carried throughout the body by the blood circulation system. These hormones are essential to the nervous system for the integration and harmonization of the body's organs activities and to the maintenance of homeostasis.

Indeed, the functioning of the nervous system depends upon the hormones. i.e. some nervous cells use a hormone known as epinephrine, as their chemical transmitter. Other hormones serve to modify the excitability of neurons. The endocrine glands are responsible for secular growth and maternal behaviours, the individual's characteristic level of energy, aptitude to stress, emotions and thoughts, which are all responsible for attitude and habits.

Some of the endocrine glands are under the control of the nervous system while others respond autonomously to the internal state of the body. We can consider an example of a fearful thought; for example, if I lost my money, it would be very problematic for me to reach my destination. Due to the fear of the loss, some changes take place in our body, similar to an actual situation of emergency. Hence we can conclude that our thoughts are able to stimulate our endocrine glands for emergency preparation.

The Pineal gland and the Sahashrara Crown Chakra
The pineal gland regulates the secretions of the other glands; it is responsible for the normal physical and mental development of the nervous system. The hormone melatonin secreted by this gland, controls the body's rhythms of sleeping and waking and it is also responsible for sexual development.

The Pituitary gland and the Anja Third Eye Chakra
This is known as the master gland, which regulate the secretions of the other glands. It is a pea shaped gland attached to the hypothalamus. It is controlled by the hypothalamus. The following hormones are secreted by the pituitary gland-

- ❖ Adrenocorticotrophic hormone which stimulates the adrenal glands to secrete steroid hormones principally cortisol
- ❖ Growth hormone which regulates growth and metabolism
- ❖ Luteinising hormone and follicle stimulating hormone known as gonadotrophins which act on the ovaries and testes
- ❖ Prolactin which stimulates milk production in the mammary glands
- ❖ Thyroid stimulating hormone which stimulates the thyroid to produce thyroid hormones

The secretions of the pituitary gland directly influence the target glands.

Thyroid gland and the Vishuddha Chakra
The thyroid gland is butterfly shaped, consisting of two maroon coloured lobes, one on each side of the trachea in the middle of the anterior portion of the neck. The hormones of this gland control metabolism, maintain the body weight, the rate of energy used and the heart rate.

The functions of the thyroid gland include:
- ❖ Regulation of the digestive system
- ❖ Preventing toxicity by secreting the iodine-rich hormones
- ❖ Balancing of the nervous system
- ❖ Control over the amount of fat in the body
- ❖ Prevention and reduced risk of goitre

Parathyroid glands

These are four, minute yellowish-brown egg-shaped bodies embedded in the two lobes of the thyroid gland. The hormones secreted by the parathyroid are known as the Parathormone (PTH).

This gland regulates the following functions:
- ❖ Ability to increase calcium level in blood
- ❖ Stimulate the bones to release stored calcium
- ❖ Increases absorption of nutrients in intestines
- ❖ Regulate the functions of the kidneys

Thymus gland and the Anahata Heart Chakra

The thymus gland is a brownish mass with two lobes, situated in the chest between the two lungs and extending up into the neck. It reaches its largest size at the beginning of puberty.

The thymus gland is a lymphoid organ, composed of lymph cells. Its secretions influence the lymph nodes, spleen and other lymphatic tissue. It helps with the stimulation of the body's immune system. It makes white blood cells which protect the body against infection. Thymus cell lymphocytes or T cells are critical to the adaptive immune system where the body adapts to specific foreign invaders. Abnormalities of the thymus can result in a decreased number of T cells and autoimmune diseases. T cells begin in the bone marrow and migrate to the thymus, each T cell has a distinct T cell receptor suited to a specific antigen. It also controls over the development and growth of sexual organs.

Adrenal Glands, Pancreas and the Manipura Navel Chakra

The Adrenal glands are a pair of two hat shaped glands that cap the two kidneys. Each adrenal gland is composed of an outer-cortex and an inner layer medulla and secretes a number of hormones that are essential for life. These regulate our brain emotions and thoughts and thus they are responsible for attitude and behaviour.

The Adrenal glands major functions include:
- ❖ The balance of salt and water in the body
- ❖ Regulation of carbohydrate, protein and fat metabolism
- ❖ Production of the fight-flight response in stressful situations

- ❖ Production of the male sex hormones
- ❖ Two important hormones of the adrenal gland are firstly Epinephrine or adrenaline and secondly nor-epinephrine or nor-adrenaline

The effects of adrenaline are excitatory and cause the following effects on the body:
- ❖ Tensed muscles and nervous system
- ❖ More sugar is released in blood from liver
- ❖ Increase blood circulation
- ❖ Increased heart rate
- ❖ Increase respiration
- ❖ Decreased digestive functions
- ❖ Immunity system is also affected

All these are in preparation of the 'fight or flight' responses in an emergency. The excitement, fear, anger and other emotions affect the secretions of the adrenal gland and vice-versa.

The Pancreas

The pancreas is also associated with this chakra. The pancreas consists of clusters of Islets of Langerhans. These are composed of alpha cells which secrete insulin which lowers blood sugar levels and delta cells, which secrete glycogen that stimulates the liver to release stored glucose into the blood.

The Gonads and the Swadhishtana Sacral Chakra

The gonads are the male and female sex organs, which are responsible for reproduction. These are the ovaries in females and the testes in males which produce the hormones oestrogen, progesterone and testosterone. The main function is to regulate the reproductive and sexual activities.

In this lesson we have explored the energetic connections and associations between the chakras and the modern anatomy and physiology understanding that we can benefit from. The linking of old wisdom and modern science gives us insight into the incredible ancient knowledge and understanding from the Yogic Gurus in the past.

Lesson 50.
Mantra or Naada Yoga and Health

Mantra is a Sanskrita word, which can be broken in two parts:

> *'Man'- which means the mind or manas*
> *'Tra'- which means the tool, instrument or vehicle*

In simple words, a mantra is an instrument or tool of the mind, a powerful sound or vibration, that a Sadhaka (spiritual seeker) can use to enter a deep state of meditation.

Mantras in the form of a sound, chant, word, or phrase are used by Yogis, Brahmins and Spiritual seekers as a form of meditation energy, to clear the mind and awaken a higher healing potential. The most ancient mantras can be found in the Vedas, the ancient Hindu Texts on the Science of Living or Spirit.

Mantras can be recited or chanted verbally, out loud or silently. In Yogic traditions mantras are often combined with rhythmic breathing and mindfulness, focussing on the meaning or a particular point like a chakra. Some of the commonly experienced benefits of mantras include: slowing down of thoughts; enhanced mental clarity; increased concentration and memory; connection with the inner self; peace of mind; releasing of tension and old negative memories.

Hinduism and various paths of Yoga like Raja, Hatha, Tantra, Jnana, etc. have incorporated Mantra as a very important aspect of Sadhana. In these systems of spiritual evolution, a mantra is a sacred sound in the form of a syllable, word, prayer or hymn in Sanskrita or other Ancient Vedic Language. A Sadhaka may chant the mantra for physical, mental, emotional, spiritual and mystic benefits.

Generally the use of Mantras, are known for invoking various gods and goddesses, seeking protection against the negative energies and fulfilment of wishes and prayers. Vedic rituals follow many mantras, hymns and chants for various ceremonies to invoke various deities for wealth, health, children, name and fame and peace and victory in life. Egyptians, Greeks, Mayans and Zoroastrians used magical chants to connect with gods and obtain boons, blessings and supernatural powers. They also used prayers and chants to cure diseases, attain freedom from evil influences and invoke deities and ancestral spirits.

Even though it seems like chants and prayers exist in many ancient cultures, the concept of mantra as a vibrational sound and its power, is uniquely followed in

Hinduism and Yoga. The Vedas reveal many mantras to invoke various auspicious energies on various occasions like birth, naming, marriage, death, harvest, etc. According to Tantra Yoga, Mantras are interpreted to be effective sounds or vibrations for awakening our Chakras and subtle energies; leading us from our mundane mind towards spiritual consciousness. Mantras are one of the most powerful tools to liberate our mind from the worldly illusion, pain and suffering and bring true abundance and joy in life.

Mantra is Not a Word

At the very beginning of my Yoga Journey, I used to think that it was very important to know the meaning of a Mantra while we were chanting or listening to it. However according to Tantra, Yoga and Samkhya Prakriti and Purusha, the Naada, Sabda or Pranava (which is OM or AUM) awakens the Purusha and Prakriti, which causes them to give rise to an energy explosion and gradually results in the manifestation of the universe and life itself. This idea is very similar to the 'Big Bang Theory" of creation. Prakriti here refers to the basic cosmic material that is the root of all beings and Purusha to the spirit or conscious energy that governs life and reality.

In Tantra Yoga a Mantra (which are the Bija Mantra of the Chakras), has a sound or vibration which resonates with various points or Bindus. Our Chakras are some of the important Bindus in our Pancha-Kosha System. These syllables (Akshara or Bija Mantras) give rise to words (Sabda). A word has the meaning which give rise to the object (Vastu) accordingly. A word gives rise to Vakya or a sentence, which leads to creation of a language (Bhasha like Sanskrita).

The true power of Mantra lies in its actual chanting or recitation by creating the vibration or Naada. Each and every cell, muscle, organ, system, whole body and all objects have their own vibration or sound. However our ears are only able to hear certain frequencies or vibrations. Through Yoga Sadhana, a Sadhaka can experience many of these subtle Bija Sounds or Vibrations and become deeply absorbed in meditation, transcending our limited sensory field of experience into transcendental or subtle fields of energy experiences. Tantra Yoga Sadhakas were initiated in many of these Mantras by their realised Gurus to keep chanting these Mantras to awaken transcendental experiences.

Yoga traditions explain the Pranava Aum as the most sacred mantra and believed it to be the sound of the divine or the nearest divine vibration that a human being can experience. These sounds are an expression of the divine itself.

Each and every word has its own power, vibration and manifestation. To understand this power, try to remember when someone gives you compliment or says something unpleasant. A word or phrase can fill your heart with joy or make you feel sad or miserable.

Just to clarify here what you may be chanting in the name of Mantras may be:

- ❖ *Bija Mantra* – These seed sounds or syllables like Lang, Vang, Rang, Yang, Hang, OM, etc.
- ❖ *Japa Mantra* – These a set of few syllables invoking the subtle and cosmic divinity in various forms. Panchakshara (one of five letters) Mantra (OM NAMAH SHIVAYA) is one of the most sacred and power Japa Mantra. Others widely known Mantras are 'RAAMA', 'HARI OM TAT SAT', 'SHIVOHAM', 'SHOHAM', 'SATCHITANANDA', etc.
- ❖ *Maha-Vakyas* – These are some of the highest valued Vedic phrases or wisdom ideas like 'AHAM BRAHMASHMI', 'SHOHAM', 'ATMA-NITYAM', 'VASUDAIVA KUTAMBAKAM', etc.
- ❖ *Gayatri Mantras* – These are prayers or slokas to invoke various aspects of divine, gods and goddess.
- ❖ *Shloka* (or Sloka) - is a poetic meter, consisting of varying number of syllables or lines, 2 lines of 16 syllables or 4 lines of 8 syllables. Both the Itihasas, Ramayana and Mahabharata are primarily written in Shloka format.
- ❖ *Sutra* - A sutra is a concise verse or thread within Hinduism, Yoga and Buddhism. In Sanskrit, sutra means 'note', 'sacred thread', or 'code'. Sutras are often used in chanting and meditation.
- ❖ *Stotra* - Stotra is a Sanskrit term which means 'praise', 'hymn of praise', 'verse' or 'tribute'. It typically refers to a genre of Hindu, Yoga and Tantra texts and prayers in praise of various aspects and incarnations of the Divine, such as Shiva, Rama, Hanuman, Vishnu, Durga and Lakshmi.
- ❖ *Richa* - Rucha or Richa refers to a shloka or verse or mantra, usually two to four sentences long, found in the Vedas written in ancient language of gods known as Devanagari or Sanskrita.

OM as the Mantra of Mantras

Pranava or Aum (OM) is the most powerful and sacred mantra in Hinduism. In the Vedas, Upanishadas, Puranas, and other sacred literature it is stated that Aum is the root of all the sounds and mantras. The pranava is a representation of the isvara/divinity. Chanting of Aum whilst concentrating on its meaning with deep heartfelt faith is the easiest way to attain Samadhi or Enlightenment according to the Yogasutras of Patanjali.

Pranava is the mantra of all the mantras. Aum is the name of God in vibration, in sound. To intone the Pranava Aum, 'the mantra of all mantras', 'the sound of sounds', is to intone or to evoke the most potent of all powers in a mantra, a vibratory energy body.

Pranava is comprised of three symbols- a, u and m. The following illustration is to relate pranava with various symbols of yoga and Hinduism-

Syllables	Mantras	God	Chakra	Sound
A	Akaar	Brahma	Anahata	Aaa…
U	Ukaar	Vishnu	Vishuddha	Uuu…
M	Makaar	Mahesh	Sahsrara	Mmm…

Omkaram, Bindu Samyuktham, Nithyam, dyayanthi yogina, Kamadam, mokshadam chaiva, Omkaraya Namo namah.

Salutations and salutations to letter 'Om', Which is meditated as a letter Om with a dot, daily by great sages, and leads them to fulfilment of desires and attainment of salvation.

AUM in the Worldwide Scripture (By Swamiji Dr. Gitananda Giriji). This is a commonly used mantra by Hindus, Jains, Buddhists, Sikhas, etc. While Aum is also found in sacred mantras of other religious.

OM in diffrent scripts

Muslims use the Aum as OM-IM (amin) to evoke Allah and as a close to their prayers. The Christians use AUM-EN (amen) similarly. In all religions a sign from God is called an OM-en (omen), while to leave God out of your life is OM-it (omit).

As a supreme God he is OM-nipotent (omnipotent). He is OM-niscient (omniscient), all light resplendent, effulgent, all knowing. He is OM-competent (omnicompetent), all-law; OM-nific (omnific), all creating; OM-nifarious (omnifarious), in all things; OM-nigenous (omnigenous), all kinds and species. He is OM-nipresent (omnipresent), far as well as near, ubiquitous, being constantly met with; OM-nivorous (omnivorous), he feeds on anything, even on himself; OM-phalic (omphalos), He is the centre the hub of the universe. He is Lingam in Yoni. AUM in the Yoga Sutra of Patajali is the word denoting God-
(Yoga Sutra I-27) Tasya vachakah pranavah

Isvara or the Supreme being is expressed and represented (vachakah) by the vibratory energy contained in the pranava (the sacred syllable, Aum).

Isvara can not be defined or limited because Isvara by definition is indefinable, infinite mind, however, can be symbolically represented by the expression of Pranava - by the vibratory essence of the sacred sound, Aum. Thus Isvara is often accessed through the Pranava which is Aum.

Tasya means 'that'. Vacakah means 'expression' from the root 'vac' to speak. Pranavah means 'the sacred syllable AUM' derived from 'pra' (before) and 'nava' (sound).

So from my limited experience of Infinite Mind (Isvara), I think that the intoning of AUM is still a conveyer, a pathway, a sadhana which leads us into the greater vibration, pulsation and inter- dimensional energetic hologram (as in beyond reality) which has no beginning or end - where both sound and words have little meaning.

Patanjali states that the Pranava is the expression of Isvara, the omniscient teacher of all the teachers. Practically speaking however all the vital and living religions agree, that it is to focus on the creator in creation. That is in the spiritual practice, so the practical meaning would be the same i.e., practice intoning Aum and/or listening for Aum as the self-existing expression of Isvara (the divine purusha).

Patanjali is thus offering this sutra as a practice that may be effective in clearing out the vrittis and obscurations that can lead us eventually to an Infinite Mind.

(Yoga-Sutra. I 28) Taj-japas tad-artha-bhavanam

Through generating (bhavanam) constant repetition (taj-japa) of the Pranava (Aum) the meaning (artha) behind the sound is realized and becomes manifest (bhavanam).

The vibratory energy contained in the vibration of the sound, Aum connects with Isvara. Japa means the repetition of mantra. Thus japa (mantra repetition of Aum) is given as a practice.

(Yoga-Sutra. I 29) Tatah pratyak-cetanadhigamo'py antarayabhavash ca

Hence through the practice of the pranava, Aum, as a dedication toward realizing Isvara (through isvara pranidhana), consciousness (cetana) is redirected inwards (pratyak) toward the realisation (adhigamo) of the intrinsic light of consciousness (pratyak-cetana-adhigamo) and (ca) also (api) obstacles and hindrances (antarayah) are thus removed (abhava).

OM in Hindu Scriptures- From The Mandukya Upanishad by Swami Krishnananda The Manusmriti, the Mahabharata, the Puranas and the Upanishads describe the nature, the constitution, the structure and the glory of Om. With Om, Brahma created this cosmos, and from Om constituted of the three isolated letters A, U, M, the Vyahritis came forth: Bhuh, Bhuvah, Svah. From these three Vyahritis, the three Padas of the Gayatri-Mantra emanated. From the three Padas of the Gayatri-Mantra, the meaning of the three sections of the Purusha-Sukta emerged, and from the meaning of the Purusha-Sukta, the meaning of the entire Vedas emanated and from this vast meaning of the Vedas, Brahma created this cosmos, say the scriptures. So important is Om, not a chant uttered by Brahma, but a vibration that rose from the Supreme Being in the initial stage of creation – a comprehensive vibration.

When we chant Om, we also try to create within ourselves a sympathetic vibration, a vibration which has a sympathy with the cosmic vibration, so that, for the time being, we are in tune with the cosmos. We flow with the current of the cosmos when we recite Om and produce a harmonious vibration in our bodily and psychological systems. Instead of tearing ourselves away from the world outside, we flow into the current of the world. Instead of thinking independently as Jivas, we start thinking universally as Isvara. Instead of thinking in relation to objects segregated from one another, we think in terms of nothing at all. There is thought thinking itself, as it were. Can you imagine thought thinking itself? This is Isvara's Thought.

When a thought thinks of an object, it is Jiva's thought. When the thought thinks only itself, it is Isvara's Thought, Isvara's Will and when we recite Om properly, with an understanding of its real connotation, we think nothing in particular. We think all things in general; this is Isvara thinking. We do not think at that time; it is Isvara who thinks through these individual minds of ours. We, as persons, cease to be for the time being. We exist as the thing-in-itself, Isvara, who exists by His own stature, mind and status. He does not exist as a Jiva (living sentiment substance) in terms of other objects. We always exist in relation to something else. Isvara exists with relation to nobody else, and we, as seekers of the status of Isvara, or Brahman, wishing to exist by a universal nature, try by this means of the recitation of Om, to flow into Isvara's Being like rivers trying to flow into the bosom of the ocean. We are like streams wanting to rush into the sea, and just as by the force of the inclination of the waters, the rivers enter the ocean, we, by the inclination of the vibration of Om, enter the Universal Form of Isvara.

When you recite Om properly, you enter into a meditative mood. You are not merely reciting a sound or a word or a phrase, you are creating a vibration. To point out once again; you are creating a vibration. What sort of vibration? Not a vibration which agitates you, irritates you, or creates a desire in your mind for a particular object, but a vibration which melts all other particular vibrations, puts an end to all desire, extinguishes all cravings and creates a desire for the Universal.

As fire burns straw, this desire for the Universal burns up all other desires. A recitation of Om, even three times, correctly done, is enough to burn up all sins, to put a cessation to all desire and make you calm, quiet and satisfied within yourself. The test of a correct recitation or chant of Om is that you become calm in your mind and feel satisfied with what you are and what you have. When you come out of your meditative mood with a desire persisting, it would only point out that your contemplation has not been perfect. The desire for things was lurking within while you were in a mood of contemplation; even the chant of Om was not properly done. The chant of Om should go together with the thought of the Universal. It is a Japa and a Dhyana combined.

While other Japas may lead you to a mood of Dhyana or meditation, while other Mantras may lead to Dhyana, the Japa of Om suddenly becomes Dhyana when it is properly done. Here, Japa and Dhyana combine, and Nama and Rupa are brought together. Here, you do not have a distinction between the designator and the designated, because the Nama (name) which is Om, being Universal, merges into the Rupa (form) which is also Universal. There cannot be two Universals; there can only be one Universal. So the designator and the designated, in the case of Om, become one. Japa and Dhyana mean the same thing in the case of the chanting of Om. It is a sudden entering into a realm which the individual mind cannot understand. A rapture of ecstasy may take possession of you if you chant Om, thus:

Omityetadaksharamidam sarvam – Om is, verily, everything.

Mantra Yoga Sadhana

Japa is an ancient practice in which a mantra or the name of a deity is recited either silently or aloud. The Sanskrit word is derived from the root, 'jap', meaning 'to repeat quietly and internally'.

Types or Stages of Mantra Japa:
- ❖ Likhita Japa- Writing the mantra
- ❖ Vachika Japa- Chanting mantra verbally and loud
- ❖ Manas Japa- Chanting or repeating mantra in Mind
- ❖ Artha or Dhyana Japa- Meditating on meaning or essence of Mantra
- ❖ Ajapa Japa- Letting go or allowing mind to be absorbed in sound, meaning and essence of mantra

Japa engages the mind spiritually and leads the practitioner to a deep meditative state. Japa meditation can be done as Manas meditation, Vachak meditation or Kirtan meditation. In Manas meditation, the mantra is chanted within the mind. In Vachak meditation, the mantra is uttered in a low voice. In Kirtan meditation, the mantra is musically chanted.

The following is an example of a Japa meditation session:
- ❖ Bathe or wash the face, hands and feet before settling down
- ❖ Assume a comfortable seated posture, preferably padmasana or sukhasana
- ❖ Face east or north
- ❖ Begin with a prayer to focus the mind
- ❖ Pronounce the mantra with clarity and repeat it at an even pace
- ❖ Use a mala to keep a count of the repetitions. Malas generally consist of 108, 54 or 27 beads and a meru, or an additional bead that symbolizes highest Truth. Japa can be performed without a mala as well.

Likhita japa, which refers to the writing of a mantra, may also be practiced.

Naam Japa Mantras

Most Mantras for Naam Japa are formed by taking the name of Ishta-Devata (deity, god or goddess you personally follow) with "AUM NAMAH ....." OR "AUM JAI ...". Some of these typically followed mantras are as follows:

Mantra	Ishta-Deva or Personal Deity
Om Namah Shivaya	*Om* Salutation to Lord Shiva
Om Namo Narayana	*Om* Salutation to Lord Vishnu
Om Namaha Bhagavate Vasudevaya	*Om* Salutation to Lord Krishna
Om Shri Ganeshaya Namaha	*Om* Salutation to Lord Ganesha
Om Namah Durgaya	*Om* Salutation to Goddess Durga
Om Jai Ram Jai Ram	*Om* Hail to lord Rama
Om Guru Jai Guru Satchidananda	*Om* Salutation to the Guru which guides to absolute bliss

Exploring Some Research on Mantra Yoga

Many Yoga, Psychology and Medical researchers are providing the theory behind the effectiveness of Mantra chanting and its applications in in bringing peace and tranquillity of mind and an enhanced relaxation response. According to Tantra teachings, mantra chanting connects our body and mind together and we can connect with the resonating subtle sounds and vibrations to reorganise our thoughts, consciousness, memories and inner self.

According to a research study conducted by Arati Amin et al., (2016) following six months of Om chanting, systolic and diastolic pressure, pulse rate, depression, anxiety and levels of stress decreased significantly. Additionally Arati Amin et al. found that the Mini-Mental State Examination (MMSE) scores improved significantly following Om chanting. Mooventhan and Vitthal Khode (2014) found that Om chanting is an important exhalation exercise and significantly improves pulmonary functions in healthy subjects and a significant decrease in the heart rate was reported following Om meditation by Telles, Nagarathna and Nagendra (1995).

Snelling (1996) in his book *A Complete Guide to Buddhist Teaching and Practice* describes how reciting a mantra continuously purifies the speech and protects the mind by maintaining a constant spiritual connection and of course it helps disperse mental chatter. If there is no religious preference, then the sound vibration OM is a universally recognized mantra.

The sound of OM or Pranava carries the meaning that it sustains life as it runs through the Prana or breath, it drives away all worldly thoughts and removes distraction and infuses new vigor in the body. The OM is composed of three letters, A, U, and M. These symbolize the practitioner's impure body, speech and mind Chanting OM (AUM) will bring us to a state of purity in body mind and soul. Yoga mantras and prayers have been found beneficial for many physiological and psychological functions of the body.

The sound Om, when chanted, vibrates at the frequency of 136.1 Hz

This is the same vibrational frequency found throughout everything in nature. Everything is in a state of vibration and when we are in a natural, resonant vibration, we are in a state of good health. But if some part of the body begins to vibrate at a wrong frequency, the energy becomes stuck and disease sets in. Therefore, through mantric chanting, one can cause the stuck energy to become released, and we can return to our natural state of resonance, thus affecting a cure.

It has been found that the sounds of specific mantras chanting will cause the left and right hemispheres of the brain to synchronize. Such chanting will also help oxygenate the brain, reduce our heart rate, blood pressure and assist in creating calm brainwave activity. There is a reason why most of the prayer/meditation on the planet is vocalized. Sound amplifies our prayers. Through positive internationalised and internalised sound, we can generate the miraculous effects. Every sound that we make is actually a composite of sounds—a fundamental frequency and geometric multiples of that sound, called harmonics or overtones. These harmonics are whole number ratios, 1:1, 2:1, 3:2, etc. These vocal harmonics make up the timbrel, tone or colour of sound and are responsible for the way our individual voices sound. It is a field of all possibilities. We can make new neural synaptic connections in the brain with vocal harmonics. Harmonics can also improve our vocal quality, hearing, change our brain pattern and even heighten our consciousness.

Dr. Ananda Balayogi Bhavanani at al., explains that slow, deep, pranayama based breathing training has been shown to be effective in reducing blood pressure (BP). The present study was undertaken to determine immediate effects of performing Pranava pranayama on cardiovascular parameters in hypertensive patients. 29 hypertensive patients who were on medical treatment and also attending yoga sessions were recruited for the present study. Supine heart rate (HR) and BP were recorded before and after performance of the pranayama for five minutes. Post intervention statistical analysis revealed a significant ($p < 0.05$) reduction in systolic pressure (SP) and a more significant (p < 0.01) reduction in HR, pulse pressure and double product (Do P). The reduction in rate-pressure product (RPP) was highly significant (p< 0.001).

Pranava pranayama is effective in reducing heart rate and systolic pressure in hypertensive patients within five minutes of the practice. This may be due to a normalization of autonomic cardiovascular rhythms as a result of increased vagal modulation and/or decreased sympathetic activity and improved baroreflex sensitivity along with an augmentation of endogenous nitric oxide production. Our findings have potential therapeutic applications in day-to-day as well as clinical situations where blood pressure needs to be brought down at the earliest. The significant fall in Rate-pressure Product (RPP is the product of heart rate and systolic blood pressure and is a reliable indicator of myocardial oxygen demand) signifies a reduction in oxygen consumption and work done by the heart. It is concluded that Pranava pranayama is a simple and cost-effective technique that can be used in the management of hypertensive patients in addition to the regular medical management. Further studies are required to enable a deeper understanding of the mechanisms involved and its usefulness in the long term management of hypertension.

Dr. Ananda goes on to mention that chanting has always been an important aspect of the spiritual life in India. Chanting Mantras, performing Japa, singing Bhajans and the use of Nada Pranayamas such as the Bhramari and the Pranava are all important parts of the Yogic life. Recent studies have shown that chanting creates sound vibrations that encourage air to move back and forth between the sinus membranes and nasal passages. This air movement helps open the tiny ducts, or ostia, that connect the nose to the sinuses, allowing the sinuses to drain properly. This can help prevent infections from settling down in the sinuses and create a healthy environment therein. All the sinuses are effectively ventilated by humming and this is an important benefit as previous research has shown that poor sinus ventilation increases the risk for sinusitis. When the sinuses are well ventilated infections have no chance of settling down at all. Recent studies have shown that humming increases nitric oxide levels fifteen fold, compared to quiet exhalations without sound. The exhalations of people with healthy sinuses tend to have high nitric oxide levels, indicating that more air is able to flow between the sinuses and the nose. The Nada Pranayamas such as the Bhramari and the Pranava are similar to the humming used in these studies. In the Bhramari Pranayama the nasal sound like a bee is used while in the Pranava Pranayama, the humming sounds of the A-U-M are used. This new light on humming and nasal ventilation can explain the scientific basis by which these Pranayamas can prevent as well as help in the management of sinusitis. This is another reason why practices like the Surya Namaskar should always be done with the chanting of the Surya Mantras and another reason why the chanting of the Mantras and scriptures should be encouraged in Yoga therapy and training.

Refences and Resources

Snelling, J. (1996), The Buddhist Handbook: A Complete Guide to Buddhist Teaching and Practice.
"The Meaning of Om" from http://www.omsakthi.org /worship/mantra.html
"The OM chant" from http://www.divinegold.com/meditation /meditationchants.htm
Arati Amin at al., Beneficial effects of OM chanting on depression, anxiety, stress and cognition in elderly women with hypertension, published in Journal of Clinical Anatomy and Physiology, July-September2016;3(3);253-255253
Bernardi L, Sleight P, Bandinelli G, Cencetti S, Fattorini L, WdowczycSzulc J, et al. Effect of rosary prayer and yoga mantras on autonomic cardiovascular rhythms: Comparative study.Br Med J.2001;323:22–9.23.
A Mooventhan and Vitthal Khode. Effect of Bhramari pranayama and OM chanting on pulmonary function in healthy individuals: A prospective randomized control trial. Int J Yoga. 2014 Jul-Dec;7(2):104–110.
Telles S, Nagarathna R, Nagendra HR. Autonomic changes during 'OM' meditation.Indian J Physiol Pharmacol.1995;39:418–20.10.
Hans, Cousto, ⊠The Cosmic Octave Turning Forks⊠, Planetware, 2009.
Gurjar, Ajay Anil and Siddharth A. Ladhake, ⊠ Analysis and Dissection of Sanskrit Divine Sound ⊠OM' using signal processing to study the science behind ⊠OM' Chanting', 7thInt. Conf. on Intelligent Systems, Modeling and Simulation, IEEE Computer Society, 2016.
Goldman, Jonathan; ⊠Shifting Frequencies⊠. Light Technology Publications, 1998.
Goldman, Jonathan; ⊠Healing Sound: The Power of Harmonics⊠, Inner Traditions,2002.
http://icyer.com/documents/pranava_IJPP2012.pdf
http://icyer.com/documents/nada_yoga-pic2011.pdf

Lesson 51.
Yoga Sutras and Mental Health

Pancha-Vrittis: Five Types of Whirlpools of Mind

Maharishi Patanjali begins the Yoga Sutra teachings with a firm statement, "yoga is a path of discipline" (atha-yoga-anushanam). Followed by mentioning that yoga is a set of kriyas and prakriyas to attain stillness of our mind (yoga-chitta-vritti-nirodhah). He concludes the glory of yoga by stating the ultimate of goal of yoga life, "yoga is to become with our own individual self (tada-drashtah-swarupe-awasthanam)."

Here some of questions you may have:
- ❖ How do we calm our mind?
- ❖ How to attain stillness from the whirlpools of our mind?

The answer is really simple, 'Yoga Abhyasa and Vairajna', do your yoga practice to clear the mind and to develop a positive mindset, along with detaching or dissociating from all that is causing distress to our mind. Swamiji Dr. Gitananda Giriji reminded us again and again in his yoga teachings that, "do your best and leave the rest".

Patanjali in V4, begins his teachings on understanding and analysing our mind, its faculties and the outcomes in the form of worldly suffering. He mentions that when we are not in a state of Union or Oneness (Samadhi or Swasthya), we are caught up in chitta-vrittis (whirlpools of the mind). These whirlpools are either coloured or manipulated (Klishta) or uncoloured or pure (Aklishta) (virttiya-panchattaya-klishta-aklishta).

Patanjali details the five fluctuations or fields of chitta-vrittis which may be painful or pleasant, pure or manipulated-

- ❖ Pramana – Valid cognition
- ❖ Viparyaya – Misconception
- ❖ Vikalpa- Imagination
- ❖ Nidra- Sleep or lack of cognition of surroundings
- ❖ Smriti- Memory or recollection of previous experiences

Pramana or Valid Cognition

It is worth contemplating that, if what we know, what we think and what we believe is valid or correct? many of the skills and lessons we have learned directly from a teacher or guide, through self-practice or self-learning, holds its own validity. For example, we all know the importance of hydration from our experience as well as what we have learned or studied. According to medical studies around 60-70 percent people are clinically dehydrated. So even though most of us are aware of the fact that we must keep hydrated for health and well-being, it gets shadowed or coloured by other mental activities or distractions we may be going through.

So the idea of Pramana or Validity is knowing what is right as well as bringing it into our practice, which can be seen in two steps: knowing what reality or true knowledge is and make it useful or applied.

Patanjali mentions three sources of Valid Cognition or Knowledge: -
❖ *Pratyaksha* (Direct experience): Direct experience by means of our five senses, mind and buddhi, for example visiting the beach or nature in gereral to experience the freshness and richness of prana or vital energy as it is described in Hatha yoga scriptures.
❖ *Anumana* (Inference, Assumptions): Using our logic, reasoning and intellectual assumptions to lead us to right knowledge, for example seeing smoke in the distance and assuming that there might a fire, which can be ascertained by following the direction of the smoke to find the truth.
❖ *Agamah* (Scriptures or Valid Sources of Knowledge): Scriptures, a Teacher, or Someone else's experience can also help us know the truth or to have right knowledge, for example you can study medical books to find the negative effects of many drugs on our body and mind and avoid substance abuse. Here the Yoga Sutra of Patanjali, the Bhagavad Gita, Yoga Vashistha, Upanishads, etc., are understood to be an Agamah.

A point to remember here is that Yoga is experiential (yoga-anubhuta-vishaya) and one should experience (anubhava) its reality by bringing knowledge in through practice (jnana-abhyasa). For example, someone may tell you that Hatha yoga and pranayama are really good for your body, mind, breath and vital energy. You may believe that person and know the benefits of yoga, but in a true sense, the only way it will become true to you is by following the Hatha Yoga and Pranayama practices to experience the benefits, which will be your own true cognition or experience (anubhava).

Viparyaya or Misconception

The second field of mental whirlpools is misconception. This is an outcome of the deceptive appearance of the object itself. The issue is rooted in the fact that instead of seeing things objectively, we see what we want to see in objects or events. Our cognition is based on our perceptions, through the five senses (pancha-jnanendriya-jaya). Our misconceptions can be the outcome of Pra-pancha-jnendriya-jaya, where 'pra-pancha-indriya' means perceiving through the deceived five senses. For example, we all may be looking at the same tree, but our perception or experience of it can be very different, based on our likes and dislikes, knowledge, interests, etc. A carpenter may see the furniture he can make from it; an artist may see a painting he can draw; a tired person may see the shelter; person feeling cold may see the wood for fire; a child may see a try to climb and have fun, etc.

Vikalpa or Imagination

This is a more subtle operating field of our mind compared to Pramana and Viparyaya. Vikalpa is an idea, a thought, or story that we create in our mind without any facts or reality. By repeating it enough times, we convince ourselves to believe it to be true. Vikalpa can also be translated as doubt, indecision, daydreaming, etc. Yoga explains that our mind cannot actually distinguish what is real and what is imagination. As a yogic sankalap you may follow some of the positive imagery contemplations: I am happy; my life is worthy and amazing; I am kind and compassionate etc. This will develop sense of positive attitude and gradually will become part of our self-identity and practice.

We all have created an imagery world of our own based on our desires, expectations, experiences and thought processes. When we are caught up with any negative mental activities, we tend towards negative and self-destructive imaginings. If we are suffering with anxiety, fears, phobias, mental instability or psychosis, we can easily get caught up in imagining terrible situations which multiply our mental suffering. Yoga guides us to develop positive, creative and spiritual thoughts to move from lower to higher states of mind.

Nidra or Deep Sleep

Nidra literally translates as 'deep sleep'. Patanjali mentions that Nidra is a state of emptiness or inability to know what is happening around us. We all know that sleep is very important for us, for our bodies and our minds. If we have one night of improper sleep, we suffer all day with tiredness, lethargy and dullness. A deep sleep helps our body and mind to rejuvenate and prepare for another day.

Maharishi Patanjali mentions that Nidra is a state when our mind is feeling heavy and absent from reality or the activities of the present moment. We all frequently experience this state, like when after reading several pages of your favourite book or story, you realise that you can't remember what you actually read. Our mind can actually be tired or caught up in imagination or other memories. This state can be the result of boredom, exhaustion, stress or other life issues.

Nidra can also be understood as the non-deliberate absence of mind, focus, thought process or perception. It is also absence of reasoning (viveka) and knowledge (jnana). Nidra can be also understood as the absence of cognition which leads to inability to explain or know what is happening in and around us.

Yoga also details many Yoga Nidra Practices to induce deep sleep to rest our body and mind to enhance our healing and homeostasis processes.

Smriti or Memory

Maharishi Patanjali explains that memory is the retention and recollection of previous experiences. All our conscious experiences are living impressions on our individual brain's and are stored as a memory. It is not so easy for our mind and brain to recognise if the memory is true, false, or imagery. If several family members write the memory of same event around a dinning table, each one of them will write different experience based on their own experience, interests and liking and disliking.

Our memories can bring a sense of joy, excitement, stress, anger, fear or agitation depending on nature of the memory and our understanding of the event. Our memories influence our day-to-day thoughts, feelings, and perceptions. For example, If someone has suffered with a bad or abusive relationship in the past, they may suffer when starting a new relationship and find taking the risk of living whole heartedly in the present moment difficult.

Also, many of our judgements around ourselves or other people are based on our memories. You may have heard, "she is untrustworthy, "I am always late", "He is so calm or peaceful", "I get angry so easily" and this is all based on our memories with those people or ourselves.

Negative, painful and traumatic memories play a huge role in mental health issues and prevent us from living in the abundance of life and having the ability to forgive or love. These memories can easily steal our present moments. We struggle to experience events without being biased, judgemental or critical, under the influence of these painful memories.

So here Patanjali in Yoga Sutras, it details Smriti or memories as one of the chitta-vrittis or whirlpool of the mind because they create thought patterns and impressions on our body, mind and experiences. Furthermore, as part of the chitta-vritties, every memory creates a new impression which leads to pleasant or painful experiences.

Yoga guides us on the path to liberate our mind from all the painful and negative mental impressions, whirlpools and mental faculties to attain the state of inner quietness or tranquillity.

Abhyasa Vairajna to attain Stillness of mind

Understanding of the Chitta-Vrittis or five modifications or functions of the mind can help us understanding the operating fields of our mind. Maharishi Patanjali provides us then with the tools which we can use to minimize them. Even the ability to be able to recognise these whirlpools of our mind and their operating fields, can help us see their true nature and separate them from the real and unreal mind fields. It is like stepping out of our mind and instead of being a victim to all these modifications or fields of the mind, we become aware and can witness them without reacting to them, allowing us to develop the ability to differentiate the mind, reality and its fluctuations.

Patanjali teaches us that by means of abhyasa or regular practice and vairajna or dissociation or detachment, one can attain stillness of mind. So the simple solution is explained well here by our Guru Swamiji Dr. Gitananda Giriji-

The 3R's- *Regularity, Repetition, Rhythm* and Do your best and leave the rest.

References and Further Resources

1. *Yoga Step By Step by Swamiji Dr Gitananda Giriji*
2. *Talks and Teachings on Yoga by Dr Ananda Balayogi Bhavanani; Youtube link :- https://www.youtube.com/user/yognat2001*
3. *Authentic Teachings of Yoga during six months intensive 2006-07, course at ICYER, Ananda Ashram, Puducheery, India with Ammaji Meenakshi Devi, Dr Ananda, Smt Devesana and Dr Nalini Devi.*
4. *Ashtanga Yoga of Patanjali by Swamiji Dr Gitananda Giriji*
5. *Yoga and Modern Man by Dr Ananda Balayogi Bhavanani*
6. *Yoga for Health and Healing by Dr Ananda Balayogi Bhavanani*
7. *Understanding of the Yoga Darshan by Dr Ananda Balayogi Bhavanani*
8. *Exploring Yoga Philosophy, 121 Authentic Yoga Lessons, By Yogachariya Jnandev*
9. *Yoga Questions and Answers by Yogachariya Jnandev*
10. *Yoga way of Life by Yogachariya Jnandev*

Kleshas: - the main causes of suffering

Klesha is a Sanskrita term, which means affliction, pain, distress, poison, or obstacle. These are internal blockages or states or modifications of our mind that arise in our mind and lead us to suffering. Kleshas can cause an intense disturbance in our inner mind fields and act like a toxic inner environment in our life. Kleshas can also be seen as mental afflictions or afflictive emotions.

Maharishi Patanjali mentions five kleshas (pancha-kleshas) as the main cause of all forms of suffering in life itself and the cause of obstacles on our spiritual path. These Kleshas are the root cause of all our pain and suffering in our human experience. We lose our ability to see the light and truth and lose our insight when we are living our life under these Kleshas. They lead us to actions, reactions with painful consequences.

These Kleshas and their fields of suffering are caused by changes in our outer and inner world, distressing experiences, samaskaras (deep behaviour patterns, impressions or desires), chitta-vrittis (whirlpools of mind), our Karma and conflicts (Dvandvas). If we are able to understand the Kleshas it can help us realise that 'change is the only reality' and instead of fighting with it, we need to learn to flow with it. Being attached to old memories, objects, places, people and possessions will gradually lead us to pain in one form or another, as what comes must also go.

The Yoga Sutras mention that we must remove these Kleshas as soon as we become aware of them arising and never let them grow. It is like clearing the weeds in your garden, is much easier in the beginning before they spread everywhere. Understanding and freeing ourselves from the Kleshas can lead us to a healthy mind and deeper spiritual yoga sadhana.

Avidya (Ignorance)

Avidya is ignorance, lack of knowledge or lack of insight. Maharishi Patanjali mentions that avidya is the source and root cause of all the other Kleshas. In a spiritual context it means 'knowing all material objects as the eternal truth' and also not knowing the eternal and all-pervading nature of atma or purusha (individual self) and Parmatman or Ishwara (the supreme self). In the case of negative thoughts, feelings and negative states of mind, many of us can easily feel trapped and believe that they there forever, but the reality is that our thoughts, emotions and feelings are all temporary and change all of the time. Unless we realise the temporary nature of our chitta-vrittis and kleshas, we cannot see the true nature of the mind which is 'sat-chita-ananda'.

Avidya or ignorance in Yogic terms is also not practising what we already know is right for us to do for our health and well-being. It is the reasoning which leads us to ignore what it is appropriate to do and to do what it is inappropriate to do. Swamiji Dr. Gitananda Giriji explains that "to grow on our spiritual path one must not avoid good for sake of pleasure".

Try to remind yourself that your true nature is love, peace, joy, health, bliss, harmony, forgiveness, patience and helping others.

Asmita (I-ness or Egoism)

Asmita is the Klesha where we see the Self as separate from everything around us. This puts the ego at the forefront of everything and values material objects and possessions as far more important than anything else in life. For this mindset, it really matters how the 'I' sees things, how things affect 'me' and what is 'mine'. This Klesha result in suffering as the ego always needs external approval and material fruits, which are not always there. Also, for the things we own, there is always a fear of losing them and that gives rise to fear and uncertainty. We may also place too high expectations on ourselves and others, which are very hard to meet.

This self-indulgence takes us away from our true nature which likes to love and care, give and take, share with others, and wants peace, harmony and abundance. We need to remind ourselves that we are far greater than the limited 'I'. We are all-connected and all-one.

Raga (Attachments or Likings)

Raga is the Klesha which means attachment to our desires, belongings, people and all that we like or feel a sense of comfort in. It becomes negative when our happiness is dependent on external things, people or accomplishments as we fear them being taken away or disappearing, which makes us feel sad. These strong attachments give rise to insecurity, fear and anxiety.

We need to remember that our true happiness resides within our hearts and minds, with the virtues of contentment, letting go, giving away things we don't need anymore, compassion and detachment. Our minds and senses are naturally looking outward and drawn to worldly objects, which takes us away from the inner joy.

Krishna in the Bhagavad Gita explains that earning and keeping what is essential for your healthy and comfortable life is important, but being greedy and accumulating what is not necessary causes loss of peace and these things should be given away to people who need it most.

Never let yourself be degraded by self-will
(The Bhagavad Gita, Ch.6: v.5).

Dvesha (Aversion, repulsion)

Dvesha means avoiding things, it may be tasks or people we dislike or feel unhappy with. This is based on the presumption that many external objects, activities or people are going to cause afflictive emotions, pain and suffering. We try our best to avoid them if we can. Even many of our desires, when we cannot fulfil them, we can develop an aversion towards them. In many ways the Raga-Dvesha or liking-disliking are two sides of the same coin and feed into each other.

Our Raga can be indulgence in watching online stuff, losing time in scrolling along social media sites. Dvesha can be feeling aversion towards going out for walk, doing some exercise or getting some work done. They both are contrary, but also feed on each other. Dvesha also causes anxiety and fear. Swamiji Dr. Gitananda Giriji mentions that "what is good may not be pleasant, while what is pleasant may not be good".

Abhinivesha (Fear of Letting Go, Attachment)

Abhinivesha is that deep clinging or attachment to life, or survival instincts. Yogic wisdom reminds us again and again that the only reality in our material world (prakriti) is change or transformation. Everything is constantly changing for the better or worse. Still one of the most common fears that we all go through, is fear of death. This fear can be for our own death or for losing someone else that we care about. It can also be fear to lose other things, for example a job, a relationship or even some of the deep-rooted negative habits or health issues. Out of the fear, we try everything to control situations, objects, people or life itself. This clinging leads us to fear, insecurity, anger, frustration, anxiety and stress.

Many of us may also suffer with fear of change as it requires letting go of our present situation. This blocks the free flow of energy and stops the abundance of flow in our lives. Each of these Kleshas lead to one another and many times you will find that you have just managed to deal with one and the next one takes over. You may have overcome attachment and aversion, but it will be followed by fear of letting go or abhinivesha. When we are caught up in the Kleshas, it is easy to forget what we already have to enjoy, appreciate and be grateful for.

The Yoga Vasistha mentions that fear and anxiety (bhaya -chinta) will gradually consume like a slow burning fire consumes everything under the shadow of smoke.

Our Karma and Kleshas

Lots of our Karmas and Actions are caused by the influence of Kleshas and we accumulate them as Seed Karma. These seed karmas will become active when it's the right opportunity for them. You can understand it by looking at flowers or fruit trees, how they wait for right season and ideal conditions to bring forth flowers and fruits. Latent impressions or modifications that are afflicted as a result of other actions (karmas) and caused by Kleshas, may become active and experienced in a present life-time or a future life time at some point.

If there are even traces of these Kleshas that remain at the subtlest level, one has to go through life-birth cycles which brings results in the type of birth, the span of life and the experiences one has to go through. Here Kleshas are seen as the root cause behind our Karma or actions and birth, life span and experiences are outcomes or fruits of actions or Karma.

Kleshas and Karmas which are of good virtue will bring pleasant fruits while ones which are of no good virtue will bring painful experiences.

Maharishi Patanjali Offers the Following Remedies:

❖ *Aparigraha* (Letting Go or non-clinging) - When the five types of modifications (kleshas) are in their subtle form, or are in their merely potential form, they must be dissolved through letting go from consciousness itself for complete cessation. These afflictions are easy to remove at the very beginning, like the weeds in your garden to be removed at the very beginning when first sprouting. Once these Kleshas become potential, they take over our Buddhi-intellect and conscious-self.

❖ *Dhyana* - These modifications of the mind at a time when they are afflictive or have some potency of impressions (klishta), they are to be removed and let go through a suitable meditation.

❖ *Viveka* (Discriminative Intelligence) - A wise, discriminating person will see all worldly experiences as painful and try to remain in balance or equanimity in every situation, because of reasoning we are able to understand that all these experiences lead to more consequences, anxiety, and deep behaviour patterns or habits (samskaras), as well as acting in opposition to our natural qualities.

❖ *Vairajna* - Detachment from worldly objects, desires and their sensual experiences.

❖ *Sraddha and Viriya* - Faith in self, life and teachings along with Viriya or life-force that gives us determination and the ability to take initiatives to find our way out from darkness to light.

❖ *Sakshi Bhava* (the attitude of witnessing our mind) - The objects to be known or experienced by a Sadhaka are by their nature of: illumination (understandability) or sentience (feeling or sensation): activity (action) or mutability (alteration); inertia (inaction) or status (condition). They contain the elements and the powers of the senses and exist for the purpose of experiencing the world and for liberation or enlightenment. Maharishi Patanjali explains that a Sadhaka should try to be aware of all these objects of experiences like the sense organs, mind, intellect and consciousness (atma-jnana) and develop the ability to be aware or witness them without being the victim or consumer.

❖ *Jnana* (Right Knowledge) - Knowing the truth about the changing nature of all the material objects and realising the eternal nature of atman or soul is known to be the subtle Truth or Reality. Developing a right mindset, positive attitude and life values can be founded in appropriate teachings.

❖ *Ashtanga Yoga* - Maharishi Patanjali provides us step by step approach by means of eight limbs of Yoga to liberate us from worldly suffering, negative thoughts, chitta-vrittis, kleshas, obstacles and all our mental, emotional and spiritual issues. These limbs are:

  ❖ Pancha-Yamas- Five moral virtues of non-violence, truth, non-stealing, energy discipline, and non greed.

  ❖ Pancha Niyama- Five ethical and moral observances of purity, contentment, discipline of practice, introspection, and faith in the divine.

  ❖ Asana- A state of being or the way we hold our body, mind and spirit. This limb extends with Hatha Yoga to prepare our body, mind and pranic energy for higher practices.

  ❖ Pranayama- Using the breath as a tool to refine and enhance the subtle pranic energies or vital life forces.

  ❖ Pratyahara- Sensory withdrawal or freeing our mind from the objects and subjects of sensory experience.

  ❖ Dharna: Effort to focus our mind on single-point, object or mindfulness concentration practice.

- ❖ Dhyana: Absorption of mind in the point of focus or dharna known as meditation.
- ❖ Samadhi: Transcending the 'I' and becoming one the our True Self, Purusha and letting the Purusha or Self to unite with the Paramatman or Supreme Self.

In this chapter we have examined the Kleshas, the internal blockages that arise in our minds and lead us to suffering. The Kleshas can cause an intense disturbance in our inner mind fields and act like a toxic inner environment in our life. We have learned that the Yoga Sutras advise that we must remove these Kleshas as soon as we become aware of them arising and never let them grow and we have the eight remedies from Maharishi Patanjali to assist us. By the practice of Sakshi Bhava we can be the witness and distance ourselves from our chameleon like mental tendencies and with this anchor, become the witnessing mind with its ability to be detached and impartial.

References and Further Resources

1. Yoga Step By Step by Swamiji Dr Gitananda Giriji
2. Ashtanga Yoga of Patanjali by Swamiji Dr Gitananda Giriji
3. Yoga and Modern Man by Dr Ananda Balayogi Bhavanani
4. Yoga for Health and Healing by Dr Ananda Balayogi Bhavanani
5. Understanding of the Yoga Darshan by Dr Ananda Balayogi Bhavanani
6. Exploring Yoga Philosophy, 121 Authentic Yoga Lessons, By Yogachariya Jnandev
7. Yoga Questions and Answers by Yogachariya Jnandev
8. Yoga way of Life by Yogachariya Jnandev

Lesson 52.
Obstacles in Yogic Evolution

In order to grow on the yoga path of spiritual evolution, and obtain maximum benefit, the Sadhaka needs to know and become aware of the obstacles that he is going to come face-to-face with, which may disrupt the yoga journey. This will enable a Sadhaka to understand life's challenges and problems. It is important to remember that to transcend the body, mind and emotions, we need to know and understand them first. Understanding the obstacles is essential to help the Yoga Sadhaka to be prepared and to be able to prevent in the now, rather than to repent and need to repair later on.

Three hundred years ago a Great unknown Rishi, author of The Shiva-Samhita cautioned his disciples in the following verses "Though there are many hard and almost insurmountable obstacles in Yoga, yet the Yogi should go on with his practice at every obstacle and problem; even were his life to come to the throat". Shiva Samhita is one of three major surviving classical treatises on Hatha Yoga, the other two being the Gheranda Samhita and the Hatha Yoga Pradipika. The Shiva Samhita is considered the most comprehensive and the most democratic treatise on Hatha Yoga. Here the author is describing that the inner journey to the Self or Consciousness is not always easy. There will be many obstacles to face and overcome. There's no denying that yoga practice can be frustrating or disappointing at times. Your situation might be not supporting your yoga practice, but you should always adhere to yoga in all and every situation. Your strong will and commitment with awareness will help you to deal with the obstacles.

In a sense, obstacles are defence mechanisms of the body and mind against the process of yogic evolution transcending body, mind and emotional conditioning. They're part of our mental conditioning historically or our attachment to living with our problems, suffering and miseries. These hold us away from experiencing the higher self and prevent us from pushing our practice along to be free and to enjoy the higher bliss. These defence mechanisms result in obstacles, where Sadhaka move away from the yogic life, ignoring the body, mind and emotions and are not able to understand the nature of negative mental processes and their destructive qualities. The Sanskrit word 'Antaraya' is translated as hindrances or obstacle here, which means 'to come between'. Thus antarayas move toward or come in between to produce a gap or interval. In classical yoga antarayas are physical, mental emotional problems or disturbances that come face to face in our yogic evolutionary process. The nine Antarayas: Impediments to progress on the path of Yoga

Probably the best-known traditional obstacles are the nine listed in the first chapter of Patanjali's Yoga Sutra (Ch.1: v.30): The first, sickness (vyadhi), is a physical obstacle. The other eight are mental obstacles: languor (styana); doubt (samshaya); heedlessness (pramada); sloth (alasya); dissipation (avirati); false vision (bhranti-darshana); non-attainment of yogic stages (alabdha-bhumikatva); and instability in these stages (anavasthitatva).

❖ *Vyadhi* Disease or Sickness - This first yoga obstacle refers to physical illnesses. Practicing yoga when health is not good, for whatever reason, is always more difficult for Sadhaka. One of the reasons behind the origin as well as the growth of Hatha-Yoga as a system itself was to gain health, fitness, and vitality; Sadhakas or followers were being able to prevent or cure physical, mental and emotional diseases. The Hatha-Yoga Pradipika of Swami Svatmaram Suri and The Gherand Samhita are a few of the scriptures enumerating yoga techniques and tools to deal with disease. Following a well-balanced and healthy life-style, a vegetarian nutritional diet, a balance of rest and exercise, practising positive thinking, contemplations and visualisation as part of yoga practices, will ensure the Vyadhi obstacle is overcome.

❖ *Styana* Languor- The next significant obstacle on the yoga journey is an advanced state of apathy. This apathy diminishes your willingness to practice yoga and commit to your responsibilities. It can lead to neglect and reluctance to practise yoga in the way that it should be practised to get the benefits from it.

❖ *Sanshaya* Doubt - The next obstacle is doubting the benefits and stages of yoga practices. This comes when you have low self-esteem. There are two kinds of doubt. In the first kind the Sadhaka may doubt the practice of yoga itself. This can be due to having a teacher or a yoga approach which is not fulfilling the sadhaka's needs or temperament or because the practice seems ineffective in overcoming obstacles. The second kind of doubt is self-doubt. Here the Sadhaka loses faith in his/her own self. The first one is easy to overcome by finding a different teacher, or approach but in the second one the Sadhaka might lose interest in yoga as they have lost their own self-interest.

❖ *Pramada Heedlessness*- The 4th yoga obstacle Pramada, occurs when the Sadhaka lacks care and negligence takes over the Yoga Sadhana. Yoga, with its combination of arts and sciences, practices, experimentation and experiences requires a unique approach and attitude. If a Sadhaka doesn't have the proper emotional and mental attitudes, it might turn the positive aspects of yoga into negative ones.

❖ **Alasya Sloth**- One cannot attain a goal in yoga with a lazy and inert state of mind and body. It is hard to deal with one's own will power and this arouses Alasya. The path to Yoga success is tough most of the time and strong will power can support you along the way. As our master Swamij Gitanada Giri states, the yoga path is like 'walking a razors edge'. A passive approach will almost certainly lead to a slow and ineffective advance so the Sadhaka should use an and conscious yoga approach to avoid or overcome this obstacle.

❖ **Avirati Dissipation**- The next obstacle is indulgence in the material world and pleasures. Physical objects hold a magnetic attraction to almost every-one. Yoga demands that you to let go of these material desires and be free of worldly attachments to progress in the realm of the spiritual evolution.

❖ **Bhrantidarshan** False vision- If you misunderstand the path, you are taking while practising yoga, it can lead to disappointment. You can counter the Bhrantidarshan obstacle by studying scriptures as well as meeting different yoga masters and listening to them to wipe out ignorance and false vision. Also keeping your hopes and expectations in close contact with reality will be a great help.

❖ **Alabdha-bhumikatva** Non-attainment of yogic stages - This yoga obstacle, often arises when a Sadhaka is not achieving the desired goals on the yoga path. It takes a long time to come out of the shell of mental conditioning and experience higher stages as well as also being victims of our own discouragement. When a failure occurs we fall into a state of self-deprecation, accompanied by pessimism. Failing to reach a step on your path to achieve your ideals can lead to worst forms of this yoga obstacle. To overcome this obstacle a Sadhaka has to keep repeating his yoga practices, regularly in rhythm. Our Master Amma always says "do your best and leave the rest".

❖ **Anavasthitatva** Instability - Many times we get to hear from our students in the first session that, "I've never done anything as incredible as this before", "Yoga is changing my whole life", "You are a great teacher and I am so pleased to find you". After this promising start, the Sadhaka slips back to what he considers to be a lower level of practice or feels the miseries of life strongly. Patanjali named obstacle as 'anavasthitva'- instability or unsteadiness. To overcome this sadhaka needs to accept the phases of yoga experiences in the moment without being frustrated or trying to force the experience.

The Four Vikshepa or Distractions

In the Yoga-Sutra (Ch.1 v.31) "Duhkha-daurmanasya-angam-ejayatva-shvasa-prashvasah vikshepa-sahabhuva", Maharishi Patanjali states that these obstacles result in four distractions (vikshepa): suffering or distress (duhkha); depression or melancholy (daurmanasya); physical restlessness (angam-ejayatva); and disturbed breathing (prashvasah). These distractions are signs that something is wrong or imbalanced with your practice.

- ❖ Duhkha - pain (mental or physical), agony, suffering, sorrow
- ❖ Daurmanasya - sadness, despair, dejection, frustration, depression, anguish
- ❖ Angam-ejayatva - shakiness, unsteadiness, movement, tremor of the limbs or body (anga - limbs or body)
- ❖ Shvasa - inhalation, inspiration (implying irregular inhalation)
- ❖ Prashvasah - exhalation, expiration (implying irregular exhalation)
- ❖ They can be accompanied by Sahabhuva - companions, accompaniments or correlates

These four distractions arise as a consequence of the nine obstacles described in the previous sutra. If you try to look into your own life then these distractions are easy to notice. When you find yourself under influence one of these, you need to find out what's going on in subtler levels and work it out. A Sadhaka can notice how easy it is to observe when someone is experiencing pain, dejection, restlessness of the body, or irregularities of the breath. You may not be able to know the root cause, but you can spot the symptoms on the surface.

Overcoming obstacles by meditation

When we observe our own body gestures, body language, general level of pain and mood, mental and emotional activities, we can easily see if something is going on at a subtler level. To try to find out what is distracting you and how it is disturbing your yoga practice, as distraction is followed by disturbance, in the Sutra (Ch.1. v.32) Maharishi Patanjali describes the solution to these obstacles, which is 'single pointed concentration, or meditation (dhyana). A Sadhaka must choose a suitable object for meditation.

Tat-pratisedha-artham-eka-tattva-abhyasah (Yoga Sutra, 1:32)

For preventing and overcoming of obstacles and their consequences, a Sadhaka should practice or cultivate the habit of focusing on a single object or principle. When the mind is focused it is less likely to be lost in worldly maya/illusion or destruction resulting in disturbances. There are many tools, objects or principles to focus, meditate or contemplate on to attain the stage of single pointed awareness or meditation.

How to work with obstacles

In the beginning of our yoga journey even before we come to face these obstacles, we can try to understand ourselves, our strengths as well as our weakness in order to avoid these obstacles. Now the first thing to find out is 'Am I ready to start my yoga journey?' Find out how much time I am going to put in it. Then think about what is involved in following the yoga path. Many Sadhakas realise that, after a few sessions of half-hearted practice that they don't really feel that they fit with the yoga path. They may not be interested in yoga practices. They may not have the time for yoga, or they may be not able to give up worldly pleasures that are not allowed on the serious yoga path. They might have to spend the time on another responsibility in their lives, or they may not see the point of the yoga practice. If you find you are not ready then let the practice go and wait for the right time or make an easy and practical space for yoga in your life and bring the changes gradually with patience. If you are ready to start, then the next step is to accept yourself as you are with love and respect - even your ignorance. In beginning of The Yoga Vashishtha it is stated that one who is not too ignorant and one who is not enlightened is eligible to study this scripture, allow yourself to accept that there is much more to learn, practice and realize and that you are not all knowing. By accepting mental processes and ignorance you can weaken their power or allow them to be dissolved. This ignorance or avidya is in respect of consciousness rather than knowledge or intelligence.

The third step is to find out how truly you want to know 'who am I'? It is very important to have a strong desire to start your yoga journey. This will push you through and help you to grow spiritually even in adverse situations. The Yoga path is not only mechanical or physical practices, it is also mental and consciousness practice.

Ramana Maharshi said that-

"Every living being longs always to be happy, untainted by sorrow; and everyone has the greatest love for himself, which is solely due to the fact that happiness is his real nature. Hence, in order to realize that inherent and untainted happiness… it is essential that he should know himself. For obtaining such knowledge, the enquiry 'Who am I?' in quest of the Self is the best means."

❖ *Faith*- In the righteousness of what you are doing as well as in your strength or ability to attain the success in your yoga path will keep motivating you in moments of distraction. "The person who has control over himself attains verily success through faith; none other can succeed. Therefore, with faith,

Yoga should be practiced with care and perseverance." (Shiva-Samhita).

- ❖ **Intention**- Your clear intention and constant mindfulness (smirti) of what you are doing and why, in regard to both short-term and long-term goals and in the subtle adjustments of everyday practice will help you to prevent as well as prepare to deal with the obstacles.

- ❖ **Contentment** (Samtosha)- Being realistic and accepting both success and failure with grace and self-respect; and also willingness to take risks and embrace uncertainty will prevent you from disappointment. "As long as one is not satisfied in the self, he will be subjected to sorrow. With the rise of contentment, the purity of one's heart blooms. The contented man who possesses nothing owns the world." (Yoga-Vashishtha).

- ❖ **Discrimination** (Viveka)- Carefully discriminating between what is right and wrong or using discernment in your yoga sadhana as to what is important what is not. Avoiding what is not important will keep you safe from obstacles.

- ❖ **Svadhyaya**- Awareness of body, mind and emotions can keep you notifying yourself about ongoing or upcoming obstacles as well as their results. "By listening to instructions, by contemplation and by being in the company of a calm and sure-minded preceptor, doubts can be removed." (Shiva-Samhita).

Maharishi Patanjali Offers following four remedies to overcome the obstacles:

- ❖ **Maitri** - Maitri is a Sanskrit word which can be translated as 'friendship', 'friendliness' or 'benevolence'. It can also be used to describe the mental union that takes place when two people are on the same wavelength. The Pali version of this word that is often used is Metta. Another way of describing maitri is a form of love which excludes the suffering that can arise from attachment (known as upadana).

- ❖ **Karuna** - Means compassion. Karuna is described as one of the nine virtuous emotions described in Hindu life-style for peace and harmony. In this life principle one needs to be free of self-centredness and feelings of pity, resentment, anger, frustration and guilt. We all must cultivate compassion in our thoughts, feelings, emotions and actions. It is a further reflective practice of friendliness towards each and every one. We can also understand the virtue of compassion or Karuna as the ability to let go and forgive. We can be extremely harsh to ourselves and others for little mistakes and things which can be one of the causal factors in many health issues.

- ❖ **Mudita** - Is detailed as one of the tools to deals with the obstacles in our lives. Mudita is state of inner joy, happiness and cheerfulness from our own as well as other's accomplishments without any form of self-interest. This is also a living concept of attitude of looking forward to every event and opportunity in life and trying to see the goodness in all. When we are happy or cheerful, it relaxes our muscles and releases endorphins or feel-good chemicals in body, which help in the healing and rejuvenation processes of our body and mind. This attitude of mudita can greatly enhance our life quality and purpose.

❖ *Upeksha* - Upeksha means detachment, a balanced mindset, tolerance and equanimity. Upeksha does not mean indifference. It is an element of true love and has as its seed the wisdom of equality that removes boundaries, discrimination and prejudice; leading to the unity where there is no self and no other. Upeksha comes from mindfulness.

Yoga explains these four elements in behaviour with ourselves and with others for living a healthy and happy life and attaining our full potential: maitri loving kindness or friendliness; karuna, compassion; mudita, joyfulness; and upeksha, detachment. These are four basic qualities of a Yogi free from all mundane, mental and emotional afflictions. The Upeksha are to be cultivated in all adverse situations and through keeping ourselves calm and not reactive to various situations or stimulus, we are able to follow our Yogic path.

In this final chapter we have considered the need to be aware of the obstacles that we can face in our spiritual path of yoga. We remember that to transcend the body, mind and emotions, we need to know and understand our strengths as well as our weakness and we need to cultivate compassion to ourselves and to others. With discrimination and right intention, being realistic and accepting both success and failure with grace and self-respect, we can follow our sadhana and progress on our Yoga path and support Sadhaka on theirs. This is our great privilege and we acknowledge the renowned teachings from my beloved Guru Yogacharini Ammaji Meenakshi Devi Bhavanani Ji, my Mentor and Guide Yogachariya Dr. Ananda Balayogi Bhavanani and all the great Sages, Rishis and Yogis who guide us here.

References and Further Resources
1. Yoga Step By Step by Swamiji Dr Gitananda Giriji
2. Ashtanga Yoga of Patanjali by Swamiji Dr Gitananda Giriji
3. Yoga and Modern Man by Dr Ananda Balayogi Bhavanani
4. Yoga for Health and Healing by Dr Ananda Balayogi Bhavanani
5. Understanding of the Yoga Darshan by Dr Ananda Balayogi Bhavanani
6. Exploring Yoga Philosophy, 121 Authentic Yoga Lessons, By Yogachariya Jnandev
7. Yoga Questions and Answers by Yogachariya Jnandev
8. Yoga way of Life by Yogachariya Jnandev

Dosha Test
(a- vata, b- pitta, c-kapha)

1. How do you describe your skin?
a. dry, rough and cold
b. fair, soft and warm
c. Pale, cold, and oily

2. Generally your hair is: -
a. dry, coarse, fine to medium thickness
b. fine, fair or reddish
c. Thick, oily, lustrous

3. Which one of the following skin problems are you more prone to?
a. dry and rough patches
b. heat rashes, spots
c. Excessive oiliness

4. How would you describe your body structure?
a. thin and tall
b. medium height and built
c. plump, stocky, large chest

5. Which one of the following describes you best?
a. hard to gain weight
b. easy to lose and gain weight
c. Hard to lose weight

5. How do you describe yourself in reference to heat tolerance?
a. high, enjoy the heat
b. poor, prefer moderate or cool temperatures
c. High, prefer hot and dry weather

6. Which one of the following describes your perspiration levels?
a. minimum
b. freely, especially when exercising
c. Moderate, clammy

7. How do you describe your body temperature?

a. low, cold hands and feet

b. high, feel warm or hot

c. low, body feels cold

8. Which type of weather do you prefer most?

a. hot, humid, sunny

b. moderate to cool

c. hot, sunny, dry and a breeze

9. How would you describe your sleeping pattern?

a. light and disturbed

b. sound sleep

c. Heavy, deep and prolonged

10. How do you describe your physical activities?

a. quick, erratic, hyperactive

b. moderate, motivated, purposeful

c. slow, steady, graceful

11. How would you describe yourself in generally?

a. clumsy, uncoordinated

b. regimented, forceful

c. Lethargic, lack of lustre

12. Which one of following describes your usual mental state?

a. restless, quick thinker, imaginative

b. intellectual, organised, perfectionist

c. Steady, calm, not easily disturbed.

13. Do you easily feel?

a. ungrounded and disconnected

b. impatient, irritable and angry

c. slow, dull and uninspired

14. Have you recently felt?

a. anxious and confused

b. critical and fanatical

c. lethargic, and resistant to change

15. You generally describe your mental attitude as
a. creative, expressive
b. determined and passionate
c. Contented and methodical

16. How would you describe your memory?
a. Good short term memory
b. generally good
c. Slow to retain, good long term memory

17. How do you describe your response to stress?
a. anxious, fearful
b. confrontational
c. Quiet, introverted

18. How do you describe your beliefs?
a. changeable, rebellious
b. strongly held
c. constant and conservative

19. How do you feel in general in your life?
a. erratic, free spirit, unplanned
b. ambitious, good planner
c. safe, steady, not comfortable with changes

20. How would you describe yourself on a good day?
a. secure, grounded, settled
b. confident, friendly, content
c. warm hearted, loving, active

Test Results

The Vata

Vata is responsible for all movement, for breathing, for transport of material within the body, and for all elimination and secretions.

Vata regulates the heartbeat and the nerve impulses.

Vata quality predominant people have a light bone structure and low weight. They don't put on weight easily and have an irregular appetite. Vata people are sensitive to noise and react sharply to sounds. As Vata quality people get cold easily, they enjoy hot temperatures and like warm foods and drinks. They are flexible, enthusiastic, imaginative and talkative.

If Vata energy is out of balance, the persona may suffer with nervousness, anxiety worries and sleep problems. Other signs of disturbed Vata are dry skin, constipation, and cold hands and feet.

The Pitta

Pitta is simply the principle of metabolism. It is responsible for the digestion, the absorption of nutrients in the intestines, the regulation of body temperature, sharpness of vision and for the intellect.

People with a predominance of Pitta quality eat a lot and generally are able to tolerate any type of food.

They have regular bowel movement. They get easily upset if they have to delay a meal.

The Pitta type people have an average body build and are good speakers, organizers and like order and resourcefulness. They are ambitious and decisive.

If Pitta quality is out of balance, they tend to suffer with perfectionism, outbursts of anger, irritability, skin rashes and inflammations.

The Kapha

Kapha holds together different parts of the body and promotes mass, immunity, and fertility.

People with predominance of Kapha quality have a strong body-build, prominent muscles, and are prone to be overweight.

These people have a strong immune system, a great stamina, and physical exercise and movement are good for them.

The Kapha personality is characterized by patience, fortitude, and gentleness.

If Kapha is out of harmony, the person tends suffer with overweight; experiencing dullness, depression or nausea; feeling full or heavy in the stomach; and prone to colds and breathing disorders.

Name	
D.O.B.	
Contact details (phone/email)	
Occupation / retired	

What is/are the health issue/s?

How does this affect your day to day life?

What treatment have you already had/are having? (Including medication, holistic therapies, self-care)

What would you like to improve/work on?

Expectations of yoga therapy?

What are your goals?
Short Term (2/3 weeks) immediate goals eg pain management

Long Term (1 month+) life changing goals of healing

Anatomical observation (darshana – observation based – Annamaya Kosha)

Posture (spine, shoulders, pelvis, how the body is held)	
Mobility The body in motion Walking Coordination Flexibility	Holding stress tension in shoulders/upper body?
Weight BMI	In healthy range?

Physiological assessment (medical history, Pranamaya Kosha)

Breathing Sectional -Lower, Mid, Upper Lung measurements if you feel it's appropriate and useful! Rhythmic / Labored	
Blood Pressure	
Pulse	
Sugar Level	
Digestion	
Bowel Movements	
Gastric Issues	
Hormonal Imbalances	
Sleep pattern Quality Duration	
Diagnosed medical conditions (genetic?) Medication? Since when? How does it impact on your daily life?	
Pain? (Scale 1min – 10max)	
Other (Supplements?)	

Mental and Emotional Health Assessment (Manomaya kosha)

Nervousness	
Mood	
Energy Levels	
Anxiety	
Stress	
Anger	
Guilt	
Traumas	
Fear/Phobia	
Thinking positive/negative	
Body self – perception (strong/weak – where?)	

What is a normal day for you? (Occupation, diet, exercise)

1a: Does any of this feel difficult to you?

What are your family, social, or economic circumstances?

What brings you joy?

General mindset/view of life? (positive or negative outlook)

	OBSERVATIONS:
Dosha type Vata - wind Pitta - Fire Kapha – Earth and water (or combination)	
Guna Sattva – Purity Rajas - action with desire Tamas - inertia	

Trivasana – inherited desires Lokah – drive for self-fulfillment Deha – physical pleasure fulfill- ment Jnana – seeking wisdom	
Prana Vayus Prana (Respiratory and Thoracic health) Apana (pelvic and lower digestive) Vyana (circulatory) Samana (digestive health) Udana (communication) Upa Prana Vayus: Naga - burping Kurma- blinking Krikara -sneezing Devadatta - yawning Dhananjaya – heart beats	
Abhyasa (current practices if any, how they are currently managing themselves and the health issues)	
Jiva Karma (current routine)	
Chetana (current consciousness/quality of thoughts)	
Vacha (current speech and expression) (Fast, slow, loud, silent, broken, etc)	
Ahara (what is the current Food of body - what they eat and mind – what they read, watch etc. Appetite, diet , fluid intake (Frequency, quality)	
Viparita Buddhi (current destructive behaviors)	

Jiva Vritti (life or bio rhythms – times of eating, sleeping, bowel movements etc.)	
Sankalpa (resolutions/intentions – current mind set)	

Advise on:	Recommendations (what/when/frequency):
Dosha type (hatha yoga, pranayamas, mudras, diet)	
Guna (practice, meditation, lifestyle, diet)	
Trivasana (tools to change outlook and attitude, specially Yamas and Niyamas)	
Prana (energy practices eg- mudras, pranayama, asanas)	
Abhyasa (lifestyle and habitual changes to work on)	
Jiva Karma (karmic routines, reflect on life choices)	
Chetana (jnana yoga practices, yogic life philosophy, yoga darshan)	
Vacha (self-confidence, working on communication, non-violent, etc)	
Ahara (diet/dosha)	
Su-Buddhi (Motivational thoughts, events, reading, Satsanga)	

Jiva Vritti (lifestyle modification, breaking negative habits)	
Sankalpa Giving affirmations towards their goal	

Any other notes:

Check list:
GDPR
Disclaimer

Next meeting date: _____

Guna Test

Do you often feel:

A   Lazy

B   Active

C   Caring and Nurturing

Generally you feel:

A   Depressed

B   Excited

C   Joyful

Often mentally you feel:

A   Confused

B   Anxious

C   Clear and focussed

You often feel:

A   Helpless

B   Anger

C   Compassion

You often like:

A   Frozen and microwave food

B   Spicy food

C   Fresh fruits and vegetable meals

You enjoy watching

A   Horror, depressing and violent movies and drama

B   Comedy and family dramas

C   Nature and spiritual documentaries

Generally you prefer to:

A   Stay in bed

B   Getting things done

C   Doing things without desires for fruits and approval

You commonly have the feelings of:

A   Guilty and resentment

B   Courage and determination

C   Friendliness and self-control

In general you are:

A   Dependent on friends and family

B   Independent

C   Providing support to others

What sorts of books do you read?

A   Horror, and dark novels

B   Exciting and adventurous books

C   Books on health, wellness and spiritualism

How so you feel towards others:

A   Apathy

B   Stress

C   Empathy

All your actions and Karmas are:

A   Done for survivals and you would not do much if you don't have to.

B   Driven by ambitions and fruits

C   To help others and done selflessly

In day to day situations you feel:

A   Shame and doubt

B   Courageous and thoughtful

C   Trust and calmness

In nature you are:

A   Lonely

B   Outgoing

C   Cheerful

Your life is:

A   Sedentary and lacks for motivation

B   Active and can be chaotic

C   Blissful and resourceful

Result:

A: Tamas

B: Rajas

C: Sattva

Your Guna can be combinations of two of them in various ratios.

Milton Keynes UK
Ingram Content Group UK Ltd.
UKHW030842121223
434223UK00009B/369